AQUIFER CHARACTERIZATION

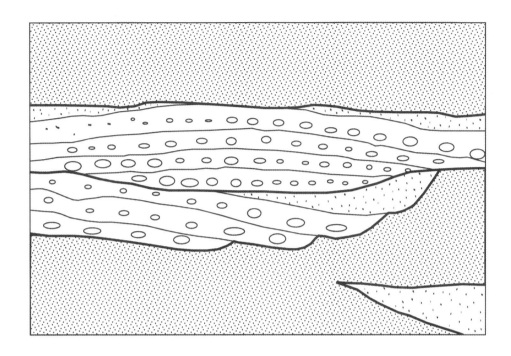

Edited by:

JOHN S. BRIDGE

Department of Geological Sciences, Binghamton University
Binghamton, New York 13902-6000, U.S.A.

AND

DAVID W. HYNDMAN

Department of Geological Sciences, Michigan State University, 206 Natural Science Building,
East Lansing, Michigan 48824-1115, U.S.A.

Laura J. Crossey, Editor of Special Publications
SEPM Special Publication Number 80

Tulsa, Oklahoma, U.S.A.   *August, 2004*

SEPM and the authors are grateful to the following
for their generous contribution to the cost of publishing

Aquifer Characterization

Emporia State University, Hydrogeology Program

INEEL Laboratory Directed Research & Development Program
under DOE Idaho Operations Office Contract DE-AC07-99ID13727

Institute of Environmental Science and Research (ESR), New Zealand

Kansas Geological Survey

Michigan State University

National Science Foundation Project no. 0208492

Contributions were applied to the cost of production, which reduced the
purchase price, making the volume available to a wide audience

 SEPM (Society for Sedimentary Geology) is an international not-for-profit Society based in Tulsa, Oklahoma. Through its network of international members, the Society is dedicated to the dissemination of scientific information on sedimentology, stratigraphy, paleontology, environmental sciences, marine geology, hydrogeology, and many additional related specialties.

The Society supports members in their professional objectives by publication of two major scientific journals, the Journal of Sedimentary Research (JSR) and PALAIOS, in addition to producing technical conferences, short courses, and Special Publications. Through SEPM's Continuing Education, Publications, Meetings, and other programs, members can both gain and exchange information pertinent to their geologic specialties.

For more information about SEPM, please visit **www.sepm.org.**

AQUIFER CHARACTERIZATION

John S. Bridge and David W. Hyndman, Editors

CONTENTS

AQUIFER CHARACTERIZATION

JOHN S. BRIDGE

Department of Geological Sciences, Binghamton University, Binghamton, New York 13902-6000, U.S.A.
e-mail: jbridge@binghamton.edu

AND

DAVID W. HYNDMAN

Department of Geological Sciences, Michigan State University, 206 Natural Science Building,
East Lansing, Michigan 48824-1115, U.S.A.
e-mail: hyndman@msu.edu

INTRODUCTION

The spatial variation of sedimentary aquifer properties (e.g., porosity and permeability) must be characterized in order to develop accurate models of groundwater flow and solute transport. Aquifer characterization should ideally involve the following steps: (1) analysis of borehole logs, cores, and hydraulic testing data to determine the sedimentological nature and origin of the strata, and their hydraulic properties; (2) stratigraphic correlation of borehole logs and cores in order to assess the lateral continuity of distinctive sediment types (facies) between boreholes; (3) use of geophysical profiles to assess the orientation and structural continuity of sequences of strata, and to recognize distinctive geophysical patterns that can be related to distinctive sedimentary facies; (4) modeling of the geometry and distribution of sedimentary facies in the volume between boreholes, and (5) distribution of properties such as porosity and permeability as a function of sedimentary facies. Unfortunately, hydrogeologists rarely incorporate information on the sedimentology of aquifers, and shallow geophysical methods are not routinely used for aquifer characterization. Furthermore, techniques for accurately modeling the sedimentary facies or hydrofacies in three dimensions are still under development. However, recent use of combined sedimentological and geophysical techniques (e.g., GPR, high-frequency seismic, resistivity, electrical conductivity) have helped to describe the spatial variation in the porosity and permeability of sedimentary aquifers. These advances are leading to quantitative, 3-D stratigraphic models that provide a link among spatial variation in porosity and permeability, different scales of stratification (defined mainly by variations in grain size, shape, and fabric), and variation in geophysical parameters such as the velocity or attenuation of radar and seismic waves.

The purpose of this volume was to bring together examples of the most recent research by sedimentologists, geophysicists, and hydrogeologists working on characterization of aquifer heterogeneity. The volume can be considered to be an outgrowth of SEPM Concepts in Hydrogeology and Environmental Geology Volume 1, entitled *Hydrogeologic Models of Sedimentary Aquifers*, which aimed to show how sedimentological information can be used in aquifer characterization and can thus help solve hydrogeologic problems. The papers in this volume demonstrate that integration of sedimentological and geophysical techniques for purposes of aquifer characterization are still in their infancy but that developments are promising.

The first five papers in the volume are concerned mainly with stratigraphic and geostatistical methods of aquifer characterization. The paper by Biteman et al. demonstrates the value of a measured stratigraphic framework for estimating hydraulic conductivity in a glacial-outwash aquifer. Tracer simulations were improved by using hydraulic conductivity values that were interpolated across lithofacies identified using cores, outcrop analogs, and geostatistical models. Weissmann et al. modeled flow and solute transport in incised-valley deposits of an alluvial fan. The aquifer was described by geostatistical (Markov chain) modeling of hydrofacies within sequence stratigraphic units. As would be expected, groundwater flow and solute transport were most rapid in the relatively coarse-grained valley fill. McKenna and Smith examine how the parameters of an object-based stochastic model of fluvial aquifers influence patterns of groundwater flow. The model predicts the geometry, proportion, and spatial distribution of channel and floodplain deposits. A single value of permeability is assigned to each deposit type. Not surprisingly, the most important parameter is the proportion of channel deposits relative to floodplain deposits. Dai et al. estimate parameters of hierarchical permeability correlation models and associated aquifer permeability. Gaud et al. show how heterogeneity of lithofacies and permeability in sedimentary rocks are closely related.

The next five papers explore the use of geophysical methods for aquifer characterization. The paper by Schulmeister et al. shows how measurements of electrical conductivity can lead to high-resolution stratigraphic characterization of unconsolidated deposits. Close et al. use ground-penetrating radar (GPR) to confirm the presence of preferential flow paths that were observed in shallow-aquifer tracer experiments. Versteeg uses time-lapse GPR data to map the density-driven flow of oil injected into saturated sediment in a laboratory experiment. Kowalsky et al. relate simulated geophysical data (GPR reflection data and cross-borehole tomography) under transient flow conditions to the nature of subsurface fluid flow in a braided stream deposit. Binley et al. also use cross-hole radar tomography to generate geostatistical models that were used to improve unsaturated flow models for a sandstone aquifer in the U.K.

The last paper examines the use of combined sedimentological and geophysical data to generate models of aquifer heterogeneity. Lunt et al. describe how sedimentological and geophysical data were used to construct a generalized 3-D model of gravelly braided river deposits that takes into account the different scales of stratigraphic unit. They discuss how such a model can be used in aquifer characterization. This paper emphasizes the importance of combining sedimentological, geophysical, and hydrogeological data. However, this approach has not yet been taken to the stage of generating 3-D aquifer models that have been used for simulation of flow and solute transport. In addition, none of the approaches in this volume have any feedback between measured transport and aquifer properties. We consider that the complete integration of all available data types for improved flow and transport simulations is the way of the future.

ACKNOWLEDGMENTS

We thank Kris Farnsworth, Laura Crossey, and other SEPM staff involved in the production of this volume. We also thank all of the authors for contributing to this volume. Finally, we thank the following reviewers for their efforts, which improved the quality of the final manuscripts: Andrew Binley, Georgio Cassiani, Jeff Daniels, Matt Davis, Alexandre Desbarats, Dave Dominic, Maggie Eppstein, Susan Hubbard, Peter Huggenberger, Mike Kowalsky, Doug LaBreque, Ian Lunt, Sean McKenna, Chris Murray, Bob Ritzi, Gary Weissmann, Brian Willis, Roelof Versteeg, and Vitaly Zlotnik.

INTEGRATION OF SEDIMENTOLOGIC AND HYDROGEOLOGIC PROPERTIES FOR IMPROVED TRANSPORT SIMULATIONS

SUSANNE E. BITEMAN, DAVID W. HYNDMAN, M.S. PHANIKUMAR, AND GARY S. WEISSMANN
Department of Geological Sciences, Michigan State University, 206 Natural Science Building,
East Lansing, Michigan 48824-1115, U.S.A.
e-mail: hyndman@msu.edu; phani@egr.msu.edu; weissman@msu.edu

ABSTRACT: Traditional geostatistical approaches for estimating distributions of hydraulic conductivity fail to reflect sharp contrasts that occur at boundaries between different stratigraphic units, thus limiting the accuracy of contaminant-transport models. We present an approach to incorporate a stratigraphic framework into geostatistical simulation at the scale of a plume, to better represent aquifer heterogeneity. The approach was developed and tested at the Schoolcraft Bioremediation Site in southwestern Michigan, where detailed estimates of aquifer properties were needed to accurately simulate multi-component reactive transport and to design an effective bioremediation strategy. The sediments at the site were deposited as glaciofluvial outwash downstream of the Kalamazoo Moraine, and consist mainly of fine to medium sands with interbedded gravels and silts. A series of 18-meter-long continuous cores was collected in the vicinity of the bioremediation-system delivery wells. These cores were assessed for sedimentary facies, grain-size distribution, porosity, and hydraulic conductivity. Sedimentologic measurements from outcrop analogs supplemented the core data from the site. On the basis of the core data, the aquifer was separated into four stratigraphic units, and the measured conductivity values were geostatistically interpolated within each stratigraphic unit. The stratigraphically based estimates of hydraulic conductivity were used as input to a high-resolution, three-dimensional model of groundwater flow and solute transport in the region. The model with stratigraphic interpolation provided better transport predictions for an injected tracer pulse than models that do not incorporate the stratigraphy.

INTRODUCTION

Accurate predictions of solute transport are commonly limited by the ability to preserve sharp gradients in aquifer parameters, yet these sharp gradients may be identified using aquifer stratigraphic analysis. Over the past few decades, several workers have shown that heterogeneity in hydraulic conductivity (K) and other aquifer parameters (e.g., porosity and storage coefficients) are controlled largely by the distribution of sedimentary material in the aquifer (e.g., Fogg, 1989; Anderson, 1989; Webb and Anderson, 1996; Davis et al., 1997; Webb and Davis, 1998; Anderson et al., 1999; Bersezio et al., 1999; Hornung and Aigner, 1999; Klingbeil et al., 1999; Ritzi et al., 2000).

The statistics of aquifer parameters also commonly vary significantly between different stratigraphic units (Davis et al., 1997; Carle et al., 1998; Ritzi et al., 2000). Thus, when using geostatistics to estimate aquifer parameters, variogram correlation lengths should be independently evaluated for each stratigraphic zone if the necessary data are available from either core measurements or outcrop analog studies. The mean and variance of aquifer parameters, such as hydraulic conductivity, also vary by stratigraphic unit and thus are not globally stationary. Geostatistical methods, from kriging to stochastic simulation, can be used more effectively to estimate aquifer parameters using different variogram models for each stratigraphic zone.

Eschard et al. (1998) and Weissmann and Fogg (1999) used the geology and stratigraphy as a framework for geostatistical realizations to avoid the assumption of global stationarity of the aquifer parameter statistics. Rather than assuming that the mean, variance, and correlation lengths are stationary across the entire area of geostatistical inference, such approaches have a less restrictive assumption that these statistics are stationary only across an individual geologic unit. These approaches were applied at the regional scale; however, point-source remediation typically requires that models of heterogeneity be developed at the smaller, plume scale.

In this paper, we present a modification of the stratigraphically based approach of Eschard et al. (1998) and Weissmann and Fogg (1999) to interpolate measured hydraulic conductivity at a plume scale. Our results show that incorporation of geologic information in the form of identified stratigraphic zonation improved our ability to predict tracer transport through a glaciofluvial aquifer in southeastern Michigan.

SITE DESCRIPTION

The Schoolcraft study site is located southeast of Schoolcraft, Michigan, on the glaciofluvial outwash plain associated with the Kalamazoo Moraine (Fig. 1; Monaghan and Larson, 1982; Rheaume, 1990; Kehew et al., 1996). The Kalamazoo Moraine, located west of Kalamazoo, Michigan, and northwest of the study site, was deposited when the Michigan Lobe ice margin stagnated during overall retreat of the Wisconsinan continental ice sheet (Monaghan and Larson, 1982).

Several contaminant plumes exist in the shallow glaciofluvial aquifer at Schoolcraft, Michigan (Hyndman et al. 2000; Dybas et al., 2002). The Schoolcraft Plume A study site (Fig. 2), the focus of this work, is located in an unconfined aquifer composed of a 27.5-m-thick succession of glaciofluvial sediments that lie directly over a regionally extensive clay-rich till and lacustrine unit (Monaghan and Larson, 1982; Lipinski, 2002). This clay-rich unit acts as an aquitard in the Schoolcraft area (Lipinski, 2002). The Plume A site is the location of a carbon tetrachloride (CT) bioaugmentation experiment, where microbes and substrate were injected to degrade aqueous and sorbed phase contaminants (Fig. 2) (Hyndman et al., 2000; Dybas et al., 2002). This CT contaminant plume is about 1.2 km long and 90 m wide, extending from roughly 8 to 26.5 m below ground surface (bgs), with CT concentrations from 5 to 150 parts per billion (ppb). The water table at this site lies at roughly 4.5 m bgs. Pilot studies indicated that sediments above 8 m depth did not have CT contamination (Dybas et al., 1998); thus we have not included these shallow

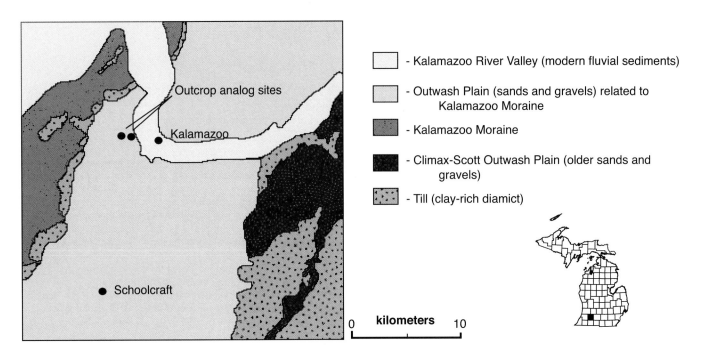

FIG. 1.—Surficial geology of Kalamazoo County, Michigan. Also shown are the locations of the outcrop analog sites used in this study. The modeling study area is located in the town of Schoolcraft. Modified from Monaghan and Larson (1982) and Rheaume (1990).

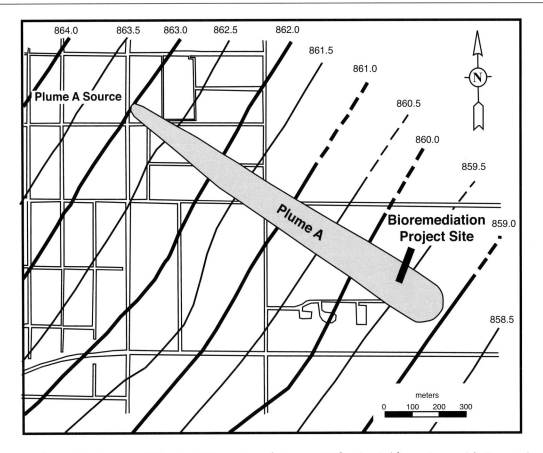

FIG. 2.—The approximate distribution of Schoolcraft Plume A in the town of Schoolcraft (shown by roads). Our study site is at the location of the bioremediation project. Contours show the water-table elevation (in feet). Modified from Mayotte (1991).

sediments in this study. This biocurtain has proven to be greater than 97% effective at removing aqueous-phase contaminants (Hyndman, et al., 2000) and effective at removing sorbed-phase CT in the biocurtain region over more than four years of operation (Dybas et al., 2002). The Schoolcraft Plume A site was chosen for this study because a large database exists that includes core descriptions, measurements of K from many wells, and many measured concentration histories collected during tracer tests.

The bioaugmentation system at this site consists of a series of closely spaced recirculation wells for delivery of microbes and nutrients (Fig. 3). Continuous core samples (approximately 5 cm in diameter) were collected from 7 of the 15 delivery well locations and from 4 monitoring well locations (Fig. 3). Cores were collected in sections 1.5 m long using the Waterloo continuous core sampler, which advances a core barrel ahead of an auger string. A vacuum-sealed core liner minimizes sample loss. Twenty-seven additional monitoring wells were drilled in both upgradient and downgradient locations relative to the biocurtain.

CORE ANALYSIS

Core samples were collected from wells D2, D4, D6, D8, D10, D12, D14, P6, P7, and P8 (Fig. 3; Table 1). These samples were cut into 15.2 cm lengths, removed from the core liner, repacked to their original volume in permeameter sleeves, flushed with carbon dioxide gas, and tested for K using a constant-head permeameter. The K measurements show that the highest K values are generally located at the base of the aquifer and lower K values are generally closer to the top of the aquifer (Fig. 4). Several discrete lenticular units of either low K or high K material,

however, are present in the section. Preliminary modeling of flow and transport by Hoard (2002) indicated that the repacked K measurements provided reasonable estimates of the actual horizontal K at the site, based on a reasonably good match between simulated and observed tracer concentration histories.

Grain-size distributions were measured for a subset of these samples using a standard sieve set (Table 1). The data show an expected relationship between grain size, sorting, and K, where coarser-grained sediment tends to have higher K than fine-grained sediment, and poor sorting reduces K (Fig. 5).

In order to gain additional insight into the aquifer stratigraphy at the study site, core from well P18 and selected samples from wells P6, P7, and P8 were analyzed for sedimentologic characteristics (e.g., grain-size distribution, vertical trends in grain size, bedding thickness, and sedimentary structures) and vertical K of minimally disturbed sediment (Fig. 6). To assess samples for vertical K, 42 subsamples (15.2 cm long) from the P18 core were kept in the sampling tube, flushed with carbon dioxide, and tested for K using a constant-head permeameter. Results show a trend in K similar to that observed in other wells, where relatively high K values exist at the bottom of the aquifer and lower K values are found in the upper part of the aquifer (Fig. 6).

The measured vertical K values from core P18 were consistently lower than the repacked K measurements on samples of the same grain size and zone from other wells by a factor of about 0.74. Because repacked K values appear to reasonably represent horizontal K at the site (Hoard, 2002), we assume that this difference represents the vertical to horizontal anisotropy in K. Therefore, the measured vertical K values from P18 were multiplied by this ratio to develop horizontal K estimates for the interpolation to the groundwater model grid. Although it is possible that this ratio is biased by the fact that horizontal K values were all measured on repacked samples and all vertical samples were measured on intact core, it is generally expected that the vertical K will be lower than horizontal K because of a higher degree of continuity of strata in the horizontal direction.

SITE STRATIGRAPHY

Four stratigraphic zones were identified in well P18 based on the observed sedimentary character and K distribution (Figs. 6 and 7). Stratigraphic boundaries were identified in cores using one or more of the following characteristics: (1) an erosional basal contact; (2) abrupt changes in mean grain size; and (3) abrupt changes in sedimentary structures and bedding thickness. Missing core (from lack of recovery) created some uncertainty for zone delineation. However, as is described in this section, detailed measurements of K and grain size (Fig. 4) provided additional evidence of these stratigraphic boundaries across the modeled region.

The basal zone, or Zone 1 (from ~ 27.5 m up to ~ 20.5 m depth), overlies the regional lacustrine clay or till and generally fines upward from cobbles in a coarse sand matrix up to medium sand. Though core was not collected across this boundary in well P18, cores from other wells indicate that this basal contact is erosional and sharp. Drilling character and cuttings from P18 and other wells indicate that the bottom one meter of this zone consists mainly of cobbles. Sands in this zone are well sorted to poorly sorted with gravel. The sediment is cross-stratified, horizontally stratified, or massive. Because stratification may be too subtle to recognize in core, the massively bedded sands may actually be stratified. Gravel typically occurs along cross-strata in the sandy beds. Bedding thickness is difficult to determine in core because of the subtle nature of stratification. However, several cross-strata sets were distinguishable in this zone, being 0.1 to 0.25 m

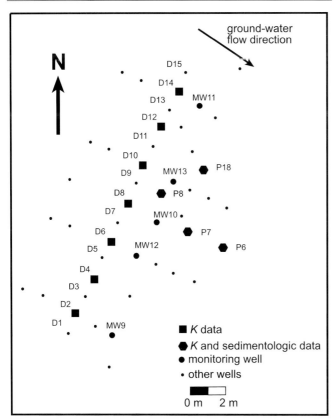

FIG. 3.—Locations of delivery wells (D) and monitoring wells (MW or P) at the Plume A Schoolcraft Bioremediation site.

TABLE 1.—Number of samples analyzed from each well for grain size, repacked *K*, or vertical *K*.
Dashes in cells indicate that no analysis was completed.

	Well Number										
	D2	D4	D6	D8	D10	D12	D14	P6	P7	P8	P18
Grain size	9	6	9	3	15	10	15	-	-	-	42
Repacked *K*	44	24	22	21	31	27	31	27	30	27	-
Vertical *K*	-	-	-	-	-	-	-	-	-	-	42

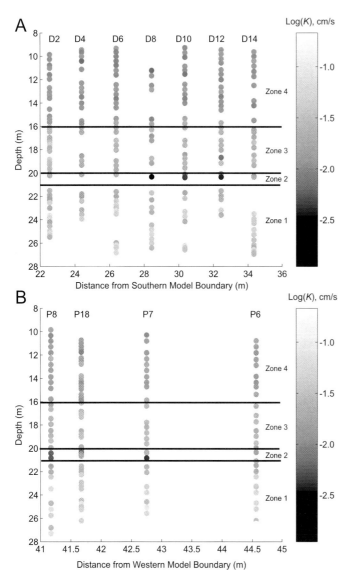

FIG. 4.—Plots showing the log-*K* data points used for interpolation and stratigraphic zonation. **A)** A transect through the delivery wells (see Figure 3 for well locations). **B)** A transect through downgradient wells where *K* data were available. Zonal boundaries were identified at 16 m below ground surface (bgs), 20 m bgs, and 21 m bgs. Modified from Hyndman et al. (2000).

thick. Measured *K* values through this zone are variable but consistently higher than observed in other stratigraphic zones. Similar relatively high *K* deposits are observed in other wells across the site through this interval (Fig. 4).

Zone 2 (from ~ 20.5 to ~ 20.25 m depth in well P18) consists of silty sand to sandy silt with relatively low *K* over much of the study area. The sediments in the silty sand portion of this interval are faintly laminated and display the lowest *K* of the stratigraphic section. Though this zone is thin, it is distinctive because a low-*K* feature is recognized at this depth in a significant number of other wells across the site (Fig. 4). As is described in the section on groundwater modeling, delineation of this zone improved the tracer-test simulation results significantly.

Zone 3 (from ~ 20.25 to ~ 15.9 m depth) consists of fine to medium sand that is moderately to well sorted. Beds in this zone are typically cross-stratified to massive; however, the massively bedded sands may have stratification that is too subtle to recognize in core. Grain size and sedimentary structures are more variable in different cross-strata cosets than observed in either Zone 1 or Zone 4. Additionally, set thickness is highly variable in this zone, ranging from 0.05 to 0.25 m. Likewise, *K* in this zone is more variable over short distances, with a mean intermediate between Zones 1 and 4 (Fig. 7). This mean and short-distance variability in *K* is also observed across the study site, thus allowing delineation of this zone in other wells (Fig. 4).

Zone 4 (from about ~ 15.9 m to < 8 m depth) consists of well sorted fine sand. A thin gravel lag was identified at the base of this zone. Individual beds appear to be relatively thin (0.05–0.15 m) and cross-stratified or horizontally stratified, with massive beds in places that may have stratification that is too subtle to recognize in core. *K* through this zone has low variability and is lower than Zones 1 or 3 (Fig. 7). Similar consistently low-*K* distributions at this depth are observed in other wells at the site, thereby allowing delineation of this zone across the study area (Fig. 4).

The stratigraphic boundaries appear to be laterally continuous and horizontal at the scale of the study area. This is consistent with observations at the outcrop analog sites, as is described in the next section. This stratigraphic character is consistent with glaciofluvial outwash deposition of a retreating ice margin (Boothroyd and Ashley, 1975; Boothroyd and Nummedal, 1978; Maizels, 1995). The basal, coarse-grained unit (Zone 1) represents proximal to medial outwash deposited as the ice margin retreated past the Schoolcraft location. The upper zones (zones 2–4) most-likely represent distal outwash deposited when the ice margin stagnated at the Kalamazoo moraine.

OUTCROP ANALOG

Cores at the study site provide an excellent sampling of vertical distributions for *K* analysis, but lateral data were lim-

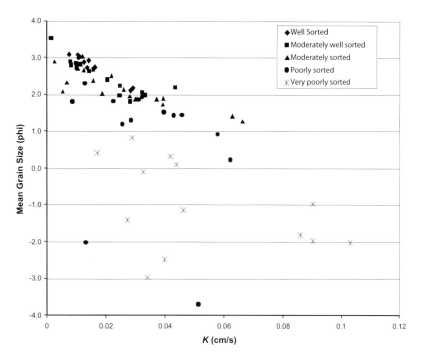

F<small>IG</small>. 5.—Plot of grain size versus *K* for the study area. Different symbols are used to indicate sediment sorting.

ited even with closely spaced cores. To supplement the core data and to aid in the interpretation of bounding-surface geometries at the site, data on lateral variability and geometry of cross-bed sets were collected on outcrop analogs. Outcrop analogs to the Schoolcraft Plume A site were selected on the basis of: (1) location within the same outwash complex, (2) comparable down-valley distance from the Kalamazoo Moraine, and (3) grain size, bed thickness, and sedimentary structures similar to those observed in the P18 core. Unfortunately, no gravel and sand pits are present in the distal outwash deposits, because of relatively high water table in these deposits. Sand and gravel pits are present, however, in proximal and medial outwash deposits on several outwash fans adjacent to the Kalamazoo Moraine. Exposures at two of these gravel pits were used as outcrop analogs for this study (Fig. 1).

Bounding surfaces and cross-bed set thickness and width were measured at the outcrop sites and recorded using photomosaics of the outcrop (Fig. 8). Sediments exposed in outcrop consist of medium- to coarse-grained, trough cross-stratified to planar-tabular cross-stratified sand. Some gravel is present along cross-strata and as discrete, cross-stratified to massive units. Maximum observed thickness of individual cross-strata sets range between 0.1 and 0.5 m. Coset bounding surfaces appear to be horizontal and as extensive as the outcrop.

Because the outcrops are oriented oblique to paleoflow, width-to-thickness ratios of several cross-strata sets could be measured. An average width-to-thickness ratio of 7.7:1 was determined for these sets. It was not possible to measure the coset or bed lengths because the outcrop is two dimensional and these lengths are longer than the scale of the outcrop. No published data were available on the ratios of bed thickness to length, likely for the reason stated above.

Bedding characteristics (e.g., grain-size distributions, bed thickness, and sedimentary structures) at these outcrop sites were similar to those observed in Zone 1 of the P18 core. Additionally, the outcrops lie within the same outwash succes-

sion and are in a medial position relative to the Kalamazoo Moraine. Thus, we use these outcrops as an analog for sediments of Zone 1.

Originally, we hoped to collect samples for *K* analysis from several cross-strata sets in outcrop, but collected samples were too disturbed to make valid *K* measurements. Additionally, outcrop instability prevented us from collecting sufficient samples to ensure statistical validity of relationships between *K* distribution and cross-strata set geometry. Instead, we assume that *K* varies little within a cross-strata set and that *K* varies more significantly between cross-strata sets in a manner similar to that described by Davis et al. (1997).

GEOSTATISTICS

We used the stratigraphic zones identified at the Schoolcraft site to separate regions for geostatistical interpolation. For each zone, experimental variograms were generated to model the correlation lengths in directions that are vertical, longitudinal to paleoflow, and transverse to paleoflow. Different variogram models are justified, if not necessary, because correlation length scales are different in each of these zones, as indicated by differences in the thickness variation of beds and cross-strata sets, grain-size variability, and *K* variability within each zone. Additionally, the means and standard deviations of *K* differ for each zone (Table 2; Fig. 7).

Experimental variograms were developed using log-*K* values from core samples. Log-*K* data were used instead of *K* in this and other geostatistical analyses because values of hydraulic conductivity were more log-normally distributed than normally distributed at this site (Hoard, 2002), as is commonly observed (Hoeksema and Kitanidis, 1985). The modeled variogram parameters for the vertical correlation length were estimated to fit the experimental variogram. Because horizontal data are sparse, the horizontal, transverse-to-paleoflow correlation lengths were determined using the 7.7:1 width-to-thickness ratio measured from the out-

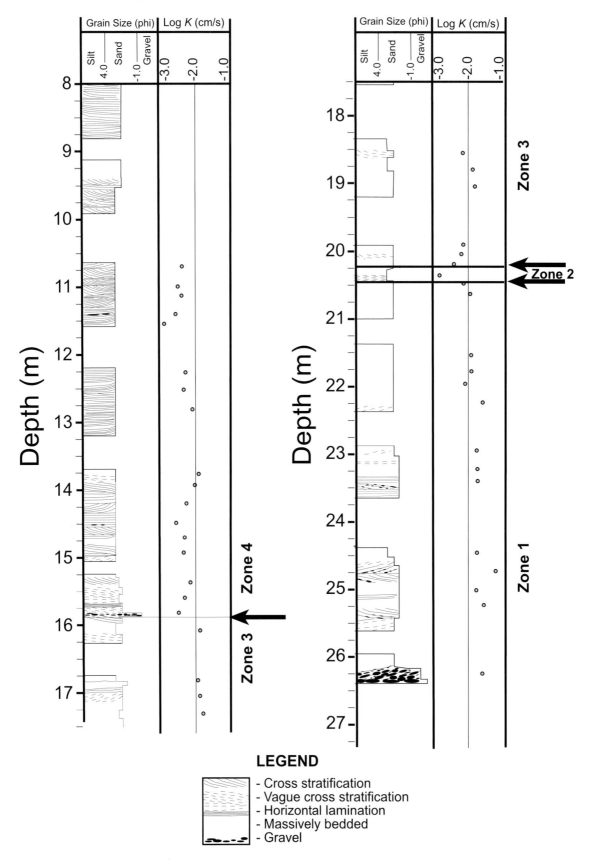

FIG. 6.—Core description for well P18 showing zonal boundaries (marked by arrows) and measured vertical *K*. See Figure 3 for location.

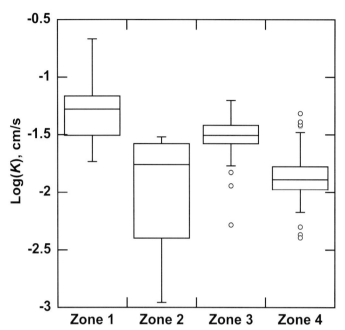

FIG. 7.—Box plots showing ranges of K for each stratigraphic zone. Each box shows the 25th, 50th (median), and 75th percentile of the population. The lines extending from the boxes show the effective maxima and minima of the data population. Outliers (circles) are points that fall outside 1.5 times the interquartile distance.

crop analogs. Because outcrop analog data were not available in the upper, distal outwash sediments (Zones 2, 3, and 4), to develop lateral variograms in these units we assumed the same width-to-thickness ratio. Although this may add uncertainty to the modeling, the effect on the final results is likely minimal. Sensitivity studies, however, may be conducted in future.

The horizontal, longitudinal-to-paleoflow correlation lengths were extended as far as Groundwater Modeling System (GMS3.1, BYU, 2000) would allow, which is approximately 18 m. We believe

FIG. 8.—A portion of the outcrop analog for medial deposits (Zone 1) at the Schoolcraft study site. A 40-cm-long shovel is shown for scale.

that this length is shorter than the true longitudinal-to-paleoflow correlation length based on the outcrop analogs and the nature of these fluvial deposits; however, the difference a slightly longer value would make is likely insignificant. Table 3 summarizes the sill, nugget, longitudinal-to-flow range, transverse-to-flow range, and vertical range for each stratigraphic unit.

Using the estimated variogram models and conditioning K data from wells, we generated a three-dimensional log-K field for each hydrostratigraphic zone using ordinary kriging. Though kriging may smooth results relative to conditional simulation, we chose kriging for this study because: (1) this approach most closely reflects current standard practice; (2) this allowed us to directly compare these results to previously published modeling results (e.g., Hyndman et al., 2000), and (3) the conditioning data are very closely spaced, thus conditional simulation results would be similar to kriging results in the region near the conductivity measurements. The kriging results from the four zones were merged to create a final log-K field surrounding the biocurtain area. This zonal kriged field preserved abrupt changes in K, especially noticeable at approximately 20–21 m depth in zone 2 (Fig. 9A).

In addition to the zonal kriged results, a log-K field was estimated by kriging without the zonal boundaries to evaluate the influence of the additional geologic information (Fig. 9B). For this model, the variogram range was set at 18.0 m (to be consistent with the zonal kriging). The nugget, sill, and range in all three orthogonal directions were fitted to the experimental variograms on the basis of core data (Table 3). In a visual comparison, the zonal kriged field had significantly more horizontal bedding-like features than the traditional kriged field, which had smoother features with less horizontal continuity. Additionally, the low-K region in Zone 2 is larger and more diffuse in the nonzonal kriged case than suggested by the core data (Fig. 9).

GROUNDWATER MODELING AND TRACER-TEST SIMULATION

We used the three-dimensional groundwater flow model, MODFLOW-96 (McDonald and Harbaugh, 1988; Harbaugh and McDonald, 1996), to predict hydraulic heads and groundwater fluxes for the region. Constant-head boundaries were used in the flow direction to provide a gradient of 0.0011 based on regional head measurements (Fig. 2). The model domain is a rectangular region 101.5 m wide (y) by 57.2 m long (x) by 27.4 m in depth (z). We discretized this region using a computational grid with 136 (y) x 86 (x) x 44 (z) cells. The delivery-well gallery is located at the center of the computational domain with fine cells (20 cm x 20 cm) approximately equal to the size of the boreholes surrounding the delivery wells, and larger cells in a geometric progression away from the well gallery. The resolution in the vertical direction varies and is discretized most finely around Zone 2 (Table 4).

During the tracer test, a conservative tracer (bromide) was injected into the seven even-numbered delivery wells and extracted from the eight odd-numbered delivery wells for five hours. During the next hour the same pumping rate was used in a flow-reversal phase in which tracer was extracted from the even-numbered wells and injected into the odd-numbered wells. We used the reactive-transport code RT3D (Clement, 1997; Clement and Jones, 1998) to simulate three-dimensional tracer transport through the site. Because the concentration of injected bromide changed during the tracer test, we divided the five-hour interval in the transport model into three stress periods with different concentrations, 18, 14, and 17 ppm, respectively.

TABLE 2.—Statistics on horizontal K (cm/s) for the four stratigraphic zones and for the entire aquifer.

	Zone 1		Zone 2		Zone 3		Zone 4		All Zones	
	K	Log-K	K	Log-K	K	Log-K	K	Log-K	K	Log-K
Mean	5.44×10^{-2}	-1.26	1.56×10^{-2}	-1.81	3.20×10^{-2}	-1.49	1.38×10^{-2}	-1.86	3.07×10^{-2}	-1.51
Median	5.28×10^{-2}	-1.28	1.74×10^{-2}	-1.76	3.12×10^{-2}	-1.51	1.27×10^{-2}	-1.90	2.59×10^{-2}	-1.59
Standard Deviation	2.90×10^{-2}	-1.54	1.11×10^{-2}	-1.95	9.40×10^{-3}	-2.03	5.40×10^{-3}	-2.27	2.43×10^{-2}	-1.61
No. of data points	106		25		82		133		346	

The one-hour-flow-reversal phase was simulated with a single stress period in which injected concentrations were 23.5 ppm. The last stress period in this simulation represents a 20-day natural gradient period with no pumping. The differences in hydraulic conductivity across the vertical extent of the aquifer cause proportional differences in the flux through different layers from the well. To represent this behavior, we used a conductivity-weighted average to compute the fluxes for the injection and extraction wells.

RESULTS AND DISCUSSION

The tracer-test comparison shows that the addition of geologic data significantly improved transport simulations in some regions whereas in others the zonal and nonzonal simulated tracers are similar (Fig. 10). In many cases, the hydrostratigraphic interpretation improves the match between simulated and observed tracer concentrations, whereas in a few cases it reduced the match slightly. Overall, the zonal model reduced the sum of squared residuals from 13.24 to 10.47, or roughly a 21% improvement. These residuals are calculated using the normalized concentrations (from 0 to 1); thus, squaring these residuals with values < 1 provides a conservative estimate of the improvement made by including the geologic information.

The largest difference between the zonal kriging model and the nonzonal model was the preservation of the abrupt nature of contacts between Zones 1, 2, and 3 in the zonal model. The most significant improvement in the tracer simulation was also in the region around Zone 2 (at 19.8 m depth), especially at wells MW10 and MW13, where the low-K silty fine sand was observed across more than half of the delivery-well area. The core descriptions and K data indicate that this unit extends through delivery wells D8, D10, and D12. MW13 and MW10 are located downgradient from delivery wells D10 and D8, respectively (Fig. 3). At the same depth in MW11 and MW12 there is no evidence for the low-K silty fine sand in Zone 2, and the simulations of tracer concentration respond similarly for both types

of kriging for these wells. No core was recovered from well D2 at this depth; however, the measured tracer breakthrough at MW9 (immediately downgradient) is very similar to the measured data from MW13, suggesting the presence of the low-K silty fine sand at this location.

At most other depths, the tracer tests simulated in the zonal and traditional kriged K fields are very similar. Slight improvements are made in MW10 and MW13 at depth 22.9 m, in MW10 and MW11 at depth 16.8 m, and MW11 at 13.7 m and 10.7 m, where the breakthrough occurs a bit earlier in the zonal kriging tracer simulation.

There are a few instances where the two kriging approaches provide similar transport results and a few sites where the nonzonal kriged K field provides a better match to the measured tracer concentrations. For example, the nonzonal kriged transport simulation better matches the measured tracer at MW12 at 17.8 m depth because the nonzonal kriging interpolated a higher K value than the zonal kriging estimated in this region.

These results show the influence that thin, low-K beds can have on tracer-test results. Though few aquifers will be characterized to the degree of the Schoolcraft site, this research demonstrates the importance of correctly identifying the stratigraphic zonation of an aquifer. The high-K and low-K features that significantly altered the measured transport at this site will generally be missed by standard aquifer characterization approaches.

CONCLUSIONS

The addition of stratigraphically significant boundaries into geostatistical interpolation methods helps preserve abrupt changes in K where they occur in the sedimentologic record. The zonal kriging approach used in this study required an understanding of the stratigraphy. We accomplished this through assessment of core for K, grain size, and bedding character. At locations where core data do not provide sufficient information to construct models of spatial variability (e.g., variograms), outcrop analogs

TABLE 3.—Variogram parameters for zonal and nonzonal models. All variograms were fitted using exponential models.

	Nugget	Sill	Range (m)		
			Parallel-to-paleoflow	Perpendicular-to-paleoflow	Vertical
Nonzonal model	0.011	0.065	18.0	6.84	2.70
Zonal models					
Zone 1	0.012	0.026	18.3	2.61	0.35
Zone 2	0.027	0.21	17.7	4.09	0.53
Zone 3	0.0017	0.020	18.0	8.33	1.08
Zone 4	0.0053	0.024	18.4	12.51	1.62

A   Zonal Kriged Results

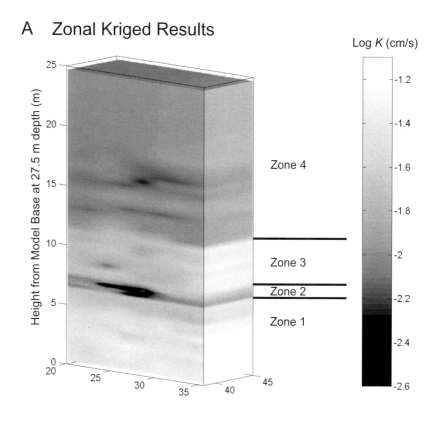

B   Non Zonal Kriged Results

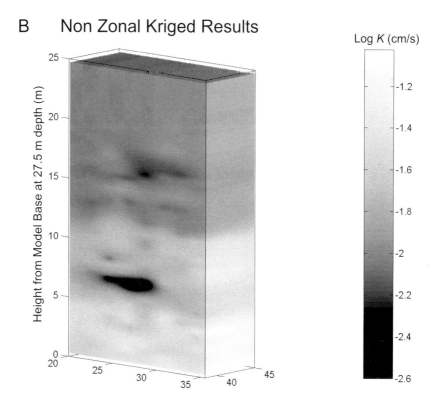

FIG. 9.—**A)** Zonal kriging results for the study site. The arrows mark boundaries of the four zones. Note that abrupt changes in *K* are preserved in the zonal kriging approach. **B)** Results of nonzonal kriging for the same area. The scale bar is in log *K* (cm/s).

TABLE 4.—Vertical discretization of layers.

Layer Number	Layer Thickness (m)
1	5.4
2 to 7	1.0
8 to 26	0.5
27 to 34	0.25
35 to 44	0.50

can be used to provide approximate lateral correlation lengths for different facies types. Importantly, the zonal model of K improved the tracer simulations most in regions with the largest degree of heterogeneity, where there was a sharp contrast in K of an order of magnitude or more.

For this site, our approach of kriging measured K values into a stratigraphic framework provided an estimated K field used in simulations that matched tracer-test results more closely. This allowed reasonable predictions of tracer breakthrough with no calibration of the conductivity values. The value of the approach would likely be more significant in regions with higher degrees of heterogeneity and sites with fewer measured conductivity

values. In this case, typical kriging provided a reasonable conductivity field because so many conductivity estimates were available. Even with such detailed characterization, inclusion of a geologic framework helped improve predictions of solute transport. In most cases, the measured conductivity data will be much more limited, thus increasing the need for geologic information.

ACKNOWLEDGMENTS

This work was funded by a grant from the Michigan Department of Environmental Quality (#Y40386) and additional funding from the Department of Geological Sciences, Michigan State University. We would like to thank M. Dybas, C. Criddle, X. Zhao, D. Wiggert, T. Voice, T. Mayotte, G. Tatara, C. Hoard, B. Lipinski, and R. Heine for their contributions to field design, data collection, and the multidisciplinary efforts that made the overall project a success. We thank Michelle Vit for her assistance in the field and laboratory. We also benefited from discussions with Grahame Larson and Kevin Kincare. We appreciate the substantive comments and reviews from Matt Davis, David Dominic, and John Bridge, which significantly improved the manuscript.

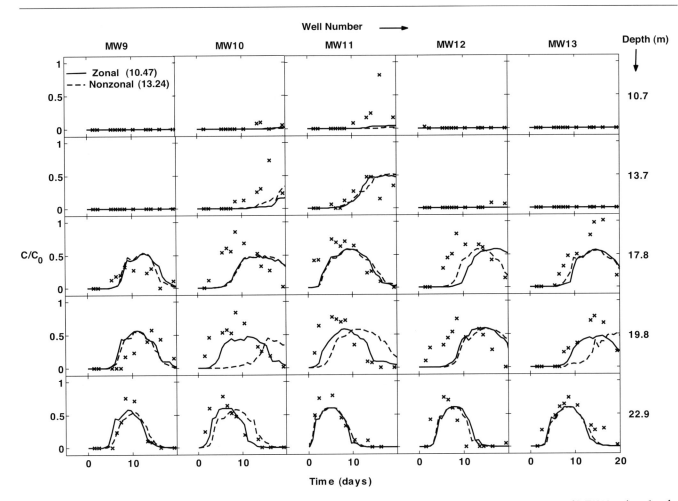

FIG. 10.—Measured tracer concentrations (shown by x) from monitoring wells MW9, MW10, MW11, MW12, and MW13 at five depths (10.7 m, 13.7 m, 17.8 m, 19.8 m, and 22.9 m), and simulated concentrations from the results of zonal kriging (solid line) and the nonzonal kriging (dashed line). Numbers listed for each of the simulation results are the sum of squared residuals. C/C_0 is measured tracer concentration normalized by the original tracer concentration released at the delivery wells.

REFERENCES

ANDERSON, M.P., 1989, Hydrogeologic facies models to delineate large-scale spatial trends in glacial and glaciofluvial sediments: Geological Society of America, Bulletin, v. 101, p. 501–511.

ANDERSON, M.P., AIKEN, J.S., WEBB, E.K., AND MICKELSON, D.M., 1999, Sedimentology and hydrogeology of two braided stream deposits: Sedimentary Geology, v. 129, p. 187–199.

BERSEZIO, R., BINI, A., AND GIUDICI, M., 1999, Effects of sedimentary heterogeneity on groundwater flow in a Quaternary pro-glacial delta environment: joining facies analysis and numerical modeling: Sedimentary Geology, v. 129, p. 327–344.

BOOTHROYD, J.C., AND ASHLEY, G.M., 1975, Processes, bar morphology and sedimentary structures on braided outwash fans, northeastern Gulf of Alaska, in, Jopling, A.V., and MacDonald, B.D., eds., Glaciofluvial and Glaciolacustrine Sedimentation: Society of Economic Paleontologists and Mineralogists, Special Publication 23, p. 193–222.

BOOTHROYD, J.C., AND NUMMEDAL, D., 1978, Proglacial braided outwash: A model for humid alluvial-fan deposits, in Miall, A.D., ed., Fluvial Sedimentology: Canadian Society of Petroleum Geologists, Memoir 5, p. 641–668.

BYU (BRIGHAM YOUNG UNIVERSITY), 2000, Department of Defense Groundwater Modeling System (GMS), Version 3.1, Provo, Utah.

CARLE, S.F., LABOLLE, E.M., WEISSMANN, G.S., VANBROCKLIN, D., AND FOGG, G.E., 1998, Conditional simulation of hydrofacies architecture: a transition probability/Markov approach, in Fraser, G.S., and Davis, J.M., Hydrogeologic Models of Sedimentary Aquifers: SEPM, Concepts in Hydrogeology and Environmental Geology no. 1, p. 147–170.

CLEMENT, T.P., 1997, A modular computer model for simulating reactive multispecies transport in three-dimensional groundwater systems: PNNL-SA-11720, Pacific Northwest National Laboratory, Richland, Washington.

CLEMENT, T.P., AND JONES, N.L., 1998, RT3D Tutorials for GMS Users: PNNL-11805, Pacific Northwest National Laboratory, Richland, Washington.

DAVIS, M.J., WILSON, J.I.., PHILLIPS, F.M., AND GOTKOWITZ, M.B., 1997, Relationship between fluvial bounding surfaces and the permeability correlation structure: Water Resources Research, v. 33, p. 1843–1854.

DYBAS, M.J., BARCELONA, M., BEZBORODNIKOV, S., DAVIES, S., FORNEY, L., HEUER, H., KAWKA, O., MAYOTTE, T., SEPÚLVEDA-TORRES, L., SMALLA, K., SNEATHEN, J., TIEDJE, J., VOICE, T., WIGGERT, D.C., WITT, M.E., AND CRIDDLE, C.S., 1998, Pilot-scale evaluation of bioaugmentation for in-situ remediation of a carbon tetrachloride-contaminated aquifer: Environmental Science and Technology, v. 32, p. 3598–3611.

DYBAS, M.J., HYNDMAN, D.W., HEINE, R., TIEDJE, J., LINNING, K., WIGGERT, D., VOICE, T., ZHAO, X., DYBAS, L., AND CRIDDLE, C.S., 2002, Development, operation, and long-term performance of a full-scale biocurtain utilizing bioaugmentation,: Environmental Science and Technology., v. 36, p. 3635–3644.

ESCHARD, R., LEMOUZY, P., BACCHIANA, C., DESAUBLIAUX, J., PARPANT, J., AND SMART, B., 1998, Combining sequence stratigraphy, geostatistical simulations, and production data for modeling a fluvial reservoir in Chaunoy Field (Triassic, France): American Association of Petroleum Geologists, Bulletin, v. 82, p. 545–568.

FOGG, G.E., 1989, Emergence of geologic and stochastic approaches for characterization of heterogeneous aquifers: New Field Techniques for Quantifying the Physical and Chemical Properties of Heterogeneous Aquifers: Dallas, Texas, March 20–23, 1989, Proceedings, National Water Well Association, Dublin, Ohio, p. 1–17.

HARBAUGH, A.W., AND McDONALD, G., 1996, User's documentation for Modflow-96, and update to the U.S. Geological Survey modular finite-difference ground-water flow model: U.S. Geological Survey, Open File Report 96-485, 56 p.

HOARD, C.J., 2002, The influence of detailed aquifer characterization of groundwater flow and transport models at Schoolcraft, Michigan: M.S. Thesis, Michigan State University, 67 p.

HOEKSEMA, R.J., AND KITANIDIS, P.K., 1985, Analysis of the spatial structure of properties of selected aquifers: Water Resources Research, v. 21, p. 563–572.

HORNUNG, J., AND AIGNER, T., 1999, Reservoir and aquifer characterization of fluvial architectural elements: Stubensandstein, Upper Triassic, southwest Germany: Sedimentary Geology, v. 129, p. 215–280.

HYNDMAN, D.W., DYBAS, M.J., FORNEY, L., HEINE, R., MAYOTTE, T., PHANIKUMAR, M.S., TATARA, G., TIEDJE, J., VOICE, T., WALLACE, R., WIGGERT, D., ZHAO, X., AND CRIDDLE, C.S., 2000, Hydraulic characterization and design of a full-scale biocurtain: Ground Water, v. 38, p. 462–474.

KEHEW, A.E., STRAW, W.T., STEINMANN, W.K., BARRESE, P.G., PASSARELLA, G., AND PENG, W., 1996, Ground-water quality and flow in a shallow glaciofluvial aquifer impacted by agricultural contamination: Ground Water, v. 34, p. 491–500.

KLINGBEIL, R., KLEINEIDAM, S., ASPRION, U., AIGNER, T., AND TEUTSCH, G., 1999, Relating lithofacies to hydrofacies: outcrop-based hydrogeological characterization of Quaternary gravel deposits: Sedimentary Geology, v. 129, p. 299–310.

LIPINSKI, B.A., 2002, Estimating natural attenuation rates for a chlorinated hydrocarbon plume in a galcio-fluvial aquifer, Schoolcraft, Michigan: M.S. Thesis, Michigan State University, 129 p.

MAIZELS, J., 1995, Chapter 12, Sediments and landforms of modern proglacial terrestrial environments, in Menzies, J., ed., Modern Glacial Environments; Processes, Dynamics and Sediments: Oxford, U.K., Butterworth-Heinemann Ltd., p. 365–416.

MAYOTTE, T.J., 1991, Village of Schoolcraft, Kalamazoo County, Michigan, Final Remedial Investigation and Feasibility Study of Remedial Alternatives, Plume A and Plume F: Halliburton NUS Environmental Corporation Project Number 4M84.

McDONALD, G., AND HARBAUGH, A.W., 1988, A modular three-dimensional finite difference groundwater flow model: U.S. Geological Survey, Techniques of Water Resources Investigations, Book 6.

MONAGHAN, G.W., AND LARSON, G.J., 1982, Surficial Geology of Kalamazoo County: County Geologic Map Series, Michigan Geological Survey, Lansing, Michigan.

RHEAUME, S.J., 1990, Geohydrology and water quality of Kalamazoo County, Michigan, 1986–88: U.S. Geological Survey, Water-Resources Investigation Report 90-4028, 102 p.

RITZI, R.W., JR., DOMINIC, D.F., SLESERS, A.J., GREER, C.B., REBOULET, E.C., TELFORD, J.A., MASTERS, R.W., KLOHE, C.A., BOGLE, J.L., AND MEANS, B.P., 2000, Comparing statistical models of physical heterogeneity in buried-valley aquifers: Water Resources Research, v. 36, p. 3179–3192.

WEBB, E.K., AND ANDERSON, M.P., 1996, simulation of a preferential flow in a three-dimensional heterogeneous conductivity fields with realistic internal architecture: Water Resources Research, v. 32, p. 533–545.

WEBB, E.K., AND DAVIS, J.M., 1998, Simulation of the spatial heterogeneity of geologic properties: an overview, in Fraser, G.S., and Davis, J.M., Hydrogeologic Models of Sedimentary Aquifers: SEPM, Concepts in Hydrogeology and Environmental Geology no. 1, p. 1–24.

WEISSMANN, G.S., AND FOGG, G.E., 1999, Multi-scale alluvial fan heterogeneity modeled with transition probability geostatistics in a sequence stratigraphic framework: Journal of Hydrology, v. 226, p. 48–65.

INFLUENCE OF INCISED-VALLEY-FILL DEPOSITS ON HYDROGEOLOGY OF A STREAM-DOMINATED ALLUVIAL FAN

GARY S. WEISSMANN
*Department of Geological Sciences, Michigan State University, 206 Natural Science Building,
East Lansing, Michigan 48824-1115, U.S.A.*
e-mail: weissman@msu.edu
Y. ZHANG
Hydrologic Sciences, University of California, One Shields Avenue, Davis, California 95616, U.S.A.
e-mail: zyong@ucdavis.edu.
GRAHAM E. FOGG
*Hydrologic Sciences, University of California, One Shields Avenue, Davis, California 95616, U.S.A., and
Department of Geology, University of California, One Shields Avenue, Davis, California 95616, U.S.A.*
e-mail: gefogg@ucdavis.edu
AND
JEFFREY F. MOUNT
Department of Geology, University of California, One Shields Avenue, Davis, California 95616, U.S.A.
e-mail: mount@geology.ucdavis.edu.

ABSTRACT: Coarse-grained, incised-valley-fill (IVF) deposits of the Kings River alluvial fan, located southeast of Fresno, California, strongly influence local recharge and groundwater flow, and thus contaminant transport, within the alluvial-fan aquifer. Alluvial-fan sequence stratigraphic concepts provide a framework for predicting the geometry and internal facies associations of the IVF and surrounding depositional sequences. Three-dimensional Markov chain models of spatial variability of facies distributions were developed for each sequence and the uppermost IVF. Facies distributions in individual sequences were simulated separately to avoid geostatistical correlation across unconformity boundaries. These individual realizations were combined to produce a final, three-dimensional, multi-scale model of aquifer hydrofacies distributions.

Modeling of groundwater flow and solute transport within this stratigraphic framework indicates that the coarse-grained IVF significantly influences groundwater flow and contaminant transport in several ways. First, the high degree of gravel/sand body connectivity within the IVF results in rapid groundwater flow relative to the surrounding, generally finer-grained fan deposits. Second, the coarse-grained nature and relatively high hydraulic conductivity of these sediments enhances vertical flow and recharge. Finally, modeling indicates that groundwater and contaminants generally flow from the IVF deposits into the adjacent alluvial-fan deposits. Thus, the IVF not only results in rapid downward and horizontal movement of contaminants but also routes non-point-source contaminants into adjacent deposits. This significantly increases the vulnerability of aquifer sediments adjacent to the IVF to contamination.

INTRODUCTION

Several workers have shown that sedimentary structures and stratigraphy significantly influence groundwater flow and contaminant transport over a wide range in scales (e.g., Fogg, 1986; Anderson, 1989; Scheibe and Freyberg, 1995; Webb and Anderson, 1996; Davis et al., 1997; Ritzi et al., 2000), yet approaches that characterize stratigraphy in a way that is useful for groundwater modeling are still needed. In the petroleum industry, sequence stratigraphic concepts provide a framework from which reservoir models can be developed. However, sequence stratigraphic models for purely continental settings have not been as well developed as those for coastal and marine settings. Shanley and McCabe (1994) suggested that such models can potentially provide similar predictive capabilities in continental settings and should be developed. Recently, Weissmann et al. (2002a) presented a sequence stratigraphic model for a stream-dominated alluvial fan, offering a framework that can potentially improve aquifer characterization. In this paper, we explore the implications of the sequence stratigraphic model for the regional groundwater flow system of a stream-dominated alluvial fan.

In the application of sequence stratigraphic concepts to the Kings River alluvial fan, Weissmann and Fogg (1999) and Weissmann et al. (2002a) identified a 30-meter-thick, coarse-grained, incised-valley-fill (IVF) deposit that originates near the fan apex, is at least 20 km long, and has an average width of about 2 km. This deposit is believed to significantly influence groundwater flow and contaminant transport in the area by providing a large zone for preferential flow (Weissmann et al., 2002a). Additionally, because this deposit has high permeability and is exposed at the fan surface, groundwater may be significantly more vulnerable to contamination within the IVF than outside this paleovalley.

In order to assess the influence of the coarse-grained, IVF deposits on groundwater flow, we conducted a study to (1) further evaluate the facies character and spatial distribution of the IVF; (2) stochastically model the spatial distribution of facies and permeability in the IVF and surrounding strata; and (3) numerically simulate groundwater flow and solute transport through the aquifer within and around the IVF. Results illuminate both the sequence stratigraphy of a stream-dominated alluvial-fan deposit and the important role of IVF deposits within the alluvial fan in controlling groundwater flow and solute transport.

Aquifer Characterization
SEPM Special Publication No. 80, Copyright © 2004
SEPM (Society for Sedimentary Geology), ISBN 1-56576-107-3, p. 15–28.

Study Area

The study area encompasses a 165 km^2 area in the medial portion of the Kings River alluvial fan, a large (approximately 3150 km^2) stream-dominated alluvial fan ("losimean fan" to "braided river fan", after Stanistreet and McCarthy, 1993) located southeast of Fresno, California (Fig. 1). This alluvial fan formed where the Kings River enters the San Joaquin Valley from the Sierra Nevada. The drainage basin upstream from the Kings River alluvial fan covers an area of approximately 4334 km^2, with a maximum elevation of 4269 m above sea level and elevation at the fan apex of 135 m above sea level. The alluvial fan has a low gradient (approximately 0.002) and drains to the west and southwest.

KINGS RIVER ALLUVIAL-FAN SEDIMENTS AND SEQUENCE STRATIGRAPHY

Many workers showed that deposition on the large alluvial fans of the eastern San Joaquin Valley, including the Kings River alluvial fan, occurred during glacial periods in the Sierra Nevada (Janda, 1966; Marchand, 1977; Marchand and Allwardt, 1981; Lettis, 1988; Huntington, 1971, 1980; Atwater et al., 1986). The large sediment supply from outwash during these glacial episodes caused aggradation on the alluvial fans. Bounding these aggradational units are reddish, clay-rich paleosols that indicate relatively long periods of exposure (Janda, 1966; Lettis, 1982, 1988; Weissmann et al., 2002a). Lettis (1988) detailed supporting evidence that this cyclic deposition was related to climatic fluctuations. Weissmann et al. (2002a) observed that this cyclic depositional pattern produced *sequences* in the Kings River alluvial fan, where a sequence is defined as "…a relatively conformable succession of genetically related strata bounded at its top and base by unconformities, or their correlative conformities" (Mitchum, 1977, p. 210). The unconformities, or sequence boundaries, are marked by the relatively mature paleosols and the bases of incised valleys on the mid to upper portions of the alluvial fan. San Joaquin Basin subsidence provided the preservation space (after Blum and Törnqvist, 2000) for these sequences. The sequence stratigraphic model, described in detail by Weissmann et al. (2002a) and briefly below, provides the framework for geostatistical simulation of facies distributions used in our groundwater modeling.

Development of sequence boundaries began on the Kings River alluvial fan at the end of glacial periods and the beginning of interglacial periods, when fan incision and a basinward shift of the fan intersection point (e.g., location on the alluvial fan below which aggradation occurs and above which incision occurs (Wasson, 1974)) occurred due to declines in the ratio of sediment supply to discharge in the Kings River. This fan incision created an incised valley in the middle and upper portions of the fan. Throughout the interglacial period, deposition was confined to the distal portions of the fan while the upper alluvial fan was exposed to erosion, soil development, or modification by eolian processes. The soils formed during the interglacial periods mark the sequence boundaries in the study area.

Rapid aggradation occurred in response to higher sediment supply during the glacial events (Lettis, 1982, 1988; Weissmann et al., 2002a). Initially, the incised valley filled with a fining-upward succession of relatively coarse-grained channel and overbank deposits. Cored wells from the IVF show that the bottom of the IVF is composed of a unit up to 8 m thick that consists of cobbles held within a very coarse sand matrix (Fig. 2B). The very coarse-grained nature of this unit, its position at the base of the IVF, and

the lack of fine sediment indicates deposition in a very high-energy river. This cobble unit grades upward into a succession of very coarse- to coarse-grained, cross-stratified to massive sand that is overlain by a mix of coarse-grained cross-stratified to massive sand interbedded with massive to laminated silt (Fig. 2B). Sedimentary textures and structures in this unit are consistent with deposition in a large fluvial system. The IVF unit is typically coarser grained at and near the surface than surrounding deposits.

The geometry of the most recent IVF was determined from core, well-log, and soil-survey data (Fig. 2). Though water-well logs are typically of low quality and carry considerable uncertainty, drillers usually identify the thick cobble unit accurately because a significant change in drilling character occurs at this contact (e.g., drilling becomes rough, and loss of drilling fluid may occur because of the very high permeability of this bed). The 2 km incised-valley-fill width is indicated on the soil survey, where older fan deposits, identified by the presence of a soil with a thick duripan or argillic horizon, surround an elongate younger fan deposit (Weissmann et al., 2002a). Additionally, in the area where the soil survey indicates the presence of this incised valley, deeper paleosols are absent, indicating that these surfaces were truncated by erosion and incision during the valley formation. This IVF appears to extend downfan at least 20 km from the fan apex.

Importantly, two distinguishing characteristics of the IVF deposit appear to significantly influence the hydrogeology of the region: (1) the basal cobble unit appears to extend across the entire base of the IVF, thus forming a conduit for groundwater flow, and (2) the incised valley truncates the sequence-bounding paleosols that form laterally extensive confining beds in other portions of the aquifer (Weissmann, 1999; Weissmann et al., 2002b; Weissmann et al., 2002c).

Continued deposition due to high ratios of sediment supply to discharge during glacial periods eventually filled the incised valley. Upon filling of the incised valley, the intersection point stabilized near the fan apex. This led to unconfined deposition across the entire alluvial-fan surface, or open-fan deposition. These open-fan deposits consist of a mix of discrete coarse-grained channel-fill deposits within fine-grained, silt-dominated overbank deposits (Fig. 2; Weissmann et al., 2002a). Sediments in the study area are predominantly open-fan deposits. The end of glaciation led to repetition of this stratigraphic cycle with subsequent decrease in the ratio of sediment supply to discharge, fan incision, basinward shift in deposition, and soil development on the upper alluvial fan.

Autogenic mechanisms related to fan-head entrenchment and depositional cyclicity, as described in experiments by Schumm et al. (1987), were considered improbable as mechanisms responsible for the depositional cycles observed on the Kings River alluvial fan, for several reasons. First, the modern incised valley is 3 m deep and, therefore, too deep to fill under the current depositional regime and too deep for a flood on the Kings River to overtop. We assume that similar conditions existed during past interglacial periods; thus, past incised valleys would also have been too deep for filling and avulsion. Additionally, the 30 m depth of the uppermost IVF is far too deep to allow autogenic filling, indicating past significant changes in depositional conditions (e.g., long-term changes in the ratio of sediment supply to discharge) to allow aggradation of this deep valley. Second, the deposits in the IVF appear to be related to gradual, albeit relatively rapid, filling because multistory channel deposits and overbank deposits exist in this deposit. Finally, the maturity of sequence-boundary paleosol is consistent with extended exposure time that would occur

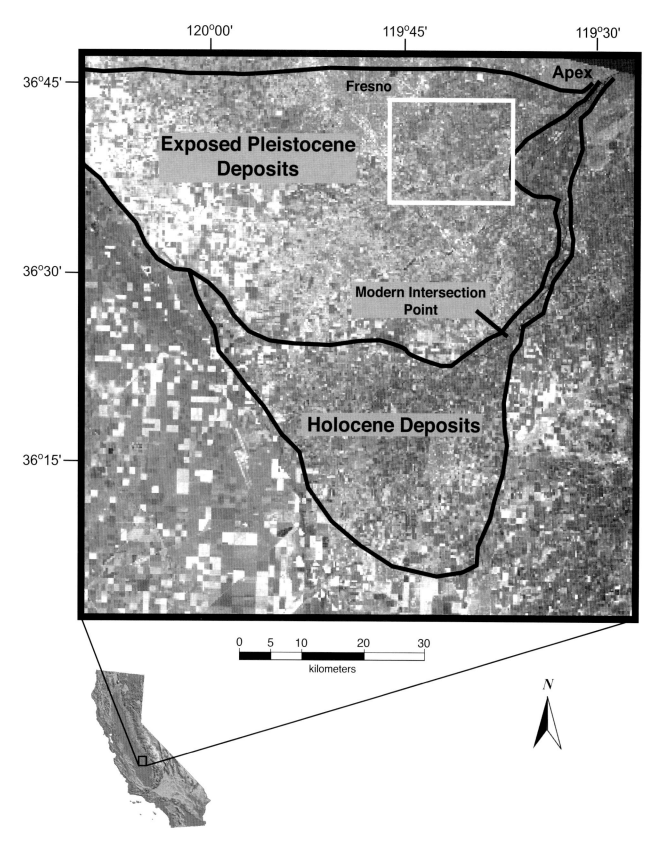

FIG. 1.—Satellite image (Landsat MSS) of the Kings River alluvial fan from the U.S. Geological Survey NALC (North American Landscape Characterization) Project. Age relationships on the fan surface were determined from soil morphologies (Huntington, 1980; Arroues and Anderson, 1986). The study area is located southeast of Fresno. The map in Fig. 2 is outlined in white.

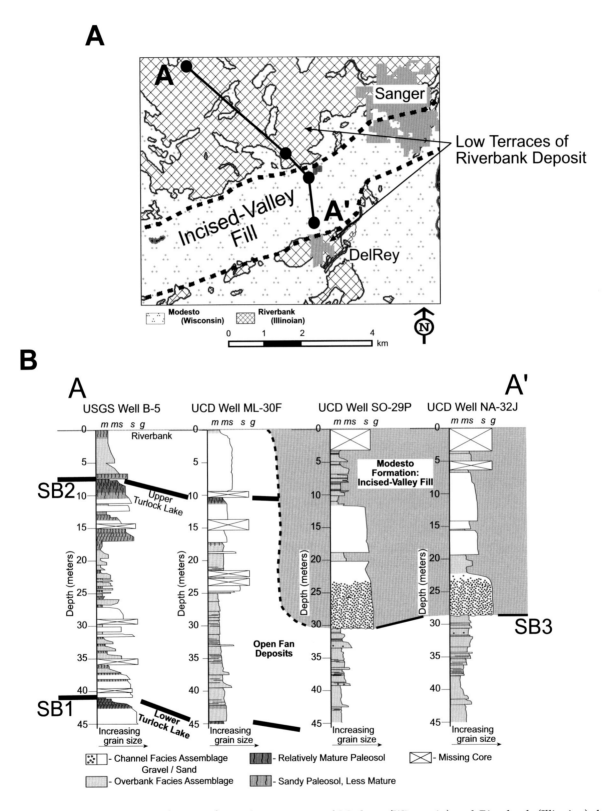

Fig. 2.—**A)** Interpreted soil survey showing the surface exposure of Modesto (Wisconsin) and Riverbank (Illinoian) deposits (modified from Huntington, 1971). Terraces of the Riverbank unit surround the IVF, indicating the lateral extent of the IVF. Wells of cross section A–A' are marked by large solid circles. The map location is noted in Figure 1. **B)** Cross section across the alluvial fan showing the laterally continuous sequence boundaries (SB1, SB2, and SB3) marked by relatively mature paleosols and the base of the IVF. A thick cobble deposit marks the IVF base. Predominant grain size is noted in the graphic core diagrams as *m* – mud (silt and clay); *ms* – muddy sand, or silt dominated sediment; *s* – sand; and *g* – gravel.

on the temporal scales of glacial cyclicity. Paleosols formed under autogenic cyclicity would be expected to display less development (Wright and Alonso Zarza, 1990; Alonso Zarza et al., 1998).

GEOSTATISTICAL HYDROFACIES SIMULATION

We applied a transition-probability geostatistical approach (Carle and Fogg, 1996; Carle et al., 1998) to simulate the distribution of hydrofacies in the Kings River alluvial-fan aquifer (Weissmann et al., 1999; Weissmann and Fogg, 1999). In this indicator geostatistical approach, transition probabilities between hydrofacies are measured in the vertical and horizontal directions and a three-dimensional Markov chain model is fitted to these measured results. The Markov chain model is then used in sequential indicator simulation followed by simulated annealing to produce realizations of the subsurface facies distributions (Carle and Fogg, 1996; Carle, 1997). Transition-probability geostatistics is a stochastic approach to modeling the distribution of facies that allows introduction of geologic reasoning (Carle et al., 1998; Weissmann et al., 1999; Weissmann and Fogg, 1999; Ritzi, 2000). Incorporation of geologic information allows development of improved Markov chain models in the typically undersampled lateral directions (Weissmann et al., 1999). Additionally, asymmetrical facies successions, such as fining-upward trends, are modeled through this approach.

Key parameters for developing the Markov chain model include proportions of each hydrofacies, mean lengths of each hydrofacies along principal directions (i.e., depositional strike, depositional dip, and vertical), and embedded transition probabilities to represent cross-correlation between different facies (Carle and Fogg, 1996; Weissmann et al., 1999), where embedded transition probability is a measure of the probability of one facies contacting another facies in a specific direction (Carle and Fogg, 1998; Weissmann et al., 1999).

Sequence stratigraphic concepts provided a framework for modeling facies distributions in the Kings River alluvial fan (Weissmann and Fogg, 1999). In this approach, we started with a deterministic model of large-scale features (e.g., sequence-bounding paleosols and sequence geometries) through well-log correlation (Figs. 2, 3). Paleosol correlation was based on stratigraphic position noted in well logs. Shallow seismic and ground-penetrating-radar surveys, conducted by Burow et al. (1997),

support these correlations. Erosional breaks through these paleosols, which were probably developed during initial reactivation of the fan surface, and the variable paleosol thicknesses were modeled stochastically. The hydrofacies distributions in each sequence were stochastically simulated using a Markov chain model appropriate for that unit, thus avoiding cross-correlation between sediments of different sequences. These individual sequence and paleosol realizations were combined to produce a final stochastic model of aquifer heterogeneity that honors the multiscale nature of these complex deposits (Fig. 4). Weissmann and Fogg (1999) detailed this modeling approach, but recently collected core from inside the IVF provide data that improve the stochastic realizations significantly. The following section reviews the approach of Weissmann and Fogg (1999) and describes the new IVF models.

Modeling Sequence Geometries

The Kings River alluvial fan consists of four sequences related to Pleistocene glacial cycles and a basal unit that represents deposition prior to major Sierran glaciations (Weissmann et al., 2002a). Correlation of these units to regional stratigraphy of the San Joaquin Valley, described by Marchand and Allwardt (1981) and Lettis (1988), were inferred on the basis of stratigraphic position, paleomagnetism, and surface exposures, and represent, from oldest to youngest, the Pliocene Lower Turlock Lake, Upper Turlock Lake, Riverbank, and Modesto units (Weissmann et al., 2002a).

The presence of laterally extensive paleosols that bound these units allowed correlation of the sequences between wells (Fig. 2B; Weissmann and Fogg, 1999; Weissmann et al., 2002a). Elevations of each sequence boundary were interpolated between wells using the TOPOGRID utility in ArcINFO (ESRI, 2001). This interpolation scheme was selected because it uses a drainage-enforcement algorithm to build surfaces that have connected drainage patterns with few sinks or undrained low areas, thus these surfaces are more consistent with regions exposed to erosion than surfaces produced by other interpolation schemes (Hutchinson, 1989, 1993; ESRI, 2001). The IVF geometry was estimated with the natural neighbor algorithm in GMS (BYU, 2000) using the soil surveys and well logs as conditioning data. Figure 3 shows the modeled distribution of sequences in the study area.

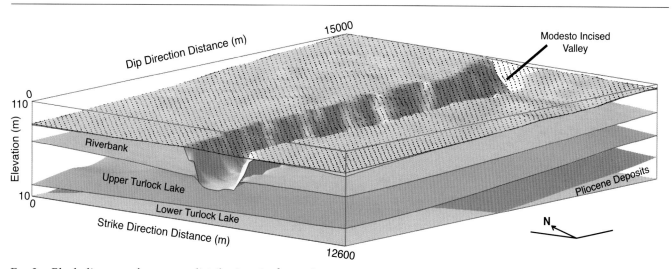

FIG. 3.—Block diagram of sequence distributions in the study area.

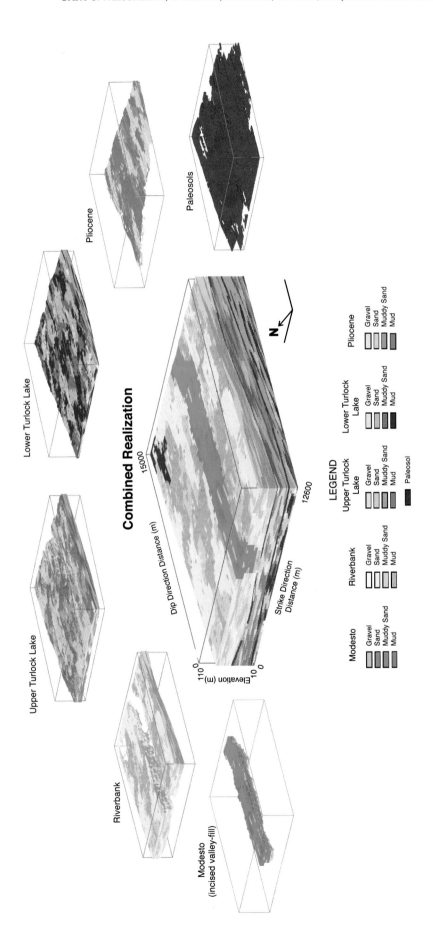

Fig. 4.—Examples of stochastic realizations for each of the stratigraphic sequences. The final combined realization is a compilation of these individual sequence realizations.

Simulation of Hydrofacies Distributions

The Riverbank, Upper Turlock Lake, and Lower Turlock Lake units were deposited on the open alluvial fan during different glacial outwash episodes, and paleosols are absent in these deposits. Relatively mature paleosols, however, separate these three sequences. In contrast, the basal Pliocene unit was deposited on the open fan during an extended period of wetter climate; thus, relatively mature paleosols exist in the open-fan strata. Finally, the Modesto unit in the study area was deposited in an incised valley and represents rapid aggradation in the incised valley during the last glacial episode (Weissmann and Fogg, 1999; Weissmann et al., 2002a). Because these units have different character, Markov chain models for each unit type were developed to account for the different internal facies geometries in each of these units.

Open-Fan-Deposit Models.—

Calculated transition rates between facies are similar between the three open-fan units (i.e., the Riverbank, Upper Turlock Lake, and Lower Turlock Lake units); thus Weissmann and Fogg (1999) used a single open-fan Markov chain model to simulate each of these sequences. These deposits consist of *gravel* and *sand* hydrofacies in the channels and *muddy sand* and *mud* hydrofacies in the overbank deposits. Thus, a four-category Markov chain model was used in simulation of these units. The sequence-bounding paleosols between these units were modeled in a later step.

The Markov chain model for these open-fan deposits reflects deposition in a fluvial setting (Table 1). Fining-upward successions, noted in core, are represented by embedded transition probabilities used in the vertical Markov chain model, where the probability of transitioning upward from *gravel* to *sand* and from *sand* to *muddy sand* (0.98 and 0.88, respectively) is significantly higher than transition probabilities upward from *sand* to *gravel* or *muddy sand* to *sand* (0.06 and 0.17, respectively) (Weissmann and Fogg, 1999). Lateral Markov chain models (Table 1) were developed from facies-embedded transition probabilities measured from the study-area soil survey and by assuming that hydrofacies have a statistically symmetrical distribution (Weissmann et al.,

1999). Figure 4 shows the resulting realizations for the three open-fan units using this model.

Pliocene-Deposit Models.—

On the basis of limited core and well-log data, the Pliocene unit was interpreted as open-fan deposits that experienced multiple periods of extended exposure (Weissmann and Fogg, 1999). Thus, the Pliocene unit contains paleosol hydrofacies along with the other four hydrofacies. Therefore, a five-category Markov chain model was developed for this unit (Table 1; Weissmann and Fogg, 1999). Because core and log data were limited, this model was developed on the basis of distributions observed in other open-fan deposits and adjusted for the presence of paleosols (Fig. 4).

Paleosol Models.—

Erosional breaks and variable thicknesses of the large-scale sequence-bounding paleosols were modeled using a two-category Markov chain model (paleosol or not paleosol) (Weissmann and Fogg, 1999). The previously described interpolated sequence-boundary elevations at each grid cell were conditioned as paleosol facies, and mean lengths were defined with large values to force a laterally continuous distribution. An exponential Markov chain model is appropriate for the paleosol units because the coefficient of variability was near unity (Ritzi, 2000). Application of this model produced simulations of laterally extensive sequence-bounding paleosols with varying thickness and erosional breaks (Fig. 4).

IVF Models.—

Markov chain models for facies in the IVF by Weissmann and Fogg (1999) were developed prior to core collection from within the incised valley; therefore, new models are presented here. Because of the striking contrast between the basal cobble deposits and the upper sandy deposits, two separate Markov chain models were developed and applied for each of the units in the incised-valley simulations (Table 2).

TABLE 1.—Embedded transition probability matrices for the Markov chain models of the open fan, Pliocene, and paleosol (from Weissmann and Fogg, 1999).

Unit	Vertical (z) direction	Strike (x) direction	Dip (y) direction
Open-Fan Deposits	$\begin{array}{c c c c c} & g & s & ms & m \\ g & \bar{L}=2.0m & 0.98 & 0.01 & 0.01 \\ s & 0.06 & \bar{L}=3.3m & 0.88 & 0.06 \\ ms & 0.03 & 0.17 & \bar{L}=1.4m & 0.80 \\ m & 0.06 & 0.39 & 0.55 & \bar{L}=1.0m \end{array}$	$\begin{array}{c c c c c} & g & s & ms & m \\ g & \bar{L}=200m & 0.70 & 0.15 & b \\ s & s & \bar{L}=625m & 0.48 & b \\ ms & s & s & \bar{L}=400m & b \\ m & b & b & b & b \end{array}$	$\begin{array}{c c c c c} & g & s & ms & m \\ g & \bar{L}=650m & 0.70 & 0.15 & b \\ s & s & \bar{L}=1500m & 0.48 & b \\ ms & s & s & \bar{L}=800m & b \\ m & b & b & b & b \end{array}$
Pliocene Deposits	$\begin{array}{c c c c c c} & g & s & ms & m & p \\ g & \bar{L}=1.0m & 0.98 & 0.01 & 0.01 & 0.00 \\ s & 0.05 & \bar{L}=3.3m & 0.80 & 0.10 & 0.05 \\ ms & 0.03 & 0.10 & \bar{L}=1.64m & 0.57 & 0.30 \\ m & 0.16 & 0.09 & 0.09 & \bar{L}=2.15m & 0.66 \\ p & 0.10 & 0.20 & 0.15 & 0.55 & \bar{L}=2.0m \end{array}$	$\begin{array}{c c c c c c} & g & s & ms & m & p \\ g & \bar{L}=150m & 0.76 & 0.10 & b & s \\ s & s & \bar{L}=625m & 0.40 & b & s \\ ms & s & s & \bar{L}=215m & b & s \\ m & s & s & s & b & s \\ p & 0.007 & 0.04 & 0.25 & b & \bar{L}=800m \end{array}$	$\begin{array}{c c c c c c} & g & s & ms & m & p \\ g & \bar{L}=500m & 0.76 & 0.10 & b & s \\ s & s & \bar{L}=1500m & 0.40 & b & s \\ ms & s & s & \bar{L}=800m & b & s \\ m & s & s & s & b & s \\ p & 0.007 & 0.04 & 0.25 & b & \bar{L}=1000m \end{array}$
Paleosols	$\begin{array}{c c c} & np & p \\ np & b & b \\ p & b & \bar{L}=1.95m \end{array}$	$\begin{array}{c c c} & np & p \\ np & b & b \\ p & b & \bar{L}=2000m \end{array}$	$\begin{array}{c c c} & np & p \\ np & b & b \\ p & b & \bar{L}=2000m \end{array}$

Entries in the matrix diagonals indicate mean lengths ($\bar{L}$) for that hydrofacies. Entries in the off-diagonal are the embedded probability values used to represent facies juxtaposition relationships. Facies abbreviations are g – gravel; s – sand; ms – muddy sand; m – mud; p – paleosol; np – no paleosol. *b* indicates the background category, and *s* indicates an assumption that the embedded transition probabilities are statistically symmetrical.

TABLE 2.—Embedded transition probability matrices used for Markov chain models in the IVF. Entries in the matrix diagonals indicate mean lengths for that hydrofacies.

Unit	Vertical (z) direction	Strike (x) direction
Basal Gravel Deposits	$\begin{array}{c} \quad g \quad\quad s \\ g\left[\begin{array}{cc} \bar{L}=2.18m & b \\ b & b \end{array}\right] \\ s \end{array}$	$\begin{array}{c} \quad g \quad\quad s \\ g\left[\begin{array}{cc} \bar{L}=1600m & b \\ b & b \end{array}\right] \\ s \end{array}$
Upper Coarse-Grained Deposits	$\begin{array}{c} \quad g \quad\quad s \quad\quad ms \quad m \\ \begin{array}{c} g \\ s \\ ms \\ m \end{array}\left[\begin{array}{cccc} \bar{L}=1.8m & 0.99 & 0.01 & b \\ 0.05 & \bar{L}=3.3m & 0.85 & b \\ 0.03 & 0.17 & \bar{L}=1.4m & b \\ b & b & b & b \end{array}\right] \end{array}$	$\begin{array}{c} \quad g \quad\quad s \quad\quad ms \quad m \\ \begin{array}{c} g \\ s \\ ms \\ m \end{array}\left[\begin{array}{cccc} \bar{L}=200m & 0.75 & 0.10 & b \\ s & \bar{L}=625m & 0.58 & b \\ s & s & \bar{L}=215m & b \\ b & b & b & b \end{array}\right] \end{array}$

Entries in the off-diagonal are the embedded probability values used to represent facies juxtapositi gravel; s – sand; ms – muddy sand; m – mud. *b* indicates the background category, and *s* indicates probabilities are statistically symmetrical.

Core and well-log data show that the basal cobble unit is dominated by the gravel hydrofacies (80% of the unit), with the rest of the unit consisting of thin (up to 1 m thick) sand lenses. Thus, a two-category model (*gravel* and *sand*) was developed to represent this basal unit (Table 2). Insufficient data were available to test the variance in these hydrofacies lengths, but we assumed that the exponential Markov chain model captured the facies variability sufficiently (Ritzi, 2000). Thus, only one parameter, the mean length of the gravel, was needed, because the other three parameters are determined by laws of probability (Carle and Fogg, 1996, 1998). Because the cobble unit appears to extend across the entire IVF, a mean length along strike equal to the average valley width was applied to the strike-direction model. Long dip direction (e.g., parallel to paleoriver flow) lengths were assumed for these units and applied to the dip-direction model.

The upper IVF models were developed in a way similar to those of the open-fan units. The vertical Markov chain models were estimated by matching transition-probability measurements from core facies distributions (Table 2). Mean lengths and juxtaposition relationships for the lateral Markov chain models were estimated from hydrofacies distributions observed in the soil survey (Weissmann et al., 1999). Proportions of each hydrofacies were assumed equal to proportions measured in core. Simulated results reasonably represent the coarse-grained nature and overall fining-upward tendency of the IVF deposit (Fig. 4).

Final Combined Realization.—

By combining these individual realizations, we produced a final realization that represents the multiscale nature of the Kings River alluvial fan study area (Fig. 4). The large-scale differences in facies distributions between Pliocene deposits, open-fan deposits, IVF deposits, and laterally extensive paleosols are preserved in this realization. Additionally, the realization shows the fining-upward nature of the channel deposits. By assigning values of hydraulic conductivity (K) to each hydrofacies (Table 3), this realization of hydrofacies distributions was used to represent heterogeneity in K in the following simulations of groundwater flow and solute transport. Values used for K of each hydrofacies (Table 3) were estimated from pumping-test, slug-test, and laboratory-core measurements, and literature estimates for similar lithologies (Burow et al., 1999; Weissmann, 1999; Weissmann et al., 2002c).

SIMULATION OF GROUNDWATER FLOW AND SOLUTE TRANSPORT

Modeling of Groundwater Flow

A three-dimensional steady-state model was used to simulate groundwater flow in the aquifer system. Although regional groundwater pumping may significantly affect groundwater flow in the study area, this was not included in this steady-state model because our goal was to assess the influence of coarse-grained IVF deposits on groundwater flow in the aquifer.

MODFLOW-96, a numerical finite-difference groundwater flow model (McDonald and Harbaugh, 1988; Harbaugh and McDonald, 1996), was used to simulate groundwater flow in the study area. The study area, with overall dimensions of 12,600 m x 15,000 m x 100.5 m in the depositional-strike, depositional-dip, and vertical directions, respectively, was discretized into a simulation grid consisting of approximately 950,000 cells. Each cell had equal dimensions of 200 m x 200 m x 0.5 m in the depositional-strike, depositional-dip, and vertical directions, respectively. Relative to average hydrofacies lengths used in the geostatistical simulation, this cell size allows several cells to be contained within individual hydrofacies units. K for the groundwater simulation was assigned to each cell on the basis of the simulated hydrofacies determined by the geostatistical realization for each scenario.

TABLE 3.—Values of hydraulic conductivity of the hydrofacies used for the simulations.

Hydrofacies	*K (m/s)*
Gravel	1×10^{-2}
Sand	1×10^{-3}
Muddy Sand	1×10^{-5}
Mud	1×10^{-6}
Paleosol	1.3×10^{-7}

General head boundary conditions (McDonald and Harbaugh, 1988) were used in the modeling to simulate inflow and outflow through the lateral and basal boundaries of the model. Head values were defined for these boundaries using an average gradient of 0.002 parallel to the stratigraphic dip direction. Minor adjustments to these head values were made along the stratigraphic dip boundaries to account for local gradient variability reported in water-elevation maps of the study area (Fresno Irrigation District, 1993). No vertical gradient was imposed, because measured vertical gradients in the area are small and locally variable (Burow et al., 1999). The boundary condition for the top of the model accounts for variable recharge rates caused by the heterogeneous distribution of hydrofacies above the water table. A constant net infiltration rate of 150 mm/yr (Burow et al., 1999) was scaled in proportion with K of overlying beds for each cell at the water table. Simulated lithologies above the water table (located at approximately 10 meters depth) were used to define the recharge rates. For example, an interconnected coarse-grained sediment body above the water table (e.g., the IVF) received a higher recharge rate than a fine-grained unit.

Simulation of Solute Transport

Simulations of solute transport employed a random-walk particle tracking method (RWPM), described by LaBolle et al. (1998) and LaBolle et al. (2000). Application of the RWPM to simulate the forward-time advection–dispersion equation simulates future particle distributions, with particle density representing solute concentration given knowledge of past distributions. Details of the RWPM are described in Uffink (1989), LaBolle et al. (1996), LaBolle et al. (1998), and LaBolle et al. (2000). We use Labolle et al.'s (2000) implementation of the RWPM in the program RWHET, in which both advection-dominated and diffusion-dominated transport are handled accurately even when lithologic transitions are sharp.

Parameter values required for the RWPM include groundwater velocities calculated from the flow simulations, molecular diffusion, effective porosity, and longitudinal (a_L) and transverse (a_T) dispersivities. Molecular diffusivity (D^*) was estimated to be approximately 6.9×10^{-10} m^2/s (Weissmann et al., 2002c). An effective porosity value of 0.33 was applied for these simulations. This porosity value was chosen because it represents an average porosity value for the unconsolidated facies in the alluvial-fan succession. The larger-scale heterogeneity, described by the hydrofacies simulations, dominates the field-scale longitudinal dispersion, making results of transport simulation insensitive to the value of local-scale a_L (LaBolle, 1999; LaBolle and Fogg, 2001). Therefore, values of a_L and a_T were both set to 0.04 m, an appropriate value for dispersivity at the scale of our simulation cells (Weissmann et al., 2002c). Sensitivity runs with a set to 0.1 and 0.01 m showed minimal effects on the results reported here (Weissmann, 1999; Weissmann et al., 2002c). Results are representative of a conservative, dissolved tracer with no chemical reactions.

Two numerical experiments were used to assess the influence of the coarse-grained IVF on groundwater flow, contaminant transport, and vulnerability of the aquifer to contamination from surface sources. In the first experiment, we released 5000 particles from two upgradient point locations at the water table, one in the IVF and the other in open-fan deposits, comparing the resulting "tracer" plume character between these two settings (Figs. 5, 6). In lieu of simulating multiple realizations, we released particles from several locations in the IVF and the open-fan deposits in order to evaluate the influence of local facies distributions on particle transport. In the second experiment, we released 10,000 particles from a line source at the water table across both the IVF and the open-fan deposits at the upgradient end of the IVF (Fig. 7).

RESULTS AND DISCUSSION

The results of these experiments show that the IVF influences groundwater flow and contaminant transport in three ways (Figs. 5–7): (1) faster downfan transport occurs inside the IVF relative to that outside the valley; (2) enhanced recharge and downward (vertical) transport occurs in the incised valley; and (3) contaminants entering the IVF may be transported relatively rapidly to adjacent open-fan deposits.

Rapid downfan transport is shown in the point-release experiment by the breakthrough of particles 6 km downfan from the release points (Fig. 5). For the IVF point releases (Fig. 5A), initial breakthrough of particles migrating through the IVF occurs after at least five years. A bimodal distribution of the particle breakthrough is apparent in all of the particle-release simulations (Fig. 5A). The larger, early-breakthrough peak, typically between 5 and 15 years, is from particles that traveled primarily through the basal cobbles in the IVF. Slight tailing on this first peak is related to particles that traveled primarily through the upper part of the IVF. Particles that moved out of the IVF into surrounding open-fan deposits take longer to travel 6 km from the source, creating the second peak of particle arrivals, typically observed between 14 to 35 years. Thus, particles that took the longest to travel the 6 km from the IVF point-release locations mostly left the IVF and entered the slower, open-fan deposits. Several particles, however, were also observed to be slowed by low-K facies near the particle release point (Fig. 6A), adding to this second breakthrough peak.

In contrast to the IVF release, particles released in the open-fan deposits typically took more than 15 years to migrate the 6 km downgradient from the source (Fig. 5B). With the exception of the point release at 2900 m, particle breakthrough occurs as a dispersed peak with a long tail. The point release at 2900 m is different because particles were released in a connected channel deposit; therefore, particles migrated downfan faster than observed in the other simulations. Comparing these results to breakthrough in the IVF releases shows that contaminants inside the IVF appear to typically travel downgradient at about twice the speed of those in the open-fan deposits.

Rapid transport in the IVF comes as no surprise because overall K is significantly higher in these deposits. Interestingly, however, overall plume dispersion in the longitudinal direction is still relatively high for the IVF release because of the disparity between fast-moving particles inside the IVF and slow particles that left the IVF and traveled through the open-fan deposits (Figs. 5, 6). Particles that travel through the basal cobbles of the IVF are transported downfan relatively rapidly; however, particles that moved from the IVF into the surrounding open-fan deposits are slowed.

In addition to rapid downfan transport in the IVF, particles released in the IVF also moved vertically downward more rapidly than those released in the open-fan deposits (Fig. 6). Two reasons for this enhanced downward transport are indicated by these simulations. First, the absence of sequence-bounding paleosols inside the IVF (because the incised valley truncates the paleosols) allows greater vertical mobility of contaminants. In the open-fan deposits, these paleosols act as laterally extensive confining beds that inhibit vertical transport (Fig. 6; Weissmann, 1999; Weissmann et al., 2002c). Second, the coarser-grained IVF has higher K, which allows greater recharge in this portion of the fan system and enhances local vertical gradients that force particles downward at a higher rate.

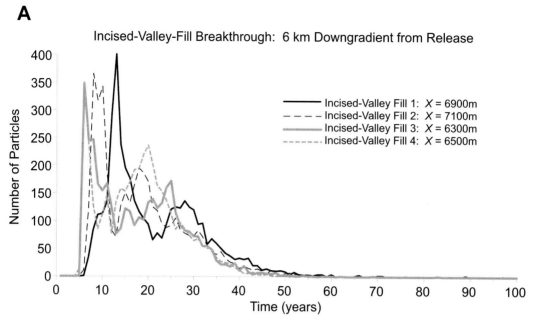

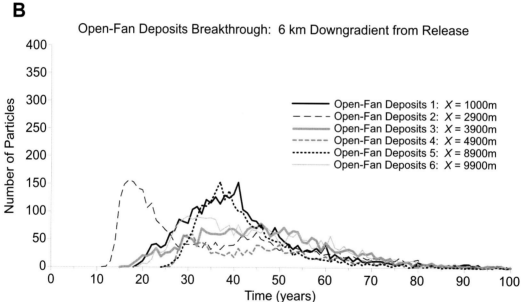

FIG. 5.—Comparing transport in IVF and open-fan deposits: **A)** Breakthrough curves 6 km downgradient from point releases at four different locations in the IVF. All point releases were located 1500 m from the upgradient boundary. The X distance notes the location relative to the northern simulation boundary. **B)** Breakthrough curves 6 km downgradient from point releases at six different locations in the open-fan deposits. All curves represent breakthrough at a plane perpendicular to the prevailing lateral flow direction.

Higher recharge rates to the IVF deposits also result in groundwater flow moving outward from the IVF to the surrounding open-fan deposits. This is indicated by the line-source experiment, in which particles were released in both open-fan and IVF deposits along a line source at the water table. Particles tend to move from the IVF into the open-fan deposits rather than from the open-fan deposits to the IVF (Fig. 7). Groundwater flow from IVF to open-fan deposits, combined with the rapid downward transport inside the IVF, allows contaminants (and recharged water) that enter the aquifer from the IVF to be transported

rapidly into deeper (30+ m) open-fan deposits below partially confining paleosols (Figs. 6, 7).

These results can be viewed as both good news and bad news in terms of aquifer management. The IVF potentially benefits groundwater managers by providing a relatively large (>40 km²) area that is conducive to enhanced groundwater recharge operations. The coarse-grained fill allows higher recharge rates, and this groundwater migrates to deeper portions of the aquifer because laterally extensive paleosols are bypassed. Unfortunately, this also provides a pathway for contaminants to more readily

A   Incised-Valley-Fill Point Release

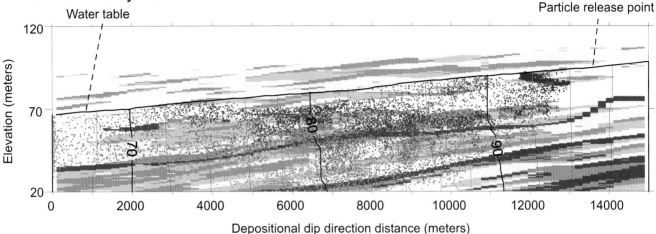

B   Open-Fan-Deposit Point Release

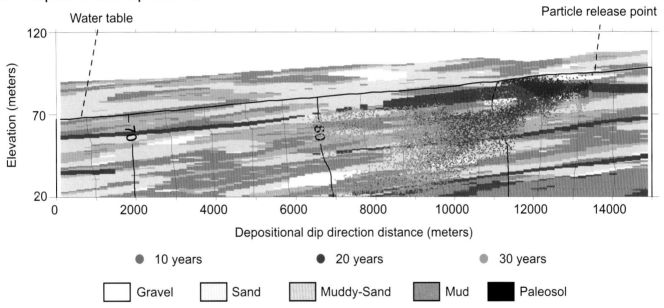

● 10 years   ● 20 years   ● 30 years

☐ Gravel   ☐ Sand   ▨ Muddy-Sand   ▨ Mud   ■ Paleosol

Fɪɢ. 6.—**A)** Particle locations at 10, 20, and 30 years for the IVF point-release experiment. Contours show the hydraulic heads. **B)** Particle locations at 10, 20, and 30 years for the open-fan-deposit point-release experiment. All particles are projected onto the 2-D vertical plane. Textural facies represent only those within a single slice through the model.

enter deeper portions of the aquifer, thus increasing the vulnerability of the aquifer surrounding the IVF to contamination.

CONCLUSIONS

A sequence stratigraphic model significantly improved our ability to model and understand spatial patterns in K that affect groundwater flow in the Kings River alluvial fan. In this stream-dominated alluvial fan, the IVF deposits are significantly more coarse-grained and lack paleosols compared to surrounding open-fan deposits. The IVF, deposited during periods of glacial outwash and rapid aggradation, generally fines upward, with a thick, cobble-dominated unit at its base that is overlain by medium to very coarse channel sand with some overbank silty fines.

In contrast, open-fan deposits contain a higher proportion of overbank deposits without thick, laterally extensive gravelly channel deposits. Open-fan units, or sequences, are separated by laterally extensive, clay-rich paleosols.

Simulation of hydrofacies distributions in the IVF and open-fan deposits, using transition-probability geostatistics in a sequence-stratigraphic framework, provided the template for modeling of groundwater flow. Without the sequence-stratigraphic framework, geostatistical and groundwater simulations would not have been able to reasonably reflect the complexity of this aquifer.

Numerical simulation of groundwater flow and solute transport indicated that: (1) most flow in the IVF moves downgradient at a higher speed than in surrounding deposits; (2) the coarse-

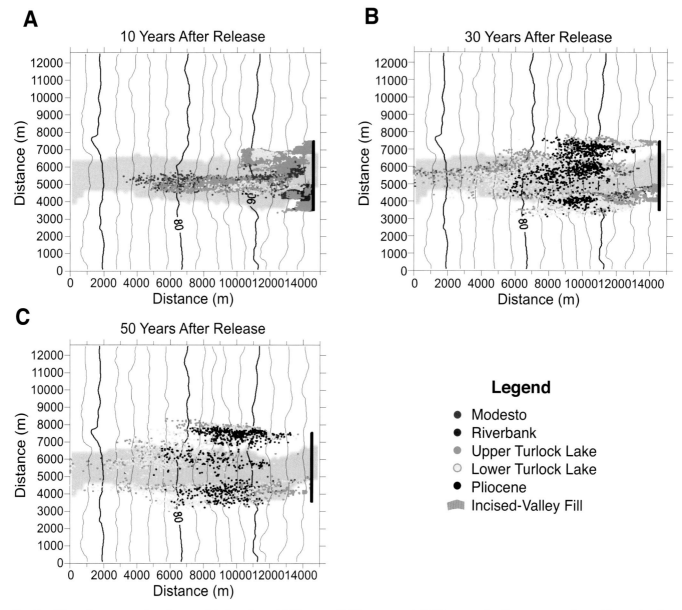

FIG. 7.—Plan-view maps showing particle locations **A)** 10 years, **B)** 30 years, and **C)** 50 years after line-source release (shown by the black bar) in and around the IVF. Particle colors indicate which sequence holds the particle. The gray shaded area outlines the IVF deposit.

grained nature of this unit enhances deep recharge to a significant portion of the aquifer system; and (3) contaminants entering the IVF can be transported relatively rapidly to deeper portions of the aquifer system, thus increasing local aquifer vulnerability to contamination.

Simplified aquifer conditions (e.g., no pumping, steady-state flow, constant porosity) used in this study indicate that the IVF deposits significantly influence transport character; however, more complete models that include realistic transient conditions could be used to better quantify these results. Additionally, the models should be validated by comparison with tracer data, potentially applying environmental tracer data to obtain tracer concentrations related to distributions of groundwater age. Simulation methods applied to modeling distributions of groundwater age from environmental tracer transport in the open-fan deposits can be used to

test whether model results are consistent with actual flow conditions (Weissmann et al., 2000; Weissmann et al., 2002c). Finally, these results are based on analysis of a single realization of aquifer heterogeneity in K. Future simulations of groundwater flow and contaminant transport will be run on multiple realizations, although we do not anticipate that the general transport results will change significantly.

ACKNOWLEDGMENTS

This research was supported by the Cooperative State Research Service, U.S. Department of Agriculture, under Agreement No. 93-38420-8792, the National Science Foundation (Award Nos. 98-70342 and 02-08492), University of California Water Resources Center (#W-901), Occidental Chemical Company,

N.I.E.H.S. Superfund Program (P42 ES04699), and the Geological Society of America (research grant 5736-95). This work would not have been possible without the data and insights provided by Karen Burow and the U.S. Geological Survey. We benefited greatly from discussions with Thomas Harter, Gordon Huntington, Michael Singer, Gil Eschel, Eric LaBolle, and Steve Carle. Comments by Dr. Robert Ritzi, Dr. Ian Lunt, and Dr. John Bridge enhanced the manuscript significantly.

REFERENCES

ALONSO ZARZA, A.M., SILVA, P.G., GOY, J.L., AND ZAZO, C., 1998, Fan-surface dynamics and biogenic calcrete development: interactions during ultimate phases of fan evolution in semiarid SE Spain (Murcia): Geomorphology, v. 24, p. 147–167.

ANDERSON, M.P., 1989, Hydrogeologic facies models to delineate large-scale spatial trends in glacial and glaciofluvial sediments: Geological Society of America, Bulletin, v. 101, p. 501–511.

ARROUES, K.D., AND ANDERSON, C.H., JR., 1986, Soil Survey of Kings County, California: U.S. Department of Agriculture, U.S. Government Printing Office, 212 p.

ATWATER, B.F., ADAM, D.P., BRADBURY, J.P., FORESTER, R.M., MARK, R.K., LETTIS, W.R., FISHER, G.R., GOBALET, K.W., AND ROBINSON, S.W., 1986, A fan dam for Tulare Lake, California, and implications for the Wisconsin glacial history of the Sierra Nevada: Geological Society of America, Bulletin, v. 97, p. 97–109.

BLUM, M.D., AND TÖRNQVIST, T.E., 2000, Fluvial responses to climate and sea-level change: a review and look forward: Sedimentology, v. 47, p. 2–48.

BUROW, K.R., PANSHIN, S.Y., DUBROVSKY, N.M., VANBROCKLIN, D., AND FOGG, G.E., 1999, Evaluation of processes affecting 1,2-Dibromo-3-Chloropropane (DBCP) concentrations in ground water in the eastern San Joaquin Valley, California: Analysis of chemical data and ground-water flow and transport simulations: U.S. Geological Survey, Water-Resources Investigations Report 99-4059, 57 p.

BUROW, K.R., WEISSMANN, G.S., MILLER, R.D., AND PLACZEK, G., 1997, Hydrogeologic facies characterization of an alluvial fan near Fresno, California, using geophysical techniques: U.S. Geological Survey, Open-File Report 97-46, 15p.

BYU (BRIGHAM YOUNG UNIVERSITY), 2000, The Department of Defense Groundwater Modeling System 3.1 (GMS): Environmental Modeling Research Laboratory, Provo, Utah.

CARLE, S.F., 1997, Implementation schemes for avoiding artifact discontinuities in simulated annealing: Mathematical Geology, v. 29, p. 231–244.

CARLE, S.F., AND FOGG, G.E., 1996, Transition probability–based indicator geostatistics: Mathematical Geology, v. 28, p. 453–476.

CARLE, S.F., AND FOGG, G.E., 1998, TPMOD: A Transition Probability/Markov Approach to Geostatistical Modeling and Simulation, User Documentation: University of California, Davis, 75 p.

CARLE, S.F., LABOLLE, E.M., WEISSMANN, G.S., VANBROCKLIN, D., AND FOGG, G.E., 1998, Conditional simulation of hydrofacies architecture: a transition probability/Markov approach, in Fraser, G.S., and Davis, J.M., Hydrogeologic Models of Sedimentary Aquifers: SEPM, Concepts in Hydrogeology and Environmental Geology no. 1, p. 147–170.

DAVIS, J.M., WILSON, J.L., PHILLIPS, F.M., AND GOTKOWITZ, M.D., 1997, Relationship between fluvial bounding surfaces and the permeability correlation structure: Water Resources Research, v. 33, p. 1843–1854.

ESRI (ENVIRONMENTAL SYSTEMS RESEARCH INSTITUTE), 2001, ARC Commands: ArcINFO 8.0 documentation manual.

FOGG, G.E., 1986, Groundwater flow and sand body interconnectedness in a thick, multiple-aquifer system: Water Resources Research, v. 22, p. 679–694.

FRESNO IRRIGATION DISTRICT, 1993, Ground-water Elevation Map, January, 1993: Fresno, California, Fresno Irrigation District, Scale 1 inch = 2.5 miles.

HARBAUGH, A.W., AND McDONALD, M.G., 1996, User's documentation for MODFLOW-96, an update to the US Geological Survey Modular Finite-Difference Ground-Water Flow Model: U.S. Geological Survey, Open File Report, 96–485, 56 p.

HUNTINGTON, G.L., 1971, Soil Survey, Eastern Fresno Area, California: U.S. Department of Agriculture, Soil Conservation Service, U.S. Government Printing Office, 323 p.

HUNTINGTON, G.L., 1980, Soil–Land Form Relationships of Portions of the San Joaquin River and Kings River Alluvial Depositional Systems in the Great Valley of California: unpublished Ph.D. Dissertation, University of California at Davis, 147 p.

HUTCHINSON, M.F., 1989, A new procedure for gridding elevation and stream line data with automatic removal of spurious pits: Journal of Hydrology, v. 106, p. 211–232.

HUTCHINSON, M.F., 1993, Development of a continent-wide DEM with applications to terrain and climate analysis, in Goodchild, M.F., Parks, B.O., and Steyaert, L.T., eds., Environmental Modeling with GIS: New York, Oxford University Press, p. 392–399.

JANDA, R.J., 1966, Pleistocene history and hydrology of the upper San Joaquin River, California: Unpublished Ph.D. Dissertation, University of California, Berkeley, 293 p.

LABOLLE, E.M., 1999, Theory and Simulation of Diffusion Processes in Porous Media: unpublished Ph.D. Dissertation, University of California, Davis, 202 p.

LABOLLE, E.M., AND FOGG, G.E., 2001, Role of molecular diffusion in contaminant migration and recovery in an alluvial aquifer system: Transport in Porous Media (Special Issue on Modeling Dispersion), v. 42, p. 155–179.

LABOLLE, E.M., FOGG, G.E., AND TOMPSON, A.F.B., 1996, Random-walk simulation of transport in heterogeneous porous media: Local mass-conservation problem and implementation methods: Water Resources Research, v. 32, p. 583–393.

LABOLLE, E.M., QUASTEL, J., AND FOGG, G.E., 1998, Diffusion theory for transport in porous media: Transition-probability densities of diffusion processes corresponding to advection–dispersion equations: Water Resources Research, v. 34, p. 1685–1693.

LABOLLE, E.M., QUASTEL, J., FOGG, G.E., AND GRAVNER, J., 2000, Diffusion processes in composite porous media and their numerical integration by random walks: Generalized stochastic differential equations with discontinuous coefficients: Water Resources Research, v. 36, p. 651–662.

LETTIS, W.R., 1982, Late Cenozoic stratigraphy and structure of the western margin of the central San Joaquin Valley, California: U.S. Geological Survey, Open-File Report 82-526, 203 p.

LETTIS, W.R., 1988, Quaternary geology of the Northern San Joaquin Valley, in Graham, S.A., ed., Studies of the Geology of the San Joaquin Basin: SEPM, Pacific Section, v. 60, p. 333–351.

MARCHAND, D.E., 1977, The Cenozoic history of the San Joaquin Valley and the adjacent Sierra Nevada as inferred from the geology and soils of the eastern San Joaquin Valley, in Singer, M.J., ed., Soil Development, Geomorphology, and Cenozoic History of the Northeastern San Joaquin Valley and Adjacent Areas, California: University of California Press, Guidebook for Joint Field Session, Soil Science Society of America and Geological Society of America, p. 39–50.

MARCHAND, D.E., AND ALLWARDT, A., 1981, Late Cenozoic Stratigraphic Units, Northeastern San Joaquin Valley, California: U.S. Geological Survey, Bulletin 1470, 70 p.

McDONALD, M.G., AND HARBAUGH, A.W., 1988, A modular three-dimensional finite difference ground-water flow model, Chapter A1: US Geological Survey, Techniques of Water-Resources Investigations, Book 6.

MITCHUM, R.M., JR., 1977, Seismic stratigraphy and global changes of sea level, part 11: glossary of terms used in seismic stratigraphy, in Payton, C.E., ed., Seismic Stratigraphy—Applications to Hydrocarbon Exploration: American Association of Petroleum Geologists, Memoir 26, p. 205–212.

RITZI, R.W., JR., 2000, Behavior of indicator variograms and transition probabilities in relation to the variance in lengths of hydrofacies: Water Resources Research, v. 36, p. 3375–3381.

RITZI, R.W., JR., DOMINIC, D.F., SLESERS, A.J., GREER, C.B., REBOULET, E.C., TELFORD, J.A., MASTERS, R.W., KLOHE, C.A., BOGLE, J.L., AND MEANS, B.P., 2000, Comparing statistical models of physical heterogeneity in buried-valley aquifers: Water Resources Research, v. 36, p. 3179-3192.

SCHEIBE, T.D., AND FREYBERG, D.L., 1995, The use of sedimentological information for geometric simulation of natural porous media structure: Water Resources Research, v. 31, p. 3259–3270.

SCHUMM, S.A., MOSLEY, M.P., AND WEAVER, W.E., 1987, Experimental Fluvial Geomorphology: New York, John Wiley, 413 p.

SHANLEY, K.W., AND MCCABE, P.J., 1994, Perspectives on the sequence stratigraphy of continental strata: American Association of Petroleum Geologists, Bulletin, v. 78, p. 544–568.

STANISTREET, I.G., AND MCCARTHY, T.S., 1993, The Okavango Fan and the classification of subaerial fans: Sedimentary Geology, v. 85, p. 114–133.

UFFINK, G.J.M., 1989, Application of Kolmogorov's backward equation in random walk simulations of groundwater contaminant transport, in Kobus, H.E., and Kinzelbach, W., eds., Contaminant Transport in Groundwater: Proceedings of the International Symposium on Contaminant Transport in Groundwater, p. 283–298.

WASSON, R.J., 1974, Intersection point deposition on alluvial fans: an Australian example: Geografiska Annaler, v. 56, p. 83–92.

WEBB, E.K., AND ANDERSON, M.P., 1996, Simulation of preferential flow in three-dimensional heterogeneous conductivity fields with realistic internal architecture: Water Resources Research, v. 32, p. 533–545.

WEISSMANN, G.S., 1999, Toward New Models of Subsurface Heterogeneity: An Alluvial Fan Sequence Stratigraphic Framework with Transition Probability Geostatistics: unpublished Ph.D. Dissertation, University of California, Davis, 279 p.

WEISSMANN, G.S., CARLE, S.F., AND FOGG, G.E., 1999, Three-dimensional hydrofacies modeling based on soil surveys and transition probability geostatistics: Water Resources Research, v. 35, p. 1761–1770.

WEISSMANN, G.S., AND FOGG, G.E., 1999, Multi-scale alluvial fan heterogeneity modeled with transition probability geostatistics in a sequence stratigraphic framework: Journal of Hydrology, v. 226, p. 48–65.

WEISSMANN, G.S., LABOLLE, E.M., AND FOGG, G.E., 2000, Modeling environmental tracer–based groundwater ages in heterogeneous aquifers, in Bentley, L.R., Sykes, J.F., Brebbia, C.A., Gray, W.G., and Pinder, G.F., eds., Computational Methods in Water Resources: XIII International Conference on Computational Methods in Water Resources, Calgary, Alberta, Canada, June 25–29, 2000, Proceedings, p. 805–811.

WEISSMANN, G.S., MOUNT, J.F., AND FOGG, G.E., 2002a, Glacially driven cycles in accumulation space and sequence stratigraphy of a stream-dominated alluvial fan, San Joaquin Valley, California, U.S.A.: Journal of Sedimentary Research, v. 72, p. 270–281.

WEISSMANN, G.S., YONG, Z., FOGG, G.E., BLAKE, R.G., NOYES, C.D., AND MALEY, M., 2002b, Modeling alluvial fan aquifer heterogeneity at multiple scales through stratigraphic assessment: Proceedings of the International Groundwater Symposium '02: Bridging the Gap Between Measurement and Modeling in Heterogeneous Media, Berkeley California, March 25–28, 2002.

WEISSMANN, G.S., YONG, Z., LABOLLE, E.M., AND FOGG, G.E., 2002c, Modeling environmental tracer–based groundwater ages in heterogeneous aquifers: Water Resources Research, v. 38, p. 1198–1211.

WRIGHT, V.P., AND ALONSO ZARZA, A.M., 1990, Pedostratigraphic models for alluvial-fan deposits: a tool for interpreting ancient sequences: Geological Society of London, Journal, v. 147, p. 8–10.

SENSITIVITY OF GROUNDWATER FLOW PATTERNS TO PARAMETERIZATION OF OBJECT-BASED FLUVIAL AQUIFER MODELS

SEAN A. MCKENNA

Geohydrology Department, Sandia National Laboratories, P.O. Box 5800 MS 0735,
Albuquerque, New Mexico 87185-0735, U.S.A.
e-mail: samcken@sandia.gov
AND
GARY SMITH

Department of Earth and Planetary Sciences, Northrop Hall, University of New Mexico,
Albuquerque, New Mexico 87131, U.S.A.
e-mail: gsmith@unm.edu

ABSTRACT: Object-based models offer a convenient means of numerically simulating the structure of sedimentary aquifers. Multiple parameters control the shapes, proportions, and spatial relationships of the objects defining the different facies in the resulting simulations. A sensitivity analysis is performed here to determine the sensitivity of several different performance measures of groundwater flow in a fluvial-basin aquifer to the parameterization of the object-based model. Unconditional realizations of the permeability field are created through an object-based model that simulates multiple facies (channel, levee, splay, and floodplain deposits) in a fluvial depositional system. A single permeability value is assigned to each facies. For each realization, Latin hypercube sampling is used to draw the input parameters from predefined distributions characterizing the uncertainty inherent in these parameters. Groundwater flow is simulated parallel to the principal channel azimuth, and the groundwater flow patterns are determined by tracking streamlines through multiple realizations of the simulated aquifer. Results on groundwater flow include points on the distributions of travel times, tortuosity of flow paths, and dispersion of the flow patterns. The values of the input parameters are compared to the results on groundwater flow using a generalized sensitivity analysis to provide a quantitative technique for the assessment of parameter sensitivity. Results of this sensitivity analysis show that a first-order characterization goal must be determination of the proportions of the high-permeability (channel) and low-permeability (floodplain) facies within the aquifer. To a lesser degree, the performance measures of groundwater flow are sensitive to the channel sinuosity, thickness, and width-to-thickness ratio. These results can be used to provide guidance towards more efficient characterization of fluvial depositional settings for groundwater studies.

INTRODUCTION

Hydrogeologists seek realistic depictions of subsurface heterogeneity to reasonably simulate groundwater flow. The principal structure of the heterogeneity is the distribution of lithofacies or lithofacies assemblages that have distinct hydraulic properties and might, therefore, be referred to as hydrofacies (*sensu* Ritzi et al., 1995). A large arsenal of methods exists for simulating the heterogeneous sedimentological framework of an aquifer (see Koltermann and Gorelick, 1996, and North, 1996, for exhaustive reviews). Once one representation, or multiple representations, of the sedimentological framework have been rendered, each component can be assigned single values of hydraulic conductivity and porosity or populated with values for these parameters drawn from distributions, possibly through geostatistical techniques. The distribution of hydrofacies components and hydraulic properties within these components thus provide a basis for groundwater-flow simulation.

One family of methods for simulating the sedimentological framework is commonly referred to as object-based simulation (Srivastava, 1994). These modeling approaches embed three-dimensional objects representing different hydrofacies into a background-matrix hydrofacies, typically of lowest hydraulic conductivity. The simplest such model might place channel sandstone bodies into a matrix of floodplain mudstone. Among the advantages of object-based models are the ability to stochastically or deterministically build a simulation that contains hydrofacies with geologically realistic shapes, and to produce realistically sharp boundaries between hydrofacies that may have strongly contrasting hydraulic properties.

Although potentially applied to any depositional system, object-based modeling of fluvial deposits is a conceptually simple way to define the spatial arrangement of different facies within an aquifer. The two-dimensional cross sections of alluvial-basin models presented by Allen (1978), Bridge and Leeder (1979), and Bridge and Mackey (1993) are examples of object-based forward modeling of fluvial stratigraphy driven primarily by basin-scale subsidence and rules adopted for channel avulsion. Models of this kind have been extended to three dimensions by Mackey and Bridge (1995) and Karssenberg et al. (2001). These models deal with two components, channel belts and floodplain, and show their possible distribution and interconnectedness. Webb (1994) and Webb and Anderson (1996) developed a forward model of braided-river deposits, at the scale of hundreds of meters. In this model, lithofacies objects were placed in accordance with a random-walk approach to describe the channel pattern on the basis of comparison to modern rivers, combined with assignment of grain size and sedimentary structure determined by the simulated channel hydraulics. Tyler et al. (1994) describe results of several stochastic object-based models that embed permeable channel bodies within less permeable mudstone and that also place elements such as bar and bedform facies within the channel bodies in accordance with their probability of size and presence in modern rivers of similar planform. Stochastic simulations require governing rules for placing objects next to one another, such as Markov analysis of facies transitions (Tyler et al., 1994;

North, 1996) and can be designed to honor conditioning subsurface data where they are available (e.g., Deutsch and Wang, 1996; Holden et al., 1998).

The main objective of this study is to gain an understanding of the relevance of parameters in an object-based model of a fluvial aquifer to groundwater-flow patterns. A secondary objective is to provide a general demonstration of an analysis technique that can be applied to specific aquifers to identify characterization needs. These two objectives are designed to guide both surface geophysical and borehole-based site characterization activities. Ideally, results of this study can be used to determine the critical parameters in a fluvial sedimentary aquifer that must be defined through field characterization. However, this result hinges on both the object-based model being an accurate portrayal of the sedimentary framework of the specific aquifer and on the accuracy of permeability structure assigned to the facies components. Determining the accuracy of an object modeling approach against a real data set is beyond the scope of this study.

METHODS

Three analytical components were employed to address the objectives. First, an object-based stochastic simulation algorithm was used to develop multiple stochastic realizations of facies arrangements in a fluvial aquifer and each facies was assigned a single permeability value. Second, a steady-state groundwater-flow solution with streamline-particle tracking was employed to characterize each aquifer simulation in terms of flow and advective transport. Third, a threshold-based sensitivity analysis was applied to evaluate the influence of each parameter in the object-based model on selected groundwater-flow and transport performance measures.

Object-Based Aquifer Model (fluvsim)

The object-based model used in this study is a recent extension (Deutsch and Tran, 2002) of the original *fluvsim* model presented by Deutsch and Wang (1996). The model allows the simulation of channel, levee, and crevasse-splay objects embedded within floodplain deposits. The characteristic shape of each of the three parameterized facies can be modified in a nearly infinite variety of ways by changing the input parameters listed in Table 1. The *fluvsim* code is capable of using simulated annealing to condition each stochastic realization to vertical and areal facies proportion curves and to borehole and geophysical data; these conditioning options are not used in this study.

The *fluvsim* stratigraphy is generated by superposing multiple planform maps of a fluvial system composed of the four facies assemblages. True fluvial stratigraphy is determined by those depositional elements that are actually preserved and is commonly biased toward channel bodies that are laterally linked to form sheets as a result of channel migration or avulsion. Deposits of this kind are simulated by *fluvsim* when a relatively high proportion of the channel facies is specified. Additionally, some ancient fluvial deposits do preserve seemingly "snapshot" views of the channel and floodplain environments (e.g., Galloway, 1977), which may be preferred when aggradation rates are large (Allen, 1978). These types of deposits are simulated by specifying a lower proportion of the channel facies, and an example of such a simulation is given in Figures 1 and 2. Therefore, simulation parameters in *fluvsim* can be implicitly adjusted to produce broad, multistory channel belts, in addition to the isolated, single-story channel belts shown in Figures 1 and 2.

In order to determine the effect of the different input parameters on the groundwater flow patterns resulting from different facies models, a distribution defining the uncertainty about each input parameter is used. Uncertainty distributions are specified for each of the 34 input parameters (Table 1). For this hypothetical study, these distributions were developed to encompass a broad range of fluvial aquifers. The uncertainty distributions used here are defined as uniform, Gaussian, or triangular. These three distributions respectively correspond to the maximum entropy distributions when (1) only a minimum and maximum, or (2) a mean and standard deviation, or (3) a minimum, most likely, and maximum value are available for the uncertain parameter. Assignment of distributions on the basis of maximum entropy ensures that no additional information beyond the constraints imposed by the knowledge of the distribution parameters (e.g., mean and standard deviation) will bias the uncertainty description (see discussion in Harr, 1987). The triangular distribution is especially attractive when basing the estimate of uncertainty on expert information. For any particular fluvial aquifer, the available data and the collective experience of the site characterization team on similar aquifers would be used to develop these uncertainty distributions. For a specific aquifer with available data, these distributions would most likely be narrower than those used in this hypothetical example.

Latin hypercube sampling (LHS) is used to draw values from specified distributions for each of the input parameters. LHS is an improvement on traditional Monte Carlo sampling; it works by dividing the distribution of the input parameter into a number of equally probable intervals and then ensures that an equal number of samples is taken from each interval (see Morgan and Henrion, 1990). This interval-based approach leads to a more efficient sampling of the parameter distribution relative to traditional Monte Carlo sampling, which just draws uniformly distributed probability values from throughout the parameter distribution.

Each distribution is sampled 200 times to create a set of 200 input vectors, where each vector contains one value of each input parameter. Each vector is used as input to *fluvism* to create one realization of the facies distribution. The aquifer simulations are created on a 100 x 100 x 50 grid where each element has dimensions of 50 x 50 x 1 m. Different views of an example realization are shown in Figures 1 and 2. Application of the LHS process to selected input parameters for *fluvsim* creates a broad range of aquifer realizations with different facies proportions (Fig. 3), which are then used to simulate groundwater flow and advective transport.

Model of Groundwater Flow and Transport

Each of the 200 *fluvsim* realizations is used as input to a flow model employing a simple set of fixed-head and no-flow boundary conditions to simulate steady-state groundwater flow with an average head gradient of 0.001 parallel to the average channel direction in the fluvial aquifer. The flow porosity for all facies is 0.10, and the hydraulic conductivity within each facies is homogeneous and isotropic (see values in Table 2). This specification was made such that the resulting groundwater flow patterns would be due solely to the proportions and arrangement of the facies, not to internal heterogeneity within the facies. The values of hydraulic conductivity assigned to the facies were taken from tabulated values (Freeze and Cherry, 1979) and range from those expected for gravel to those of a silty sand. For the steady-state flow model and fixed-head boundary conditions used here, it is the magnitude of the differences in hydraulic conductivity between the facies that govern the flow patterns, not the absolute value of the hydraulic conductivity values.

A regular orthogonal grid of 500,000 elements with the same orientation and discretization as the output of the *fluvsim* code is

TABLE 1. Input parameters for the object-based model and corresponding distributions.

Num.	Parameter Description	Distribution	Lower (Mean)	Mode (Std. Dev.)	Upper	Units
1	Floodplain Proportion	Uniform	0.1	N/A	0.9	None
2	Channel Proportion	Uniform	0.1	N/A	0.9	None
3	Levee Proportion	Uniform	0.0	N/A	0.50	None
4	Crevasse Proportion	Uniform	0.0	N/A	0.50	None
5	Channel Orientation	Gaussian	0.0	10.0	N/A	Degrees
6	Deviation of Channel Orientation	Gaussian	20	5	N/A	Degrees
7	Channel Sinuosity Departure	Triangular	100	200	300	Meters
8	Deviation in Channel Sinuosity Departure	Triangular	0.0	50	100	Meters
9	Channel Sinuosity Correlation Length	Triangular	200	500	1500	Meters
10	Deviation in Correlation Length	Triangular	0.0	100	200	Meters
11	Channel Thickness	Triangular	1	4	10	Meters
12	Deviation in Channel Thickness	Triangular	1	2	3	Meters
13	Channel Thickness Undulation	Triangular	0.1	0.5	2	Relative to Channel Thickness
14	Deviation in Thickness Undulation	Constant	N/A	0.1	N/A	Relative to Channel Thickness
15	Channel Undulation Correlation Length	Triangular	200	500	1500	Meters
16	Deviation in Undulation Correlation Length	Triangular	50	100	200	Meters
17	Ration of Channel Width to Thickness	Triangular	5	50	250	None
18	Deviation in Width-to-Thickness Ratio	Constant	5	5	5	None
19	Channel Width Undulation	Triangular	0.5	1	2	Relative to Channel Width
20	Deviation in Channel Width Undulation	Constant	N/A	0.5	N/A	Relative to Channel Width
21	Horizontal Correlation Length for Width Undulation	Triangular	200	500	1500	Meters
22	Deviation in Width Undulation Correlation Length	Triangular	50	100	200	Meters
23	Levee Width	Triangular	50	200	500	Meters
24	Deviation in Levee Width	Triangular	50	100	150	Meters
25	Levee Height	Triangular	0.1	0.3	0.6	Relative to Channel Thickness
26	Deviation in Levee Height	Constant	N/A	0.1	N/A	Relative to Channel Thickness
27	Levee Depth below channel top	Triangular	0.1	0.2	0.5	Relative to Channel Thickness
28	Deviation in levee depth below top	Constant	N/A	0.1	N/A	Relative to Channel Thickness
29	Crevasse attachment length	Triangular	100	500	1500	Meters
30	Deviation in attachment length	Triangular	0.0	50	100	Meters
31	Crevasse thickness next to channel	Triangular	0.2	0.4	0.6	Relative to Channel Thickness
32	Deviation of thickness next to channel	Triangular	0.0	0.1	0.2	Relative to Channel Thickness
33	Areal extent of crevasse (diameter)	Triangular	150	250	500	Meters
34	Deviation in areal extent of crevasse	Triangular	50	100	150	Meters

used for the flow model. Steady-state flow conditions are solved for each realization using the FEHM finite-element groundwater flow code (Zyvoloski et al., 1999). A total of 4000 streamlines are tracked from the starting locations to the downstream end of the model. The starting locations of the streamlines are determined with a flux-weighted scheme inside of a 25,000 m² (50 x 10 elements) plane orthogonal to the average flow direction located 500 meters from the upstream end of the model.

For each stochastic realization of the aquifer, the 4000 streamlines define a distribution of travel times through that realization. From this distribution, the 5th, 50th, and 95th percentile travel times are extracted and examined as representative of the fast, median, and slow portions, respectively, of the groundwater travel-time distribution. The 5th and 50th percentile travel times are similar to groundwater-travel-time requirements used in regulating nuclear waste repositories and municipal landfill programs. The 95th percentile travel time and the difference between the 95th and 5th percentile arrival times, the "residence" time, indicate the ability of the aquifer to store, or retard, the flow of a dissolved contaminant. The 4000 streamlines also define a distribution of flow-path lengths through each realization. From this distribution of path lengths, the median path length is selected as an indicator of the flow-path tortuosity in the aquifer. Three dispersivity values define the spread of the arrival times in

the longitudinal direction and the spreading of the streamlines in the transverse horizontal and vertical directions. The flow-path tortuosity and dispersion are the result of different processes. For example, if all pathlines follow a tortuous, but nearly identical, path, the tortuosity will be high, but the amount of dispersion will be small.

The longitudinal and transverse dispersivities are calculated from the particle arrival times and the transverse displacements of the particles. The transverse displacements are determined from the starting locations to the point where each particle crosses a plane oriented normal to the mean flow direction 4500 meters down gradient of the starting locations. For this model setup and a flux-weighted, instantaneous injection of particles, Kreft and Zuber (1978) present an analytical solution for the longitudinal dispersivity, a_L:

$$\alpha_L = \frac{x}{2}\left(\frac{\sigma_t(y)}{m_t(y)}\right)^2$$

where $m_t(y)$ and $s_t(y)$ are the mean and standard deviation of the arrival times at travel distance x. The horizontal (H) and vertical (V) transverse dispersivities are calculated as

$$\alpha_H(y) = \frac{\psi_{22}(y)}{2y} \qquad \alpha_V(y) = \frac{\psi_{33}(y)}{2y}$$

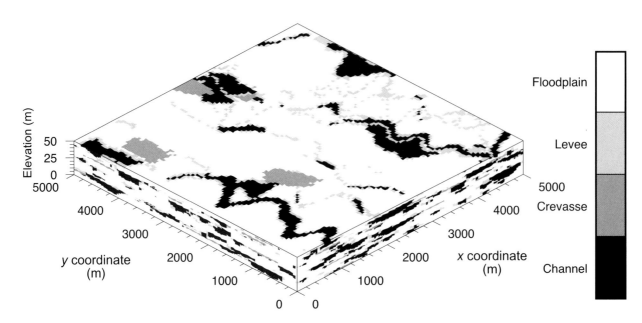

F$_{\text{IG}}$. 1.—A three-dimensional view of an example object-based model realization (realization 22) showing the relationships between the different facies. The vertical exaggeration is 12x.

where $\Psi_{22}(y)$ and $\Psi_{33}(y)$ are the variances of the differences between the transverse particle-arrival position at travel distance y and the initial coordinates of the particle at the source location. These variances are calculated across all particles for both the transverse x and z directions, respectively. These variances are used to approximate the transverse second-order spatial moments defined in macro-dispersive theory. This approximation has been used successfully in previous studies to evaluate transverse dispersion (Follin and Thunvik, 1994; Wen and Gomez-Hernandez, 1998).

Sensitivity Analysis

Results on travel time, path length, and dispersivity are examined in order to determine the most sensitive input parameters with respect to these outputs. This sensitivity analysis is conducted using a generalized sensitivity analysis (GSA) approach (see Spear and Hornberger, 1980; James, et al., 1996) outlined in Figure 4. Each vector of input parameters defining a single *fluvsim* realization is placed into one of two sets: those that create results that exceed a specified threshold value, and those that do not exceed the threshold. This behavioral classification of the input vectors into two sample sets allows quantitative examination of the differences between the two sample sets as a function of each parameter contained in the input vectors.

Eight different measures of groundwater flow performance are considered (Table 3) in the GSA. These different performance measures were selected to determine the effect of the parameters in the object-based aquifer model on three major aspects of groundwater flow paths: timing, tortuosity, and dispersion. The specific threshold values used here (Table 3) were selected to fully exercise the GSA approach by ensuring that nearly equal numbers of realizations exceeded and did not exceed each threshold value. In a practical application, these threshold values might be set by a regulatory agency, in the case of groundwater travel times, or some physical process, such as the necessary flow path length that allows for a critical amount of surface area for sorption of a contaminant. The thresholds for the longitudinal and hori-

zontal transverse dispersivity (Table 3) in this example were selected as 10 and 1 percent, respectively, of the distance from the particle release location to the downstream end of the model.

A strength of GSA over other sampling-based techniques of sensitivity analysis, such as rank regression, is its use of a threshold-based classification. As the value of the threshold is changed, the sensitivity of the more, or less, extreme results to each input parameter changes. By varying the threshold values, the fine-scale sensitivity structure of the outputs to the inputs can be elucidated. However, for this first look at the sensitivity of groundwater flow paths to object-based model parameters, only the single set of thresholds shown in Table 3 is used. Future work will examine the changes in sensitivity structure as a function of different threshold values for the performance measures.

GSA provides both qualitative and quantitative techniques to examine the sensitivity of the results to a given parameter. The qualitative results are a graph of cumulative density functions (CDFs) for each parameter, where the CDF of the parameter within the vectors that exceeded the threshold value is compared to the CDF within the vectors that did not exceed the threshold. A large difference between the CDFs indicates that the results are sensitive to that parameter with respect to that threshold.

GSA provides quantitative results by using a nonparametric statistical test of the difference between the two CDFs. The test used here is the Kolmogorov-Smirnov (K-S) test (e.g., Conover 1980), in which the maximum vertical difference between the two CDFs, d, is determined. This maximum can occur at any value of the selected parameter. The K-S test also provides a determination of the probability, P, that the maximum distance between the two CDFs could occur if the two sample distributions were obtained from a single population. The lower this probability, the more certainty that the CDFs are significantly different.

RESULTS

The results are examined in terms of the sensitivity analysis and the relation of the object-based model parameters to the three categories of the performance measures of groundwater flow.

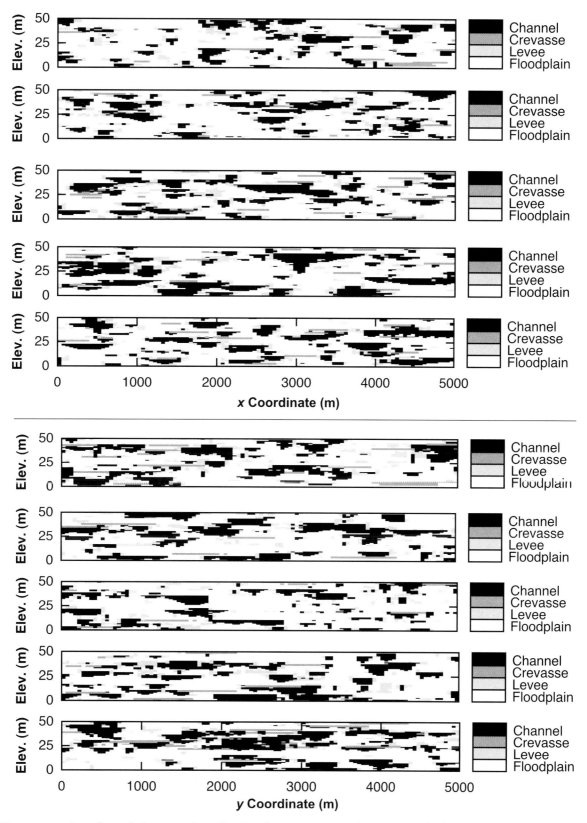

FIG. 2.—Ten cross sections through the example realization shown in Figure 1 (realization 22). The top five cross sections are in the x–z dimension and are taken at y coordinates of 500, 1500, 2500, 3500, and 4500 meters from bottom to top, respectively. The bottom five cross sections are in the y–z dimension and are taken at x coordinates of 500, 1500, 2500, 3500, and 4500 meters from bottom to top, respectively. The vertical exaggeration is 12x for all cross sections.

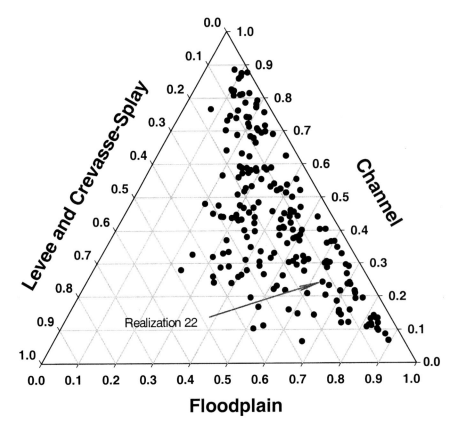

FIG. 3.—The proportions of each facies for the 200 realizations created with *fluvsim*. The location of realization 22 (shown in Figs. 1 and 2) in ternary space is shown by the arrow.

Results of Sensitivity Analysis

GSA compares the CDFs of the parameter distributions for those parameter values that are associated with results that fall below the threshold value and those that exceed the threshold value. The distance between the two CDFs gives a visual indication of the sensitivity of the results to the chosen parameter. As an example, the 5th percentile travel time is very sensitive to the proportion of the channel and floodplain facies in the model (Fig. 5A, B) but less sensitive to the proportion of levee and crevasse-splay facies (Fig. 5C, D). The probability, P, that the two CDFs could have been obtained from the same underlying population is used here as a quantitative measure of sensitivity.

The results of the sensitivity analysis are summarized in Figure 6. Figure 6 shows the value of P for each parameter and each of the performance measures of the eight flow model. In Figure 6, the *fluvsim* input parameters are divided by vertical

gray lines into four groups (from left to right): the proportions of the four facies (1–4); parameters controlling the shape of the channels (5–22); parameters controlling the levee facies (23–28); and the parameters controlling the crevasse facies (29–34). As shown in Table 1, parameters 14, 18, 20, 26, and 28 are held as constant values for this analysis and therefore are not shown in Figure 6.

The P values in Figure 6 are the probability that the input parameters that caused the results to exceed the threshold could be derived from the same underlying population as those that caused the results to fall below the threshold. The lower the P value, the more sensitive the groundwater performance measure is to that aquifer model parameter. It is noted here that the first four parameters, the proportions of the different facies, are not independent—changes in one of these proportions cause changes in at least one of the other proportions. All of the other parameters are sampled independently of one another. In this analysis, P

TABLE 2. Values of hydraulic conductivity and permeability assigned to each facies.

Facies	Hydraulic Conductivity (m/s)	Permeability (m²)
Floodplain	1.8×10^{-5}	1.0×10^{-12}
Levee	1.8×10^{-3}	1.0×10^{-10}
Crevasse Splay	1.8×10^{-2}	1.0×10^{-9}
Channel	1.8×10^{-1}	1.0×10^{-8}

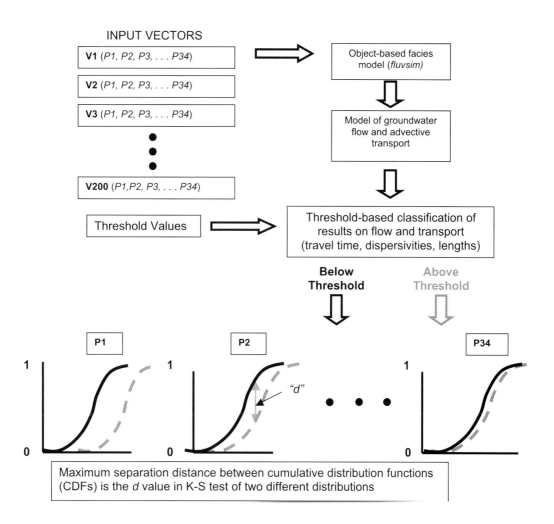

FIG. 4.—Schematic diagram of the generalized sensitivity analysis (GSA) framework.

values of 0.10 or less are considered as evidence for a significant level of sensitivity of the results to that input parameter. The results are examined in terms of the three main categories of groundwater-flow performance measures: timing, tortuosity, and dispersion.

A total of 200 stochastic models of the aquifer were created using *fluvsim*. The question of whether or not 200 realizations are enough to get stable estimates of the groundwater-flow performance measures is addressed by calculating the running average of several of the performance measures from 1 to 200 realizations. If the average stabilizes to a constant or nearly constant value, then it is concluded that 200 realizations are adequate. Figure 7 shows the running averages for four of the performance measures. For all four of these measures, the fluctuations of the average values vary generally less than ± two percent of the final average value after 150 realizations, and we take this as evidence that 200 realizations are enough to produce stable estimates of the performance measures.

Flow-Path Travel Times

The sensitivities of the four different travel-time results to the input parameters are shown on the left side of Figure 6. These results indicate that it is the proportions of the floodplain, channel and levee facies (1–4) and several of the parameters controlling the geometry of the channel bodies (8, 9, 11, 13, and 17) that exert the most influence on the groundwater travel-time metrics. To a lesser extent, the width and height of the levees (23 and 25) has some influence on the 5th and 50th percentile travel times and the crevasse geometry (29, 32, and 33) influences the 95th percentile travel time and the residence time (difference between the 95th and 5th percentile travel times).

All four of the performance measures of groundwater travel time are consistently most sensitive to the proportions of the channel and floodplain facies (1 and 2). As an example, the 5th percentile travel time is very sensitive to the proportion of the channel and floodplain facies in the model (Fig. 5A, B). The example CDFs shown in Figure 5 B indicate that it is lower proportions of channel facies that produce travel times greater than 50 days (the solid-line CDF). This result implies that higher proportions of channel bodies in the model domain lead to well-connected pathways that are capable of relatively fast transport of groundwater through the aquifer. The relative positions of the floodplain proportion CDFs (Fig. 5A) are reversed relative to the channel proportion, indicating that the realizations with high proportions of low-hydraulic-conductivity floodplain material result in the longest (slowest) 5th percentile travel times.

All of the different measures of time for groundwater to flow from one end of the model domain to the other are sensitive to parameters 9, 11, and 13 (Fig. 6). These three parameters are the

TABLE 3. Performance measures of groundwater flow and the thresholds used in the generalized sensitivity analysis (GSA).

Performance Measure	Threshold
0.05 Travel Time	50 days
0.50 Travel Time	100 days
0.95 Travel Time	200 days
0.95–0.05 Travel Time	500 days
Median Path Length	4950 meters
Longitudinal Dispersivity	450 meters
Transverse Horizontal Dispersivity	4.5 meters
Transverse Vertical Dispersivity	0.10 meters

correlation length, or wavelength, of the channel sinuosity (9); the channel thickness (11), and the amount of undulation in the channel thickness (13). The greater the value for each of these three parameters, the greater the likelihood that channel bodies intersect one another. Intersections increase the interconnectedness of high-permeability channel facies to permit more continuous and faster transport pathways. The channel-thickness undulation creates vertical connections with other channels, providing more continuous and faster transport pathways.

With the exception of the 50th percentile (median) travel time, all of the travel-time results are also very sensitive to the ratio of channel width to thickness (17). This result indicates that the extreme travel times, fast and slow, are much more sensitive to the width-to-thickness ratio than are the median travel times. This result may be due to extremely wide channels making enough connections with other channels to produce well-connected flow paths through the aquifer, whereas low values of the ratio are associated with narrow channels that do not provide connections of this type.

The distribution of groundwater travel times through the aquifer is much less sensitive to the levee (23–28) and crevasse-splay (31–34) parameters relative to the channel parameters.

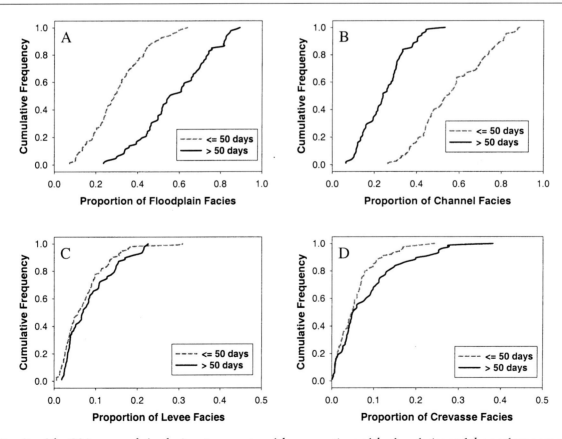

FIG. 5.—Results of the GSA approach for the input parameter of the proportions of the four facies and the performance measure of the 5th percentile travel time. Parts A, B, C, and D show the CDFs for the floodplain, channel, levee, and crevasse-splay facies, respectively. The threshold applied to these travel-time results is 50 days.

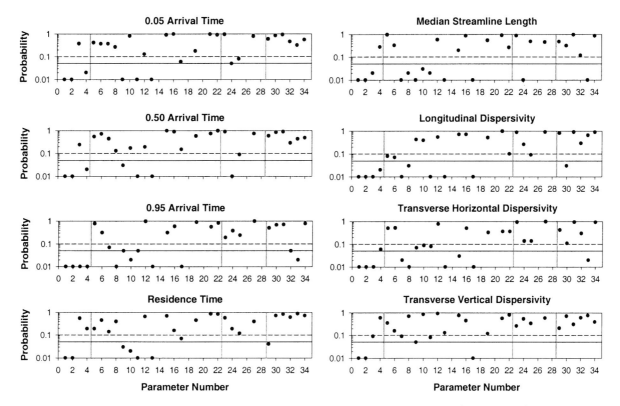

FIG. 6.—Results of sensitivity analysis for the performance measures of groundwater flow. The y axis is the probability that the distributions of each input parameter that created the results that exceeded the threshold and those that did not exceed the threshold could have come from the same underlying population. The solid and dashed horizontal lines at probabilities of 0.05 and 0.10, respectively, are provided to aid in interpretation of the results.

The levee parameters have no effect on the 95th percentile travel time and the residence time. The 5th and 50th percentile travel times are sensitive to deviations in the levee width (23) and levee height (25). Although levees have lower permeability than the channel facies, these deviations in the levee width and height can provide flow connections between high-permeability channel bodies. The diameter (33) and the thickness (31) of the crevasse-splay deposits near the channel are important in determining the 95th percentile travel time through the aquifer, whereas the crevasse attachment length (29), or the frequency with which crevasses appear along the channel, is important in determining the residence time of the groundwater within the aquifer.

Flow-Path Tortuosity

The right side of Figure 6 shows the results of sensitivity analysis for the median path length (tortuosity) and dispersivity outputs. These results are sensitive to a greater number of the input parameters relative to the travel-time results,. The median groundwater travel length is sensitive to the proportions of the floodplain, channel, and levee facies (parameters 1, 2, and 3; top right graph of Figure 6). While these results are not sensitive to the proportion of the crevasse facies, they are sensitive to the size of the individual crevasse splays coming off of channels (33). Almost all of the parameters controlling the channel sinuosity and thickness (7–11 and 13) are important for defining the tortuosity of the groundwater flow paths, as is the ratio of channel width to thickness (parameter 17). Tortuosity of groundwater flow paths is sensitive to only a single levee parameter, the deviation in levee

width (24) which controls the effective width of the channel and levee together. These results are somewhat intuitive in that the channel bodies provide the main pathways for flow and that the flow-path tortuosity is controlled by the sinuosity and thickness of these channel bodies. Additionally, large crevasse-splay bodies can connect separate channels and provide relatively high-permeability flow connections between them. These crevasse-splay connections, or the lack thereof, also control the tortuosity of the flow paths.

Flow-Path Dispersion

The longitudinal dispersivity is a measure of the spread in the travel times and is sensitive to all of the facies proportions (parameters 1–4; Fig. 6, second graph from the top right) as well as a large number of the parameters controlling the orientation, sinuosity, and thickness of the channel facies (5, 6, 7, 8, 11, 13, and 17). The results on longitudinal dispersivity are sensitive to the channel orientation (5), whereas the travel-time results are not. This result indicates that the mean channel orientation and the variation about that mean exert a strong influence on the variation in travel times but not in the average value of those times. These results reinforce the interpretation of the tortuosity results that the shapes of, and connections between, the channel bodies exert a strong control on the groundwater flow patterns. The results on longitudinal dispersivity are also sensitive to the deviation in the crevasse attachment length along the channels. This deviation exerts some control on the variability in travel times through variation in the cross-channel connections created by these crevasse-splay deposits.

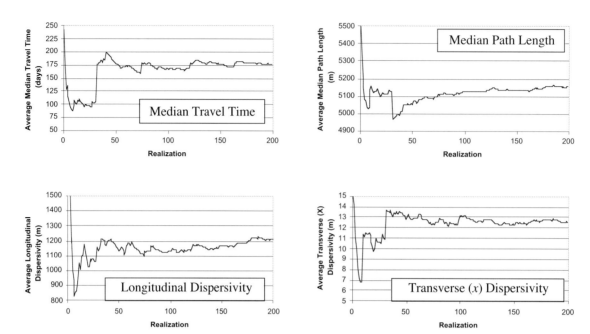

FIG. 7.—The average of four different performance measures of groundwater flow as a function of the number of results included in the average.

Transverse horizontal dispersivity is a measure of the spread of the groundwater flow paths in the horizontal direction orthogonal to the mean direction of the flow. These dispersivity results (Fig. 6, third graph from the top right) are sensitive to many of the same parameters defining the distribution of the channel facies that controlled flow-path tortuosity. A notable difference between these two results is the sensitivity of the flow-path tortuosity to the deviation in levee width (24) and the sensitivity of the transverse horizontal dispersivity to the proportion of the crevasse facies (4) in addition to the size of the individual crevasse bodies (33).

The results on vertical transverse dispersivity (Fig. 6, bottom graph on the right) are relatively insensitive to all input parameters with the exception of the floodplain and channel facies proportions (parameters 1 and 2) and the ratio of channel width to thickness (17). These results are slightly sensitive to departures in the channel sinuosity (7), the correlation length of the channel sinuosity (9), and the channel thickness (11).

SUMMARY

These results of sensitivity analysis indicate that the channels act as the main flow conduits and that the crevasse-splay deposits and, to a lesser extent, the levee deposits act as connectors between the channels. The higher hydraulic conductivity of the crevasse facies compared to the levees and the areal extent of these deposits can provide strong horizontal connection between the channels. The presence or absence of these connections in any single realization has a strong influence on the transverse horizontal dispersion, the tortuosity of the flow paths, and the slower portion of the arrival times. The levees increase the effective width of the channels, and this exerts some influence on the tortuosity of the flow paths. Because the levees can build up above the channel to which they are connected, they also create vertical connections between individual channel bodies. The 5th and 50th percentile travel times as well as the longitudinal

dispersion are sensitive to these vertical connections created by the levee deposits.

Figure 8 shows a summary of the results of sensitivity analysis across all of the different performance measures of groundwater flow. In Figure 8, the sum of the probabilities across all eight performance measures is shown for each parameter. The lower the sum of the probabilities, the more sensitive are the eight different performance measures of groundwater flow to that parameter. Figure 8 shows that the two most important parameters to define in order to predict the timing, tortuosity, and dispersion of groundwater in the modeled basin are the proportions of the facies with the highest and lowest hydraulic conductivity: the channel facies and the floodplain deposits. For the models created here, these two parameters are relatively strongly correlated, and determining the proportion of one of these two facies provides significant information on the proportion of the other. The next most important parameters to characterize, those in Figure 8 with probability sums between 0.1 and 1.0, are the correlation length of the channel sinuosity, the channel thickness, the undulation of the channel thickness, and the ratio of channel width to thickness.

It would be easy to apply these results to guide efforts to characterize fluvial aquifers. Geophysical logging and/or coring of existing boreholes in the aquifer would provide a relatively inexpensive means of estimating proportions of the channel and floodplain deposits in the subsurface. The important parameters defining the shape of the channel deposits (e.g., channel thickness and the ratio of channel width to thickness) could be inferred from outcrop analog studies (e.g., Gaud et al., this volume; Bridge and Tye, 2000) or 3-D seismic information if available. It is necessary to keep in mind that the permeability of each facies must also be adequately determined.

CONCLUSIONS

This study has demonstrated some of the capabilities of an object-based approach applied to modeling a fluvial sedimen-

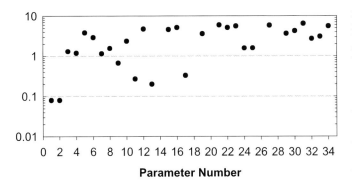

Fig. 8.—Results of sensitivity analysis for all eight of the performance measures. The probability values shown here are the sum of the probabilities shown in Figure 6 for each parameter

tary aquifer with uncertainty in the parameters defining the shapes and sizes of the facies objects. A powerful technique for sensitivity analysis, GSA, was used to determine the important parameters for a number of results on groundwater flow. If borehole and/or geophysical conditioning data and/or outcrop analog data are available, this object-based approach could readily be tailored to simulate a specific aquifer and the most important parameters for the groundwater-flow question being addressed could be determined for that aquifer. The coupling of object-based modeling and GSA could prove useful in the investigation of any specific aquifer across a wide range of fluvial deposits.

In the general case examined here, the GSA approach has elucidated a number of features in the object-based facies models that are important in controlling groundwater flow patterns. It is noted that all of these results are for the boundary conditions, permeabilities, and performance thresholds specified in this study. The most far-reaching conclusion that can be drawn from this study is that groundwater travel times, path lengths, and the amount of dispersion are all sensitive mainly to the proportions of the different facies within the aquifer, especially the highest-permeability and lowest-permeability facies. Fortunately, determination of the facies proportions is generally one of the more readily obtainable goals of aquifer characterization.

For the situation studied here, the other model parameters that control the flow patterns are the shape and connectedness of the high-permeability channel facies. The GSA results indicate that the parameters controlling the geometry of the channel facies exert control on the 5th and 50th percentile travel times and on the amount of longitudinal and horizontal transverse dispersion. The crevasse-splay facies also influence horizontal dispersion by creating relatively high-permeability pathways between the channels. With the exception of the proportions of the channel and floodplain facies, and the ratio of channel width to thickness, transverse vertical dispersion was only mildly sensitive to several of the channel-sinuosity and thickness parameters.

ACKNOWLEDGMENTS

The authors gratefully acknowledge C. Deutsch for providing us with an early copy of the *fluvsim* code and guidance on its use. This work benefited from thoughtful reviews by John Bridge, Chris Murray, Gary Weissmann, and Erik Webb. Portions of this work were reported at the SEPM/IAS Research Conference "Environmental Sedimentology: Hydrogeology of Sedimentary Aquifers" held 24–27 September 2000 in Santa Fe, New Mexico. Sandia is a multiprogram laboratory operated by Sandia Corporation, a Lockheed Martin Company, for the United States Department of Energy under contract DE-AC04-94AL850000.

REFERENCES

ALLEN, J.R.L., 1978, Studies in fluviatile sedimentation: an exploratory quantitative model for the architecture of avulsion-controlled alluvial suites: Sedimentary Geology, v. 24, p. 253–267.

BRIDGE, J.S., AND LEEDER, M., 1979, A simulation model of alluvial stratigraphy, Sedimentology, v. 26, p. 617–644.

BRIDGE, J.S., AND MACKEY, S.D., 1993, A revised alluvial stratigraphy model, *in* Marzo, M., and Puigdefabregas, C., eds., Alluvial Sedimentation: International Association of Sedimentologists, Special Publication 17, p. 319–336.

BRIDGE, J.S., AND TYE, R.S., 2000, Interpreting the dimensions of ancient fluvial channel bars, channels, and channel belts from wireline logs and cores: American Association of Petroleum Geologists, Bulletin, v. 84, p. 1205–1228.

CONOVER, W.J., 1980, Practical Nonparametric Statistics, Second Edition: New York, John Wiley & Sons, 493 p.

DEUTSCH, C.V., AND TRAN, T.T., 2002, FLUVSIM: A program for object-based stochastic modeling of fluvial depositional systems: Computers & Geosciences, v. 28, p. 525–535.

DEUTSCH, C.V., AND WANG, L., 1996, Hierarchical object-based stochastic modeling of fluvial reservoirs: Mathematical Geology, v. 28, p. 857–880.

FOLLIN, S., AND THUNVIK, R., 1994, On the use of continuum approximations for regional modeling of groundwater flow through crystalline rocks: Advances in Water Resources, v. 17, p. 133–145.

FREEZE, R.A., AND CHERRY, J., 1979, Groundwater: Englewood Cliffs, New Jersey, Prentice Hall, 604 p.

GALLOWAY, W.E., 1977, Catahoula Formation of the Texas coastal plain: depositional systems, composition, structural development, groundwater flow history, and uranium distribution: Texas Bureau of Economic Geology, Report of Investigations 87, 59 p.

HARR, M.E., 1987, Reliability-Based Design in Civil Engineering: New York, McGraw Hill Book Co., 291 p.

HOLDEN, L., HAUGE, R., SKARE, O., AND SKORSTAD, A., 1998, Modeling of fluvial reservoirs with object models: Mathematical Geology, v. 30, p. 445–468.

JAMES, B.R., GWO, J.-P., AND TORAN, L., 1996, Risk-cost decision framework for aquifer remediation design: Journal of Water Resources Planning and Management, v. 122, p. 414–420.

KARSSENBERG, D., TÖRNQVIST, T.E., AND BRIDGE, J.S., 2001, Conditioning a process-based model of sedimentary architecture to well data: Journal of Sedimentary Research, v. 71, p. 868–879.

KOLTERMANN, C.E., AND GORELICK, S.M., 1996, Heterogeneity in sedimentary deposits: A review of structure-imitating, process-imitating and descriptive approaches: Water Resources Research, v. 32, p. 2617–2658.

KREFT, A., AND ZUBER, A., 1978, On the physical meaning of the dispersion equation and its solutions for different initial and boundary conditions: Chemical Engineering Science, v. 33, p. 1471–1480.

MACKEY, S.D., AND BRIDGE, J.S., 1995, Three-dimensional model of alluvial stratigraphy: Theory and application: Journal of Sedimentary Research, v. B65, p. 7–31.

MORGAN, M.G., AND HENRION, M., 1990, Uncertainty; A Guide to Dealing with Uncertainty in Quantitative Risk and Policy Analysis: New York, Cambridge University Press, 332 p.

NORTH, C.P., 1996, The prediction and modeling of subsurface fluvial stratigraphy, *in* Carling, P.A., and Dawson, M.R., eds., Advances in Fluvial Dynamics and Stratigraphy: New York, John Wiley & Sons, p. 395–508.

RITZI, R.W., JR., DOMINIC, D.F., BROWN, N.R., KAUSCH, K.W., MCALENNEY, P.J., AND BASIAL, M.J., 1995, Hydrofacies distribution and correlation in the Miami Valley aquifer system: Water Research, v. 31, p. 3271–3281.

SPEAR, R.C., AND HORNBERGER, G.M., 1980, Eutrophication in Peel Inlet II. Identification of critical uncertainties via generalized sensitivity analysis: Water Research, v. 14, p. 43–49.

SRIVASTAVA, R.M., 1994, An overview of stochastic methods for reservoir characterization, *in* Yarus, J.M., and Chambers, R.L., eds., Stochastic Modeling and Geostatistics: Principles, Methods, and Case Studies: American Association of Petroleum Geologists, Computer Applications in Geology, no. 3, Chapter 1, p. 3–16.

TYLER, K., HENRIQUEZ, A., AND SVANES, T., 1994, modeling heterogeneities in fluvial domains: A review on the influence of production profile, *in* Yarus, J.M., and Chambers, R.L., eds., Stochastic Modeling and Geostatistics: Principles, Methods, and Case Studies: American Association of Petroleum Geologists, Computer Applications in Geology, no. 3, Chapter 8, p. 77–90.

WEBB, E.K., 1994, Simulating the three-dimensional distribution of sediment units in braided-stream deposits: Journal of Sedimentary Research, v. B64, p. 219–231.

WEBB, E.K., AND ANDERSON, M.P., 1996, Simulation of preferential flow in three dimensional, heterogeneous conductivity fields with realistic internal architecture: Water Resources Research, v. 32, p. 533–545.

WEN, X-H., AND GOMEZ-HERNANDEZ, J.J., 1998, Numerical modeling of macrodispersion in heterogeneous media: A comparison of multi-Gaussian and non-multi-Gaussian models: Journal of Contaminant Hydrology, v. 30 (1–2), p. 129–156.

ZYVOLOSKI, G.A., ROBINSON, B.A., DASH, Z.V., AND TREASE, L.L., 1999, User's Manual for the FEHM Application: FEHM UM SC-194, Los Alamos National Laboratories, Los Alamos, New Mexico, 178 p.

ESTIMATING PARAMETERS FOR HIERARCHICAL PERMEABILITY CORRELATION MODELS

ZHENXUE DAI, ROBERT W. RITZI, Jr., AND DAVID F. DOMINIC

Department of Geological Sciences, Wright State University, Dayton, Ohio 45435, U.S.A.
e-mail: zhenxue.dai@wright.edu; rritzi@wright.edu; ddominic@wright.edu

ABSTRACT: The spatial covariance of ln(k) can be modeled with a hierarchy of covariance structures corresponding to the organization of bedding within and among the lithofacies of a sedimentary sequence. Such a model accounts for the spatial correlation of ln(k) within and across bedding units defined at any one level (Ritzi et al., 2004). This is related to correlation of ln(k) at a higher level (larger scale) through the spatial correlation of indicator variables representing the proportions, geometry, and juxtaposition patterns of the units at the lower level. In this paper the fitting of the components of the hierarchical model, written as nested functions, is considered in developing a hierarchical covariance model for use in estimation, simulation, or analytical derivation of macrodispersivity models. The least-squares criterion, along with parameter prior information and other weighted constraints, is used as the objective function of the inverse problem, which is solved by the Gauss–Newton–Levenberg–Marquardt method. The method is tested on synthetic data and illustrated with real data from a site with glaciofluvial sand and gravel deposits.

INTRODUCTION

The spatial variation of permeability in sediments has been recognized as a control on the dispersion of groundwater contaminant plumes. Spatial covariance or semivariogram models developed from measurements of natural-log permeability, $Y = \ln(k)$, are important in developing macrodispersivity models (Dagan, 1989). We have in mind the general methodology used in the Borden site and Cape Cod site studies, where large numbers of measurements of ln(k) with small measurement support scale (of the order of 10^{-2} m) are made in unconsolidated sediments over a scale of the order of 10^2 m (Sudicky, 1986, Leblanc et al., 1991). In this approach, the measurements are considered to be scalar point values, $Y(\mathbf{x})$, and their variance and two-point spatial correlation are used to develop macrodispersivity models or effective permeability tensors for the larger (10^2 m) scale.

We consider the case where such sediments can be conceptually divided into lithofacies types, as shown in Figure 1. Although $Y(\mathbf{x})$ appears to be unimodally distributed if values from all lithofacies are examined together, the data from within each lithofacies have slight but statistically significant differences in the mean (e.g., Gaud et al., this volume). Thus, $Y(\mathbf{x})$ has a weakly multimodal distribution, with each mode corresponding to a lithofacies (just facies hereinafter).

In such cases, one could characterize and model the spatial correlation of [$Y(\mathbf{x})$, $Y(\mathbf{x}')$] by fitting a model to the global sample auto-covariance or auto-semivariogram determined from all of the data, as in previous studies. However, there are advantages to modeling the sample auto- and cross-covariance or semivariogram for each facies type separately and then combining those models to develop the global model. One advantage is that we can gain greater insight into how attributes of the facies assemblage influence the global spatial correlation (e.g., Rubin, 1995; Barrash and Clemo, 2002; Ritzi et al., 2004). These attributes might include: the proportions of the facies, the mean and variance in the length of the facies in any particular direction, the pattern in how the facies are juxtaposed, the mean, variance, and spatial correlation of $Y(\mathbf{x})$ within facies, and the spatial correlation of $Y(\mathbf{x})$ across facies. Another advantage is that we can improve our ability to extrapolate the model into

regions for which we have no permeability data but do have some knowledge of these attributes of the sediment.

Ritzi et al. (2004) developed a hierarchical model that can be used for this purpose. The model can be written to span any number of hierarchical scales of organization, but here the focus is on just two scales: facies and facies assemblage. The auto- and cross-semivariograms among the N facies can be related to the global semivariogram for the facies assemblage by

$$\gamma_Y(h) = \sum_{k=1}^{N}\sum_{i=1}^{N} \gamma_{ki}(h) p_k t_{ki}(h) \tag{1}$$

And the auto- and cross-covariances among the facies can be related to the global covariance for the facies assemblage by

$$C_Y(h) = \sum_{k=1}^{N}\sum_{i=1}^{N} \{C_{ki}(h) + m_k m_i\} p_k t_{ki}(h) - M_Y^2 \tag{2}$$

Furthermore, the mean and variance of the facies are related to the global mean and variance of the facies assemblage by

$$M_Y = \sum_{k=1}^{N} p_k m_k \tag{3}$$

$$\sigma_Y^2 = \sum_{k=1}^{N} p_k \sigma_k^2 + \sum_{k=1}^{N}\sum_{i>k}^{N} p_k p_i (m_k - m_i)^2 \tag{4}$$

Here, $\gamma_Y(h)$ is the global semivariogram, $\gamma_{ki}(h)$ is the auto-semivariogram ($k = i$) or cross-semivariogram ($k \neq i$) among facies; p_k is the volume proportion, $t_{ki}(h)$ is the transition probability, $C_Y(h)$ is the global centered covariance, $C_{ki}(h)$ is the auto-covariance ($k = i$) or cross-covariance ($k \neq i$), m_k and σ_k^2 denote the mean and variance of $Y(\mathbf{x})$ in facies k, and M_Y and σ_Y^2 denote global mean and variance, respectively.

Ritzi et al. (2004) applied these equations to data representing a cross-bedded point-bar deposit, where there was negative correlation across bed types. In such deposits, the cross-terms ($i \neq k$) in Equation 1 predominate. Ritzi et al. (2004) focused on the development and application of the hierarchical model in order to understand the factors that dictate the shape of the global sample semivariogram in cross-bedded

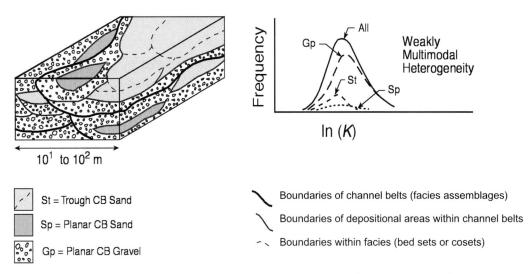

St = Trough CB Sand   Boundaries of channel belts (facies assemblages)

Sp = Planar CB Sand   Boundaries of depositional areas within channel belts

Gp = Planar CB Gravel   Boundaries within facies (bed sets or cosets)

FIG. 1.—Conceptual diagrams showing cross-bedded (CB) sedimentary facies and the corresponding histograms of permeability.

deposits. They did not consider the issues of fitting spatial correlation models and estimating model parameters.

In this paper we focus on the problem of fitting model functions to the auto- and cross-semivariograms or covariances, and to the transition probabilities among the facies. This procedure is required if Equations 1 or 2 are to be used for estimation that involves kriging, and for analytical derivations of macro-dispersivity models, as with Rubin (1995). If kriging is involved, the functions that are fitted have restrictions. Specifically, they must lead to non-negative definite matrices in the system of kriging equations. The six most commonly used and permissible models, reviewed by Deutsch and Journel (1998), are the exponential, spherical, Gaussian, power, linear, and cosine functions. For some functions, such as the cosine, the permissibility may be limited by the dimensionality of the analysis. However, the permissibility conditions required for models used in kriging do not restrict development of macrodispersivity models. Because we are interested in the latter, we do not restrict functions to be permissible for kriging.

For the transition probabilities, it has been shown that the parameters of these functions represent the proportions, geometry, and pattern of the facies (Carle and Fogg, 1996; Ritzi, 2000). Note that when the indicator correlation can be represented by summing exponential functions, the continuous Markov chain model can be used. Ritzi (2000) showed that continuous Markov chain models arise in binary systems from unimodal distributions of facies lengths with the coefficient of variation, c_v, of the order of unity. Multimodal distributions of facies lengths can give rise to transition probabilities that appear to have nested structures, in which the number and types of functions needed is related to the modality, mean, and variance in length of the facies. These relationships between indicator correlation and facies length restrict the functions that can be used. Ritzi (2000) pointed out that the nugget and Gaussian functions cannot be used, and furthermore that the parameters are constrained by probability laws, considered further below. With these relationships defined, geologic information (soft data or prior information) can be incorporated in the process of fitting the models.

Kitanidis and Lane (1985) advocated maximum likelihood parameter estimation of hydrologic spatial processes. To estimate the spatial covariance structure of intrinsic or nonintrinsic random functions from point or spatially averaged data, Samper

and Neuman (1989) described a cross-validation method. Woodbury and Sudicky (1991) modeled the experimental semivariogram data from the Borden aquifer with an exponential function by the constrained simplex approach and the Levenberg–Marquardt method separately. Kitanidis (1997) reviewed the methods for fitting functions to sample semivariogram and covariance models and the estimation criteria that might be used.

If the application of model functions is known, the fitting process could have an estimation criterion based on that application. For example, if the models are to be used for kriging and point estimation, cross validation can be used with an estimation criterion based on differences between kriging estimates and observations. If the models are to be used in analytically derived macrodispersivity models, an estimation criterion could be based on differences between computed and observed spatial moments of mass in the plume.

Here the application is unspecified, so we focus on differences between the model functions and the sample semivariograms, covariances, and transition probabilities. We adopt a least-squares estimation criterion and use the Levenberg–Marquardt method. We impose constraints so that the transition probability models obey probability laws, and we include the ability to incorporate prior information, specifically geologic (soft) information, into the transition probability models. As with most data inversion methods, we gain confidence by first testing the method on synthetic data and then presenting an application to real data and evaluate the results.

NESTED STRUCTURE AND CONSTRAINTS FOR TRANSITION PROBABILITY MODELS

Here, a linear combination of semivariogram, covariance and transition probability functions, $\mathbf{u}_{ki}(h)$, is established:

$$\mathbf{u}_{ki}(h) = \sum_{j=1}^{n} w_j u_j(h) \quad (k, i = 1, 2, ..., N) \qquad (5)$$

$$\sum_{j=1}^{n} w_j = 1 \qquad (6)$$

where w_j is the weighting coefficient for the jth function u_j, u_j is exponential when $j = 1$, spherical when $j = 2$, linear when $j = 3$, cosine when $j = 4$, power when $j = 5$, and Gaussian when $j = 6$, and n is the number of functions. For the semivariogram and covariance, $n = 6$. For the transition probability, only the first four functions ($n = 4$) are defined (Ritzi, 2000).

Developing model functions with the sample data by Equation 5 becomes an inverse problem in which a number of parameters need to be estimated. For an assemblage of N facies we must fit a nested set of n functions to each of N^2 semivariograms, N^2 covariances, and N^2 transition probabilities. For each function there are N_p parameters (including parameters within the function such as structural ranges, variance or proportion, and also weights). Thus, there are $N^2 \times n \times N_p$ parameters that must be estimated for the semivariograms, for the covariances, and for the transition probabilities. In application, we can reduce the number of parameters by applying geologic insight and reducing n and N_p.

The linear combination of functions can be established for auto- and cross-semivariograms and covariances without more constraints on the parameters of the functions beyond that of Equation 6. However, additional constraints are required for those of the transition probability functions. The nested transition probability models must satisfy the basic conditions

$$\sum_{k=1}^{N} p_k = 1 \quad \text{and} \quad \sum_{k=1}^{N} t_{ki}(h) = 1 \tag{7}$$

$$0 \leq p_k \leq 1 \quad \text{and} \quad 0 \leq t_{ki}(h) \leq 1 \tag{8}$$

Furthermore, the formulae of the basic functions of the auto-transition probabilities are different from those of the cross-transition probabilities. For example, the exponential model for the auto-transition probability is

$$t_{kk}(h) = p_k + (1 - p_k)\exp(-\frac{3h}{a_k}) \tag{9}$$

and the cross-transition probability model is

$$t_{ki}(h) = p_k - p_k \exp(-\frac{3h}{a_k}) \tag{10}$$

Here we determine the constraints on the parameters of the nested functions for the auto- and cross-transition probabilities such that conditions in Equations 7 and 8 are satisfied,

$$t_{kk}(h) = \sum_{j=1}^{4} w_j u_j = w_1[p_k + (1-p_k)\exp(-\frac{3h}{a_k})] + w_2$$

$$\{1 - (1-p_k)[1.5h/a_k - 0.5(h/a_k)^3]\} + w_3[1 - (1-p_k)h/a_k] \tag{11a}$$

$$+ w_4[p_k + (1-p_k)\cos(\frac{\pi h}{b_k})] \quad (h < a_k)$$

$$= w_1[p_k + (1-p_k)\exp(-\frac{3h}{a_k})] + w_2 p_k$$

$$\tag{11b}$$

$$+ w_3 p_k + w_4[p_k + (1-p_k)\cos(\frac{\pi h}{b_k})] \quad (h \geq a_k)$$

where a_k and b_k are structure ranges for different functions.

Because $\sum_{j=1}^{n} w_j = 1$, Equation 11b can be simplified to

$$t_{kk}(h) = p_k + (1-p_k)[w_1 \exp(-\frac{3h}{a_k}) + w_4 \cos(\frac{\pi h}{b_k})] \tag{12}$$

For any values of the parameters in Equation 12, $t_{kk}(h) \leq 0$. However, to satisfy $t_{kk}(h) \geq 0$, it is necessary that

$$w_1 \exp(-\frac{3h}{a_k}) + w_4 \cos(\frac{\pi h}{b_k}) \geq \frac{-p_k}{1-p_k} \tag{13}$$

On the left-hand side, under the extreme minimum conditions of $\cos(\frac{\pi h}{b_k}) \to -1$, or the minimum points $h = (2m+1)$ bk ($m = 0, 1, 2, 3, ...$), we can obtain

$$\frac{b_k}{a_k} \leq -\frac{1}{3(2m+1)} \ln \frac{w_4(1-p_k) - p_k}{w_1(1-p_k)} \tag{14}$$

From Equation 11a, the same criterion can be derived as Equation 14 but $m = 0$.

For the nested model of cross-transition probability we have the similar criterion,

$$\frac{b_k}{a_k} \leq -\frac{1}{3(2m+1)} \ln \frac{(w_4 + 1)p_k - 1}{w_1 p_k} \tag{15}$$

Because Equations 7, 8, 14, and 15 define the constraints of parameters for the nested auto- and cross-transition probabilities, we apply more than one function (i.e., nested functions) to fit the sample transition probabilities.

FORMULATION OF INVERSE PROBLEM

Objective Function

The most common tool for parameter identification is the generalized least-squares criterion (Neuman and Yakowitz, 1979; Sun, 1994; Dai, 2000). Let $\mathbf{p} = (\mathbf{p}_1, \mathbf{p}_2, \mathbf{p}_3, ..., \mathbf{p}_M)$ be the optimal parameter vector. Then the least-squares criterion E($\mathbf{p}$) can be expressed as

$$E(\mathbf{p}) = \sum_{m=1}^{Ne} W_m E_m(\mathbf{p}) \tag{16}$$

where Ne is the number of different types of data, $E_m(\mathbf{p})$ is the least-squares for each type of data, and W_m are the weighting coefficients for the mth type of data. As for data types, $m = 1$ when data are sample semivariograms, covariances, or transition probabilities and $m = 2$ when they are prior information about parameters. Weighting coefficients, W_m, are defined according to Carrera and Neuman (1986), Sun (1994) and Dai and Samper (2004) as

$$W_m = \frac{W_{0m}}{\frac{E_m(\mathbf{p})}{L_m}} \quad (m = 1, 2, ..., Ne) \tag{17}$$

where W_{0m} are user-defined initial weighting coefficients of different types of data and L_m is the number of mth type of sample data. Generally, $W_{0m} = 1$. For optimization, however, the preference of a modeler can be expressed through the values chosen for W_{0m}, which rank the importance of different types of data. It should be noted that W_{0m} are dimensionless. However, W_m have dimensions that are reciprocal to those of $E_m(\mathbf{p})$, which are generally the square of the units of mth type of data

$$E_m(\mathbf{p}) = \sum_{l=1}^{L_i} w_{lm}^2 (\mathbf{u}_{lm}(\mathbf{p}) - F_{lm})^2 \quad (m = 1, 2) \tag{18}$$

where $\mathbf{u}_{lm}(\mathbf{p})$ are the values of nested models, F_{lm} are sample semivariograms, covariances, or transition probabilities ($m = 1$)

and prior information of the parameters ($m = 2$), and w_{lm} are weighting coefficients for individual sample data, and their values depend on the accuracy of samples. Here we have dropped the k, i (k, i = 1, 2, …, N) notation for simplicity, with the understanding that $\mathbf{u}_{lm}(\mathbf{p})$, F_{lm}, w_{lm}, and $E_m(\mathbf{p})$ are defined for specific k, i combinations.

Generally, the smaller the lag distance, the larger are the assigned weighting coefficients, w_{lm}, because smaller lags are based on more pairs of data. So, w_{lm} can be computed as

$$w_{lm} = \frac{w_{lm0} Np_{lm}}{Ntp} \tag{19}$$

where w_{lm0} are user-defined initial weighting coefficients for each lag class of a sample semivariogram, covariance, or transition probability; Np_{lm} are the number of pairs in each lag class, and Ntp is the total number of pairs. For prior information ($m = 2$), $Np_{lm} = Ntp$, and w_{lm0} is inversely proportional to the value of a parameter that represents prior information.

Prior Information of Parameters

From the statistical analysis of the measurements, we can easily obtain as prior information the variance and the structural range from permeability data, and the proportion and the structure range from the indicator data. These values of independent prior information about parameters can be incorporated in the objective function and used to define lower and upper bounds, as well as initial values for the optimization process. A set of weights must be given to each piece of prior information according to Equations 17 and 19. In practice, by giving different initial weighting coefficients, one can assign the weights in accordance with the extent to which one wishes each article of prior information to influence the parameter estimation process.

Prior information is very important, because it helps in deciding upon a range of acceptable values that a parameter can take during the optimization process. Moreover, incorporating prior information into the objective function improves the structure of the covariance matrix and alleviates the ill-posedness of the inverse problem, allowing the system to supply a unique set of parameters.

Optimization Methods

Equation 16 can be solved using different optimization methods such as Newton, Gauss–Newton, modified Gauss–Newton (Sun, 1994), conjugate gradient (Carrera and Neuman, 1986), and the simplex method (Woodbury and Sudicky, 1991). In this paper, the Gauss–Newton–Levenberg–Marquardt method is used. It is a robust algorithm for small-residual problems (Dai, 2000). Statistical measures of goodness of fit, as well as measures of parameter uncertainty (approximate confidence intervals), have been derived from the covariance matrix of parameter estimates to evaluate the estimation accuracy.

In order to conduct the different stages of inverse analysis, three similar computer codes were developed for estimating parameters in nested semivariogram, covariance, and transition-probability models. There are more parameters to be estimated in one run for nested transition-probability models than for semivariograms because it is necessary to couple all of the individual models together in order to make the estimated parameters satisfy Equations 7, 8, 14, and 15.

SYNTHETIC EXPERIMENTS

In order to test the proper performance of the codes (i.e., checking that the codes properly solve the equations they are intended to solve), synthetic examples, in which the true model parameters are known exactly, are used to demonstrate the accuracy of the estimated parameters. The codes were tested with synthetic semivariograms created with many different nested models. Here two examples are presented.

Synthetic Model I

The synthetic sample semivariogram is computed from the sum of an exponential and a cosine model, which is corrupted with different levels of noise having a lognormal distribution. Although we are ultimately interested in macrodispersion models, which are insensitive to the nugget of covariance models, here we include a nugget function in the synthetic model I for more general testing of the inverse code. The true parameter values used and the estimated parameters under different levels of noise are listed in Table 1. Figure 2A shows the synthetic semivariogram corrupted with noise having a standard deviation of 0.1 and the model results reproduced by the inverse code. Figure 2B presents the relationship of relative parameter errors and the objective function to the levels of noise. With no noise the estimated parameters are the same as the true parameters. When the standard deviation of the noise in corrupted data is increased, the error of the estimated parameters increases. Most of the relation curves of relative parameter errors and measurement errors are

TABLE 1.—Estimation results using synthetic semivariogram data containing different degrees of log-normally distributed noise (mean $\mu = 1$).

Parameter		Estimated results for different standard deviation (σ) in added noise						
Name	True value	$\sigma = 0$	$\sigma = 0.01$	$\sigma = 0.05$	$\sigma = 0.1$	$\sigma = 0.25$	$\sigma = 0.5$	$\sigma = 1$
w_1	0.8	0.8	0.7976	0.7884	0.7788	0.7934	0.9187	0.9309
w_4	0.2	0.2	0.2024	0.2116	0.2212	0.2066	0.0813	0.0691
a_k	12	12	12.28	13.56	15.76	36.36	190	272.1
b_k	3	3	3.001	3.005	3.009	3.018	2.998	2.95
σ_k^2	0.4	0.4	0.4006	0.4035	0.4096	0.4913	1.195	1.65
Nugget	0.1	0.1	0.1007	0.1038	0.1079	0.1226	0.1117	0.0613
Objective function		$4.51 \cdot 10^{-8}$	$5.60 \cdot 10^{-4}$	0.014	0.0567	0.362	1.507	6.441

A

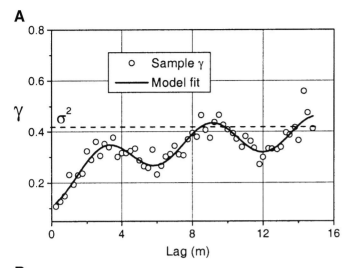

B

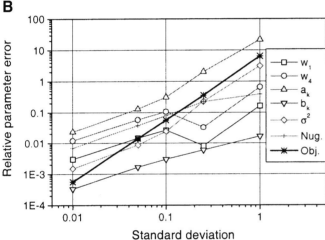

Fig. 2.—**A)** The synthetic sample semivariogram corrupted with noise having a standard deviation 0.1 and the corresponding model fit. **B)** Relative parameter errors and objective function versus standard deviations (s_l).

close to straight lines on a log–log plot. The objective function increases with the standard deviation along a straight line with a slope of 2. This feature results from the form of the least-squares objective function (Dai, 2000).

Synthetic Model II

A synthetic transition-probability model that consists of the sum of an exponential and a cosine model for three facies is set up to estimate 15 parameters by using the synthetic sample transition probabilities corrupted with different levels of log-normally distributed noise. The true parameter values and the estimated results are listed in Table 2. Figure 3A presents the fitting of model transition probabilities to the synthetic ones corrupted with noise at the 0.1 standard deviation level. The t_{11} is the auto-transition probability; the t_{12} and t_{13} are cross-transition probabilities. Like Figure 2B, Figure 3B also shows that the objective function increases with the standard deviation of the sample synthetic transition probabilities along a straight line of slope of 2. This result, along with other tests, indicates that the inverse codes are robust and reliable.

APPLICATION TO HAMILTON SITE

The conceptual model in Figure 1 is derived from our studies of buried-valley aquifer systems in the North American mid-continent (Dominic et al., 1996, Ritzi, 2000; Ritzi et al., 2002). These aquifers occur within the extent of Pleistocene glaciation. A variety of depositional processes (e.g., fluvial, lacustrine, glacial) created complex mixtures of two main facies associations: (1) sand and gravel, which predominates, and (2) mud and diamicton. Data were collected from the Miami Valley aquifer system as shown in Figure 4 (Ritzi et al., 2002). The distributions of air-permeameter measurements from the sand and gravel facies associations (Fig. 4B–D) have a central tendency that corresponds closely to pumping-test measurements (Fig. 4A), adding to confidence that they are representative. Figure 5 shows that the air-permeability data have more variance than pumping-test data because the individual occurrences of relatively higher-permeability and lower-permeability facies are "hydraulically averaged" in estimates derived from pumping tests.

The field site at Hamilton, Ohio, is located in a bedrock valley partially filled with Pleistocene glacial deposits. The facies in a sand and gravel facies association exposed in a quarry are associated with in-channel dunes and bars. Facies include planar cross-bedded gravel (Gp), planar cross-bedded sand (Sp), and trough cross-bedded sand (St) (Titzel, 1997; Ritzi et al., 2002). Permeability data were collected with an air permeameter on the outcrop as shown in Figure 6A within two areas (boxes), each of which was 2 m (vertical) by 5 m (horizontal); the boxes are separated by 5 meters (Fig. 6B; Titzel, 1997). The sample spacing for permeability measurements is 0.25 m in the horizontal direction and 0.1 m in the vertical direction. Each point has five repeated permeability measurements. The average of these five measurements was used as the $\ln(k)$ measurements. The statistics of the field measurements for individual facies are listed in Table 3.

The mean of $\ln(k)$ in the facies is 5.43 ln(darcys) for Gp, 5.11 ln(darcys) for Sp, and 4.78 ln(darcys) for St; for the combined facies it is 5.32 ln(darcys). All facies show significant overlap in their permeability ranges. An analysis of covariance (ANCOVA) of the permeability data was conducted to determine if the mean permeabilities of the facies were significantly different. Two ANCOVAs were performed under different conditions (Chen, 1997). One is based on all sample data, and the other is based on a randomly sampled subset. Both tests concluded that the facies means were significantly different. By using Equations 3 and 4 and the data listed in Table 3, we can calculate that M_Y = 5.32 ln(darcys) and σ_Y^2 = 0.44. These values are identical to the results calculated directly from all data.

The facies occurrences across the entire outcrop were mapped, and those maps were converted to an indicator data set with a spacing of 0.5 m (horizontal and vertical directions) for computing the facies proportions (Table 3) and their transition probabilities. From permeability data the m_k and σ_k^2 in each facies were computed (Table 3). The l_k is the mean horizontal length for individual facies (meters). The σ_k^2 and p_k listed in Table 3 will be taken as the prior information for model fitting.

Semivariogram Model

The $Y(x)$ data were used to calculate sample auto- and cross-semivariograms. Here we present the results for the $+y$ direction (horizontal, from left to right in Fig. 6A). A nested model was fitted to the individual sample semivariograms. Although we have a parameter estimation tool, not everything in the approach is automatic, nor should it be (Carrera and Neuman, 1986). Trial

TABLE 2.—Estimation results using synthetic transition probability data containing different degrees of log-normally distributed noise (mean $\mu = 1$).

Parameter			Estimated Results for different standard deviation (σ)						
Name		True value	$\sigma = 0$	$\sigma = 0.001$	$\sigma = 0.01$	$\sigma = 0.1$	$\sigma = 0.25$	$\sigma = 0.5$	$\sigma = 1$
t_{11}	w_1	0.5	0.5	0.5004	0.502	0.548	0.468	0.402	0.363
	w_4	0.5	0.5	0.4996	0.498	0.452	0.532	0.598	0.637
	a_k	20	20	20	19.98	21.08	18.05	18.01	21.58
	b_k	6	6	6	6.001	6.009	5.988	5.912	5.732
	p_1	0.64	0.64	0.6399	0.639	0.620	0.650	0.665	0.652
t_{12}	w_1	0.5	0.5	0.4998	0.498	0.488	0.459	0.509	0.641
	w_4	0.5	0.5	0.5002	0.502	0.512	0.541	0.491	0.359
	a_k	20	20	19.95	19.52	14.57	16.68	6.347	3.603
	b_k	6	6	6	5.998	5.979	5.968	6.025	6.429
	p_2	0.21	0.21	0.21	0.211	0.222	0.204	0.195	0.201
t_{13}	w_1	0.5	0.5	0.4998	0.498	0.488	0.459	0.516	0.740
	w_4	0.5	0.5	0.5002	0.502	0.512	0.541	0.484	0.260
	a_k	20	20	19.97	19.54	14.58	16.7	6.034	3.941
	b_k	6	6	6	5.997	5.979	5.968	6.026	6.433
	p_3	0.15	0.15	0.1501	0.150	0.158	0.146	0.140	0.147
Objective function			$8.33 \cdot 10^{-8}$	$2.23 \cdot 10^{-5}$	$2.16 \cdot 10^{-3}$	0.248	1.399	5.829	22.28

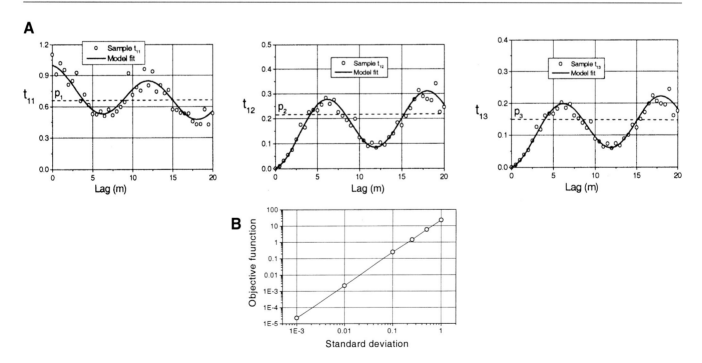

FIG. 3.—**A)** Noise-corrupted sample transition probability with a standard deviation 0.1 and the corresponding model fit. **B)** Optimum values of objective function versus standard deviation of sample transition probabilities.

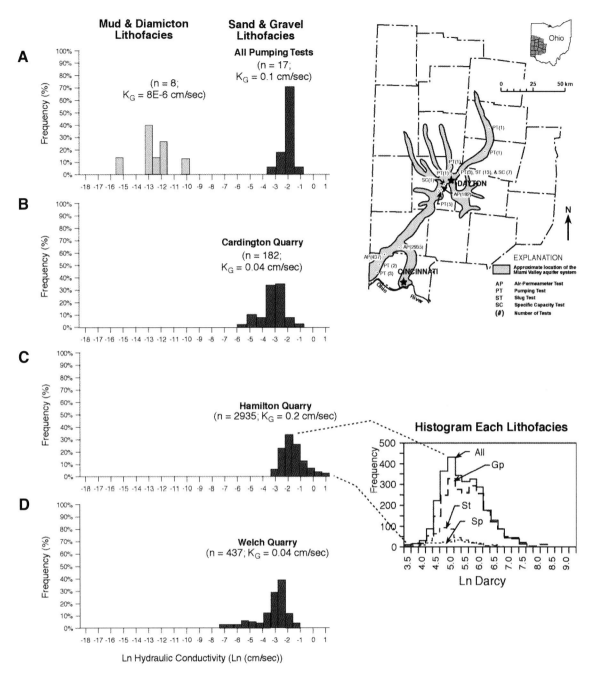

FIG. 4.—Histograms of permeability measurements in the Miami Valley aquifer system. The measurements in sand and gravel include those made with **A)** pumping tests and **B–D)** air permeameters on outcrops, as located at the upper right (adapted from Titzel, 1997). K_G refers to the geometric mean of all data, and n is the number of data.

and error is still carried out in the estimation procedure by modifying the parameter bounds, initial parameter values, and initial weighting coefficients. Personal judgment helps to determine the set of estimated parameters on the basis of model parsimony, values of objective functions, the coefficients of variation for parameters, as well as the characteristics of the sedimentary units (mean length and proportions).

The estimated model parameters are listed in Table 4, and the results are plotted in Figure 7. There is no transition between Sp and St along the $+y$ direction because Sp occurs in the upper part

of the region whereas St occurs in the lower part (Fig. 6). Therefore, there are no cross terms for the semivariogram, covariance, or transition probability for these facies. We assume that this pattern repeats for the scale of interest and therefore that the cross terms for these facies in the model are zero.

Five of the semivariograms (Gp–Gp, Gp–St, Sp–Gp, Sp–Sp, and St–Gp) are fitted with nested combinations of exponential and cosine models ($w_2 = w_3 = w_5 = w_6 = 0$); two others (Gp–Sp and St–St) only with exponential models. The fits for most of the individual semivariograms are better at small lag distances than

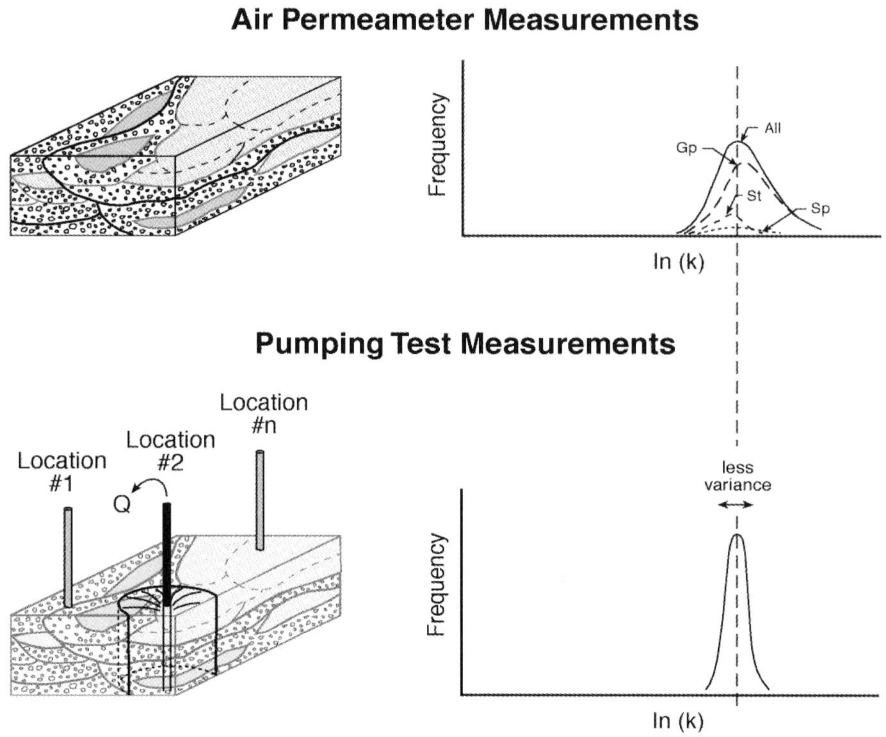

Air Permeameter Measurements

Pumping Test Measurements

FIG. 5.—Comparing measurements from small and large support scales (adapted from Ritzi et al., 2002).

those at large lag distances, because the sample semivariograms are unstable from decreasing numbers of lag pairs; we prescribed relatively small weighting coefficients at large lags. Nugget does not affect macrodispersivity, and here we are not interested in measurement error; therefore, there is no reason to model nugget, and it is taken as 0. The estimated sill of Gp–Gp ($C_0 = 0.53$) is slightly higher than the prior information (0.42), but those of Sp and St are very close to the prior information listed in Table 3. Generally, the confidence intervals on b_k and C_0 were small, but for parameters w_1, w_4, and a_k they were large. For example, the estimated wavelength (b_k) of Gp–Gp is 15.66 m and the 95% confidence interval of b_k is (13.64–17.68 m), and the estimated w_1 of Gp–Gp is 0.46 and its 95% confidence interval is (0.15–1.0). Because of correlation between the parameters and the weights of different functions, confidence intervals must be viewed with caution.

Covariance Models

The $Y(x)$ data were also used to calculate the sample auto- and cross-covariance. First the general nested model Equation 5 was fitted with the inversion procedure to the sample covariance. The estimated C_0 from the auto-covariance model were equal to the univariate variance for each facies. The range of correlation of Gp was 2.72 m, of Sp was 0.85 m, and of St was 2.76 m. The sample Gp–Sp cross-covariance is random; we cannot identify a suitable function to express it, so a straight line with 0.0 for C_0 was used.

However, the shapes of the sample covariances of Gp–St, Sp–Gp, and St–Gp (Figure 8) show that the hole effect is damped out with increasing lag distance. We could not obtain a good fit with the above inversion procedure. In order to improve the fit, then, a damped hole-effect model was used for the Gp–St, Sp–Gp, and St–Gp cross-covariance models:

$$C_{ki} = C_0[1 - \exp(-\frac{3h}{a_k})\cos(\frac{\pi h}{b_k})] \qquad (20)$$

This expression is no longer linear, and it was not included in the inverse code. The function was fitted to the sample cross-covariances by manually adjusting C_0, a_k, and b_k. Note that the parameter a_k here is different from the correlation range in an exponential function. It is the distance at which 95% of the hole effect is damped out. b_k is the half-wavelength. The results indicate that at about 23.5 to 25 m the hole effect in each of the three cross-covariances is damped out. The estimated half wavelength is 4.13 m for Gp–St, 0.98 m for Sp–Gp and 1.21 m for St–Gp. These models lower the values of the objective functions compared to what we derived using Equation 5 with the inverse code. This indicates that finding an appropriate model structure is more important than estimating the parameters alone. As it turns out, these three cross covariances do not contribute much to Equation 2, as we will see below, so further attempts to improve the inverse procedure here did not seem warranted.

Transition Probability Models

The indicator data taken from the entire outcrop at the Hamilton site were used to calculate the sample transition probabilities. A nested model of exponential, spherical, linear, and cosine functions was fitted to the sample transition probabilities. The weights for the spherical and linear models were zero ($w_2 = w_3 = 0$). The results are presented in Table 6 and Figure 9. The hole effect of the sample transition probabilities for St–Gp and St–St is damped out with increasing lag distance. Therefore, the damped hole-effect model similar to Equation 20 was used for transition probability St–Gp and manually fitted.

Because the sedimentary structures repeat, all of the seven transition probability models include a cosine function. The

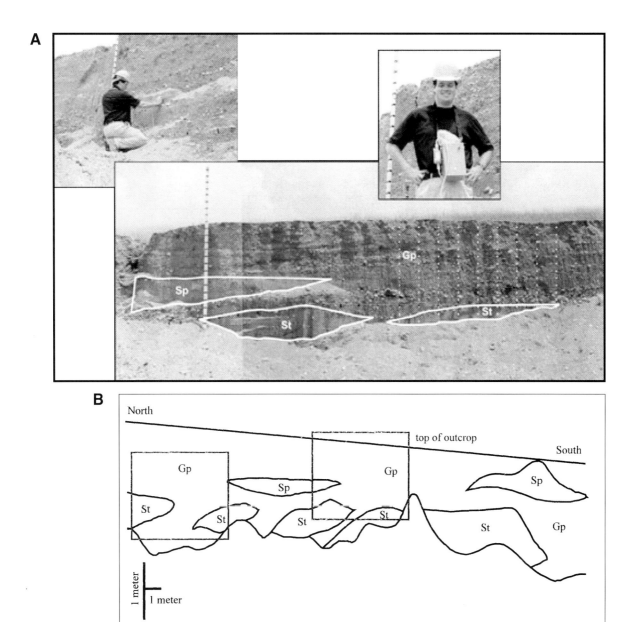

F$_{IG}$. 6.—**A)** Collection of permeability data at the Hamilton site. The air permeameter injects air at a constant pressure and the resulting flow rate is a known function of the permeability of the sediment (Davis et al., 1994). A part of the sampling grid used by Titzel (1997) within the right box (6B) is indicated with white dots over a portion of the outcrop (6A). Sets of cross strata within the St and Sp facies are not readily discerned in the photo but are easily seen close up. **B)** Map of the Hamilton outcrop showing facies and the location of permeability data collection grids (boxes) (adapted from Titzel, 1997)

half wavelength for Sp is about 7.5 m, for Gp it is 6.9 m, and for St it is 2.6 m. The estimated proportions for Sp in the model for t_{Sp-Sp}, St in t_{St-Gp} and in t_{St-St} are larger than the prior information because of the absence of Sp–St and St–Sp transitions in the $+y$ direction and are modeled this way in order to satisfy the condition $\sum_{k=1}^{N} p_k = 1$.

Global Semivariogram

Figure 10 shows the result of combining all fitted functions for $\gamma_{ki}(h)$ and $t_{ki}(h)$ according to Equation 1, the global model, as compared to the global sample semivariogram. Note that combining the sample p_k, $\gamma_{ki}(h)$, and $t_{ki}(h)$ according to Equation 1 gives exactly the same result as computing the global sample semivariogram directly from all data. The circles represent both of these procedures (Ritzi, et al., 2004). Examining the global model, we see that the periodicity in the individual semivariogram and transition-probability models is mostly damped out when they are combined according to Equation 1. We see that the global model reproduces the sample global semivariogram very well except at lag distances 5 m and 15 m. There is a jump in the sample semivariogram at the lag distance of 5 m. This is because the permeability samples were collected in the two boxes which were separated by a distance of 5 m. At this lag distance we shift from

TABLE 3.—Statistics for individual facies.

Parameter	m_k	σ_k^2	p_k	$\bar{l}_k$
Gp	5.43	0.42	0.72	6.82
Sp	5.11	0.31	0.08	2.35
St	4.78	0.22	0.20	3.34

taking pairs defined within each box to pairs taken along the inside edge of each box. There is a sudden drop in the number of pairs that are defined and a sudden change in proportions. Thus, the jump is an artifact of sampling. The sample semivariogram is also affected by declining numbers of pairs as the lag distance approaches 15 m. Thus, the global model, developed from the facies pattern over the whole outcrop, not just the boxes, may better represent the spatial structure of permeability than does the sample semivariogram. Note that the global model represents the spatial structure of permeability only inasmuch as the transition probability terms represent the proportions, geometry, and arrangement of the facies. To the extent that these attributes of the facies exposed in outcrop repeat beyond the exposure, the model can be applied, but not further.

When the cross-semivariogram terms are neglected, the sum of the auto-semivariogram terms has the same trend and shape as that of the global semivariogram but is lower than the sample semivariogram. The cross-semivariograms between facies and the auto-semivariograms within facies are both important to the global semivariogram. These results are different from those

TABLE 4.—Parameter estimates for semivariograms of Gp, Sp, and St.

Parameter	Gp–Gp	Gp–Sp	Gp–St	Sp–Gp	Sp–Sp	St–Gp	St–St
w_1	0.46	1.0	0.56	0.88	0.65	0.72	1.0
w_4	0.54	0	0.44	0.12	0.35	0.28	0
a_k	0.001	0.71	0.001	0.96	2.63	2.19	6.62
b_k	15.66	—	5.14	1.12	1.01	3.36	—
c_0	0.53	0.24	0.31	0.52	0.32	0.65	0.23

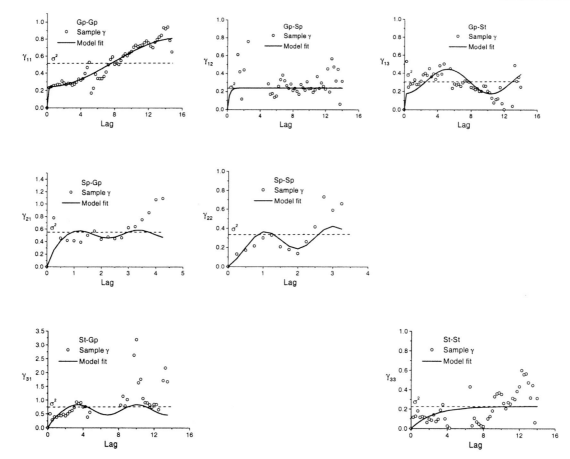

FIG. 7.—Model fit of the semivariogram with the sample data. Lag distance is in meters.

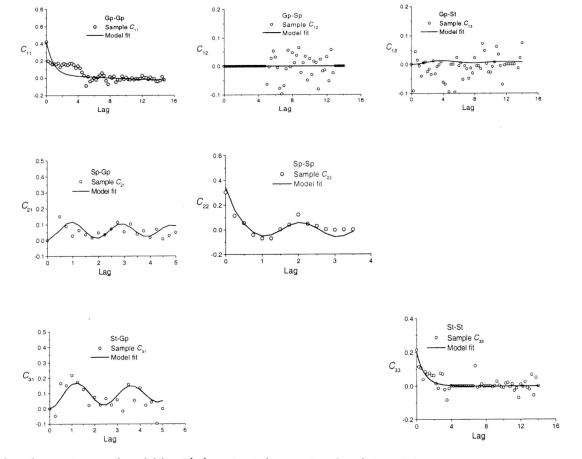

FIG. 8.—Sample covariance and model fit with the estimated parameters. Lag distance is in meters.

obtained by Ritzi et al. (2004). In that study, negative correlation of permeability across sedimentary unit types caused the cross-terms in Equation 1 to dominate in defining the global semivariogram; the auto-terms were negligible.

Global Covariance

Using the estimated parameters of nested covariance and transition probability models, the global covariance model is formed by Equation 2. The results are plotted in Figure 11.

As shown in Figure 11, neglecting the cross-covariance terms gives nearly the same result as the model that includes these terms. In Figure 8, the cross-covariance functions Gp–Sp, Gp–St, Sp–Gp, and St–Gp are close to 0. Therefore, these terms have little contribution to the global covariance, and the auto-covari-

ances dominate in defining the global covariance. So, in this case, the cross-covariance terms between facies can be ignored. Generally, the global semivariogram and covariance functions are thought to be equivalent ways of expressing the spatial continuity of measurements. However, the difference between cross-semivariograms and cross-covariances can be seen from their expressions,

$$\gamma_{ki}(h) = \frac{1}{2}\left\langle (Y_k(\boldsymbol{x}) - Y_i(\boldsymbol{x}'))^2 \right\rangle \qquad (21)$$

$$C_{ki}(h) = \left\langle (Y_k(\boldsymbol{x}) - m_k)(Y_i(\boldsymbol{x}') - m_i) \right\rangle \qquad (22)$$

Equation 21 is sensitive to the difference in mean permeability between facies k and i, whereas in Equation 22 the mean is

TABLE 5.—Parameter estimates for nested covariance models.

Parameter	Gp–Gp	Gp–Sp	Gp–St	Sp–Gp	Sp–Sp	St–Gp	St–St
w_1	0.94	0.31	—	—	0.91	—	0.99
w_4	0.06	0.69	—	—	0.19	—	0.01
a_k	2.72	—	23.52	25.18	0.85	25.0	2.76
b_k	15.51	—	4.13	0.98	1.02	1.21	8.53
C_0	0.42	0.0	0.01	0.06	0.31	0.09	0.22

TABLE 6.—Parameter estimates for nested transition-probability models.

Parameter	Gp–Gp	Gp–Sp	Gp–St	Sp–Gp	Sp–Sp	St–Gp	St–St
w_1	0.74	0.61	0.99	0.46	0.46	—	—
w_4	0.26	0.39	0.01	0.54	0.54	—	—
a_k	20.19	15.25	18.81	2.57	2.57	18.21	18.21
b_k	6.85	7.07	0.001	7.53	7.53	2.61	2.61
p_k	0.65	0.17	0.18	0.65	0.35	0.74	0.27

removed and thus Equation 22 is not. To the extent that differences in mean permeability across facies contributes to the global variance in permeability, the cross-terms will contribute to the global semivariogram but not to the global covariance.

CONCLUSIONS

Here we further consider the hierarchical spatial random functional model (Ritzi et al., 2004) that links permeability to sedimentary organization. The global spatial correlation of permeability is expressed as a function of facies proportions, transition probabilities, and the auto- or cross-semivariograms or covariances. The focus in this paper is on fitting models for the transition probabilities, semivariograms, and covariances at a lower hierarchical level, to be used in developing a model for a higher level expressed as a function of those lower-level models. Lower-level models for semivariograms, covariances, and transition probabilities were fitted with nested functions. The inverse procedure was here defined with the least-squares objective function along with defining constraints so that the models obey probability laws.

We demonstrated the inverse methodology by first testing it on two sets of synthetic data and then applying it to field data taken from an outcrop of glaciofluvial sand and gravel. The final global semivariogram and covariance models obtained from the estimated parameters compare well to the sample ones from the field site. The model results have also been used to examine alternative assumptions about correlation between facies, spe-

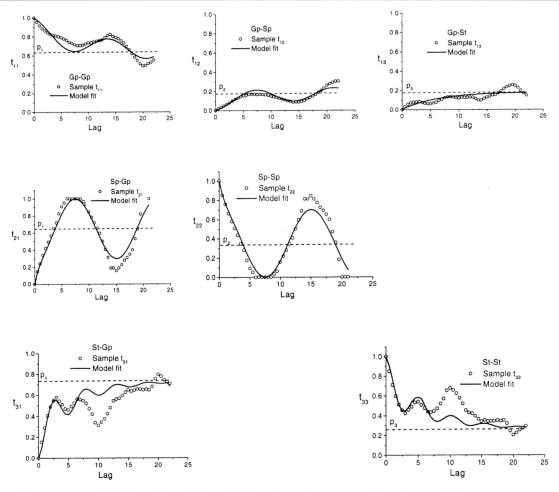

FIG. 9.—Sample transition probability and model fit with the estimated parameters. Lag distance is in meters.

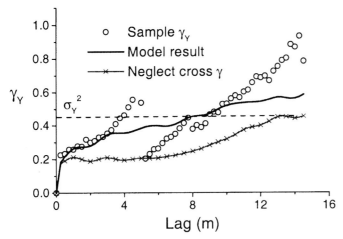

FIG. 10.—Sample semivariogram for the facies assemblage at the Hamilton site, and the model with fitted functions.

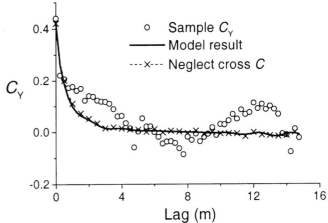

FIG. 11.—Sample covariance at the Hamilton site and model result computed with Equation 2 by using the estimated parameters.

cifically the relative importance of auto- and cross-correlation. For the global semivariogram model, the cross-semivariograms generally cannot be ignored. For the global covariance model, the cross-covariances are generally unimportant and the auto-covariances dominate. This is because the centered cross-covariance does not represent the difference in means across facies boundaries, but the cross-semivariogram does.

The global semivariogram or covariance model represents permeability structure beyond the outcrop from which it was developed only to the extent that the transition probabilities represent the proportions, geometry, and juxtaposition pattern of the facies beyond the outcrop.

ACKNOWLEDGMENTS

This work was supported by the National Science Foundation under grant NSF-EAR 00-01125. Any opinions, findings, and conclusions or recommendations expressed in this paper are those of the authors and do not necessarily reflect those of the National Science Foundation. We thank the reviewers of this paper, Drs. David Hyndman, Sean Mckenna, and an anonymous reviewer, for their constructive comments.

REFERENCES

BARRASH, W., AND CLEMO, T., 2002, Hierarchical geostatistics, multi-facies systems, and stationarity: Boise Hydrogeophysical Research Site, Boise, Idaho: Water Resources Research, 38 (10), dot:1029/2002WR001436.

CARLE, S.F., AND FOGG, G.E., 1996, Transition probability–based geostatistics: Mathematical Geology, v. 28, p. 453–476.

CARRERA, J., AND NEUMAN, S.P., 1986, Estimation of aquifer parameters under steady-state and transient condition: 2. Uniqueness, stability, and solution algorithms: Water Resources Research, v. 22, p. 211–227.

CHEN, M., 1997, ANCOVA for Hamilton lithofacies: Wright State University, Statistical Consulting Report, 12 p.

DAGAN, G., 1989, Flow and Transport in Porous Formations: New York, Springer-Verlag, 465 p.

DAI, Z., 2000, Inverse problem of water flow and reactive solute transport in variably saturated porous media: Ph.D. Dissertation, University of La Coruña, La Coruña, Spain, 334 p.

Dai, Z., and Samper, J., 2004, Inverse problem of multicomponent reactive chemical transport in porous media: formulation and ap-

plications: Water Resources Research, v. 40, doi:10.1029/2004 WR003248.

DAVIS, J.M., WILSON, J.L., AND PHILLIPS, F.M., 1994, A portable air-minipermeameter for rapid in situ field measurements: Ground Water, v. 32, p. 258–266.

DEUTSCH, C.V., AND JOURNEL, A.G., 1998, GSLIB, Geostatistical Software Library and User's Guide, 2th Edition: Oxford, U.K., Oxford University Press, 369 p.

DOMINIC, D.F., RITZI, R.W., AND KAUSCH, K., 1996, Aquitard distribution in a northern reach of the Miami Valley aquifer: 2) three-dimensional analysis of facies: Hydrogeology Journal, v. 4, p. 12–24.

KITANIDIS, P.K., AND LANE, R.W., 1985, Maximum likelihood parameter estimation of hydrologic spatial processes by the Gauss Newton method: Journal of Hydrology, v. 79, p. 53–71.

KITANIDIS, P.K., 1997, Introduction to Geostatistics; Applications in Hydrogeology: Cambridge, U.K., Cambridge University Press, 249 p.

LEBLANC, D.R., GARABEDIAN, S.P., HESS, K.M., GELHAR, L.W., QUADRI, R.D., STOLLENWERK, K.G., AND WOOD, W.W., 1991, Large scale natural gradient tracer test in sand and gravel, Cape Cod, Massachusetts. 1. Experimental design and observed tracer movement: Water Resources Research, v. 27, p. 895–910.

NEUMAN, S.P., AND YAKOWITZ, S., 1979, A statistical approach to the inverse problem of aquifer hydrology, 1. Theory: Water Resources Research, v. 15, p. 845–860.

RITZI, R.W., 2000, Behavior of indicator semivariograms and transition probabilities in relation to the variance in lengths of hydrofacies: Water Resources Research, v. 36, p. 3375–3381.

RITZI, R.W., DAI, Z., DOMINIC, D.F., AND RUBIN, Y., 2002, Spatial structure of permeability in relation to hierarchical sedimentary architecture in buried-valley aquifers: centimeter to kilometer scales, in Findikakis, A., ed., Bridging the Gap Between Measurements and Modeling in Heterogeneous Media: International Association of Hydrological Sciences and Lawrence Berkeley Laboratory, on CD-ROM.

RITZI, R.W., DAI, Z., DOMINIC, D.F., AND RUBIN, Y., 2004, A general spatial covariance model with hierarchical organization, and application to permeability in cross-bedded sediment: Water Resources Research, in press.

RUBIN, Y., 1995, Flow and transport in bimodal heterogeneous formations: Water Resources Research, v. 31, p. 2461–1468.

SAMPER, F.J., and Neuman, S.P., 1989, Estimation of spatial covariance structure by adjoint state maximum likelihood cross validation, 1, Theory: Water Resources Research, v. 25, p. 351–362.

SUDICKY, E.A., 1986, A natural gradient experiment on solute transport in a sand aquifer: spatial variability of hydraulic conductivity and its role in the dispersion process: Water Resources Research, v. 22, p. 2069–2082.

SUN, N.-Z., 1994, Inverse Problems in Groundwater Modeling: Dordrecht, The Netherlands, Kluwer Academic Publishers, 364 p.

TITZEL, S., 1997, Quantification of the permeability distribution within sand and gravel lithofacies in a southern portion of the Miami Valley Aquifer: Master's Thesis, Wright State University, 113 p.

WOODBURY, A.D., AND SUDICKY, E.A., 1991, The geostatistical characteristics of the Borden aquifer: Water Resources Research, v. 27, p. 533–546.

RELATING SMALL-SCALE PERMEABILITY HETEROGENEITY
TO LITHOFACIES DISTRIBUTION

MICHAEL N. GAUD AND GARY A. SMITH

Department of Earth and Planetary Sciences, University of New Mexico, Albuquerque, New Mexico 87131, U.S.A.
e-mail: gsmith@unm.edu

AND

SEAN A. MCKENNA

Geohydrology Group, Sandia National Laboratories, P.O. Box 5800 MS 0735, Albuquerque, New Mexico 87185-0735, U.S.A.
e-mail: samcken@sandia.gov

ABSTRACT: Aquifer heterogeneity at small scales (meters to tens of meters) can be characterized with hydrofacies. We investigate the feasibility of translating lithofacies into hydrofacies by testing the hypothesis that the permeability frequency distributions of different lithofacies are distinct. We mapped 11 lithofacies and performed more than 1800 *in situ* permeability measurements at an outcrop exposing poorly cemented, nonmarine, clastic sediment. The lithofacies represent both channel and interchannel deposits, are both ribbon-form and tabular, and vary in grain size from clay to sandy gravel. For each lithofacies permeability sample, we calculated variograms to define correlation lengths that were used to select spatially uncorrelated subsamples from each sample. The frequency distributions of permeability subsamples from the various lithofacies were compared using nonparametric statistical tests. The statistical tests generally support the claim that the lithofacies permeability distributions are distinct from one another.

INTRODUCTION

Small-scale aquifer heterogeneity, defined by variability over meters to tens of meters, strongly influences groundwater advection and dispersion (Koltermann and Gorelick, 1996, and references therein). It is, therefore, important to characterize aquifers at this scale, which is smaller than (or sometimes as small as) the volume typically sampled by borehole hydraulic tests. Hydraulic properties are the result of geologic processes, and hydraulic properties should, therefore, correlate with genetically interpretable geologic units. Hydrofacies are defined as interpretable, three-dimensional geologic units with distinct permeability frequency distributions ("hydrogeologic facies" of Anderson, 1989; see also Poeter and Gaylord, 1990; McKenna and Poeter, 1995; Ritzi et al., 1995; Ritzi et al., 2000). Aquifer models constructed of hydrofacies can capture small-scale heterogeneity, if the hydrofacies are defined at that scale.

For sedimentary deposits, we expect to translate lithofacies, geologic units defined by lithologic properties with geologically interpretable origins (Anderton, 1985), into hydrofacies, with definitive hydrologic properties (Poeter and Gaylord, 1990; Klingbeil et al., 1999). An advantage of translating lithofacies into hydrofacies is that an interpretation of lithofacies origin may lead to simultaneous predictions of the distribution, orientation, size, and shape of the lithofacies and, thus, of its associated hydrofacies.

Lithofacies are typically smaller and more restrictively defined units than architectural elements, which previously have been considered as hydrofacies (Davis et al., 1993). Architectural elements typically contain a variety of lithofacies ranging widely in grain size (Miall, 1985; Davis et al., 1993) and, by implication, ranging widely in permeability. We focus on lithofacies rather than architectural elements because lithofacies, being simpler categories defined largely by grain size, are more likely to translate into well-defined hydrofacies. Lithofacies are also more likely to characterize aquifers at the scale of meters to tens of meters.

To explore the feasibility of translating lithofacies to hydrofacies, we defined and mapped lithofacies, and measured permeability *in situ*, at an outcrop. Outcrop-analogue studies are used in both reservoir and aquifer characterization (e.g., Dreyer et al., 1990; Kittridge et al., 1990; Goggin et al., 1992; Davis et al., 1993; North and Taylor, 1996; Robinson and McCabe, 1997; Klingbeil et al., 1999; Willis and White, 2000). These studies investigate field-defined lithofacies, which is important because it is in the field that sedimentologists collect descriptions of grain size and sedimentary structures that routinely define lithofacies.

Lithofacies must be hydrogeologically distinct from each other in order to translate to meaningful hydrofacies. We hypothesize that permeability frequency distributions within field-based lithofacies are either statistically distinct between lithofacies, or else lithofacies with similar permeability distributions have significantly different geometries. Differences in geometry are important, because even if permeability-frequency distributions are similar, the lithofacies geometries affect the distributions of hydrogeological properties in the aquifer. The hypothesis is not rejected if a small number of lithofacies are not hydrogeologically distinct, because as long as the hypothesis applies generally, the translation of lithofacies to hydrofacies is a useful procedure. This paper, then, tests the hypothesis that lithofacies and hydrofacies can be linked, one for one, and illustrates the rigorous statistical methodology necessary to establish such a linkage.

FIELD AREA AND GEOLOGIC HISTORY

We studied an outcrop of the middle Miocene Tesuque Formation in the Española Basin, near Española, New Mexico (Fig. 1). This outcrop is well exposed and accessible for detailed observation and measurement (Fig. 2). The outcrop is ca. 370 m long, oriented approximately along structural strike, and exposes ca. 30 m of stratigraphic thickness. The strata are loosely consolidated to slightly cemented, which permits investigation of the influence of depositional processes on the hydrogeologic properties without the added complications of diagenesis and lithification. The Tesuque Formation was deposited on an alluvial slope (Smith, 2000; Kuhle and Smith, 2001) on the hanging-wall piedmont of a continental rift basin, and is comparable to other basin-

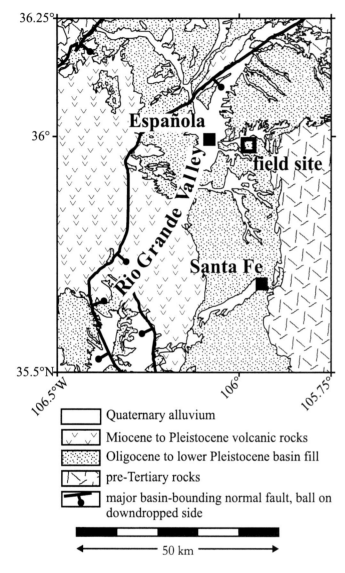

FIG. 1.—Geologic map of the Española Basin, New Mexico (modified from Anderson et al., 1996). The Tesuque Formation is part of the basin fill.

fill aquifers in the American Southwest. Fluvial and eolian processes deposited mostly sand and silt with less abundant clay and gravel (Table 1; see also Kuhle and Smith, 2001). Streams flowed from northeast to southwest (Cavazza, 1986, 1989; Kuhle and Smith, 2001).

METHODS

Field Methods

We defined and mapped 11 lithofacies (Table 1; Fig. 2; see also Gaud, 2002), using grain size and lithofacies shape as distinguishing characteristics. Grain size was estimated by comparing loose samples with size-comparator cards. Shape was distinguished as ribbon or tabular by applying the critical thickness-to-width ratio of 1:15 (Friend et al., 1979). Grain size correlates strongly to permeability (e.g., Chilingar, 1964; Beard and Weyl, 1973; Byers and Stephens, 1983; Shepherd, 1989; Vukovic and Soro, 1992;

Detmer, 1995; Koltermann and Gorelick, 1995), and lithofacies shape can be equated to three-dimensional units in aquifer models. Focusing on these two properties increases, therefore, the likelihood that the lithofacies can be translated to hydrofacies. Sedimentary structures are commonly used in lithofacies definitions but are not distinctive in the Tesuque Formation because of the dominance of massive, bioturbated beds (Table 1). The distinctive grain sizes and lithofacies shapes were defined as narrowly as possible in order for each lithofacies to occupy the smallest reasonable area for the scale of the map, and are referred to by abbreviations listed in Table 1. Mapping was completed on outcrop photographs, which were digitally registered to a topographic grid constructed from an electronic-total-station survey of the site (Gaud, 2002). The topographic grid is in a local coordinate system in which the x–y plane ("horizontal") is parallel to the dipping bedding planes, with the y axis parallel to outcrop strike.

We measured *in situ* permeability at more than 1,800 locations with a portable air mini-permeameter (design of Davis et al., 1994) over as much of the whole outcrop as physically feasible. The measurements are irregularly spaced at approximately 1 m intervals. These measurements form a three-dimensional data set because although the outcrop is approximately a two-dimensional panel (Fig. 2), the outcrop topography varies as much as 65 m in the outcrop-perpendicular direction. The outermost 0.5–5 cm of sediment was removed by trowel and brush to form a fresh, flat surface for measurement. Uncommon areas of discontinuous nodular and stratiform cement were avoided. Two to ten measurements were made at most sites and geometrically averaged. We surveyed every permeability measurement location in the local coordinate system with an electronic total station and recorded the lithofacies at each measurement site. The whole set of permeability measurements in each lithofacies is the "sample" for that lithofacies. Additional measurements were made at more than 1,350 locations on smaller-scale (cm to dm) grids at nine places in the field area. Except where specified, all analyses are performed only on the larger, ca. 1-m-scale, data set. Data analysis was undertaken using natural-logarithm transformed permeability measurements because permeability tends to be log normally (Gaussian) distributed (Freeze, 1975)

Statistical Methods

The Mann–Whitney test and the squared-ranks test for variances were employed to compare permeability frequency distributions between permeability samples. These tests are nonparametric (do not assume a particular frequency distribution), are based on ranks, and test the likelihood that the frequency distributions of two samples are the same (Conover, 1999, p. 271–286, 300–310). We use nonparametric tests, rather than the more commonly employed t-test, because the sample frequency distributions are not in every case Gaussian, even after transforming the data to natural-log units (Fig. 3). The Mann–Whitney test is sensitive to differences in sample means, whereas the squared-ranks test for variances is sensitive to differences in sample variances.

We used variograms (or, strictly, semivariograms) to describe the spatial correlation of the natural-log-permeability samples. The variogram is a measure of variance (one-half the average squared difference between sample values) that is a function of the separation distance ("lag") between data points (Olea, 1994). Variograms are calculated along different azimuths to characterize anisotropy. The calculations of γ based on measured data are the experimental variogram; the function fitted to the experimen-

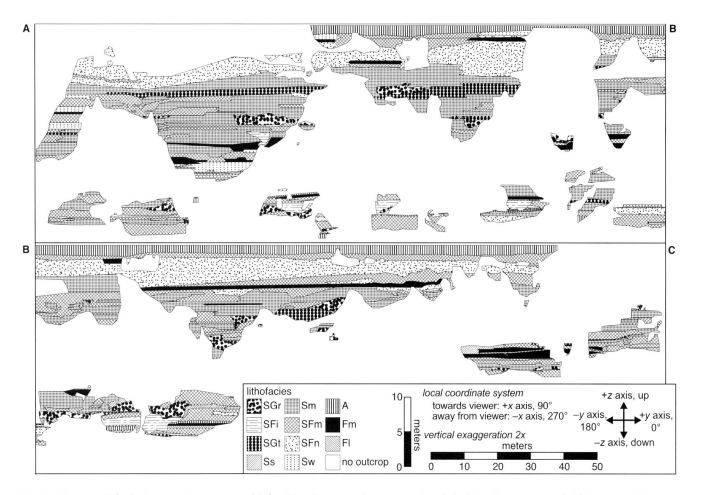

FIG. 2.—Outcrop lithofacies map, in two parts (right side of top panel corresponds to left side of bottom panel). This is a profile view, with the bedding planes parallel to the local coordinate system x and y axes ("horizontal"). The strike of the outcrop is parallel to the y axis; the viewer is looking approximately west (Fig. 1). The map has been vertically exaggerated to emphasize thin beds. Paleocurrent direction is perpendicular or oblique into the page. See Table 1 for lithofacies descriptions.

tal variogram is the model variogram (Olea, 1994). Model values are low at short lags, increase at increasingly longer lags, and usually form a constant-value plateau (the "sill") at lags longer than some distance (the "range"). The sill value is usually equal to the variance of the sample. The range is the correlation length, meaning that data points spaced closer than the range tend to be relatively similar to one another, whereas data points spaced farther apart than the range do not tend to be any more or less similar to each other than to any other data point. The value of γ at zero lag is the "nugget."

Experimental variograms were calculated both parallel to and perpendicular to bedding planes, and then fitted with model variograms (Fig. 4, Table 2). The variogram azimuths were chosen to characterize the maximum anisotropy of permeability, after calculating variograms at all azimuths. For the majority of the experimental variograms, at least half of the points are calculated from 30 or more pairs of permeability measurements. Variogram values for lags longer than half the maximum lag are retained only where the number of pairs of measurements is large, following Johnson and Dreiss (1989). The model variograms were fitted to the experimental variograms to obtain values for sills, ranges, and nuggets (Fig. 4, Table 2). The model variograms were fitted most closely to

experimental variogram points with 30 or more pairs of measurements, if possible (following Journel and Huijbregts, 1978, p. 194; Olea, 1994; Gringarten and Deutsch, 2001).

RESULTS

The Lithofacies, Their Depositional Origins, and Their Textural and Spatial Characteristics

The lithofacies are grouped into channel and interchannel associations on the basis of their interpreted origins (Table 1). The hypothesis tested in this paper is not dependent on the origin of the lithofacies, so the reader desiring further description and interpretation is referred to Gaud (2002).

Three lithofacies were deposited in fluvial channels defined by scoured bases and at least partial exposure of banks. Two of these lithofacies, SGr and SFi, are ribbon shaped, and appear on the outcrop map (Fig. 2) as narrow bodies typically with rounded bases, because the paleoflow direction was perpendicular or oblique to the strike of the outcrop. The third channel lithofacies, SGt, is tabular. The two sandy gravel channel lithofacies (SGr and SGt) are the coarsest grained and have the poorest sorting of all the lithofacies. In contrast, lithofacies SFi is relatively fine grained

TABLE 1.—Lithofacies.

Name	Code	Texture	Shape	Sedimentary structures	Other observations	Interpretation
ribbon-form sand with gravel	SGr	dominantly medium to coarse sand, with common gravel and minor silt; poorly sorted	ribbon	horizontal stratification, low-angle scour-and-fill stratification; rare trough and planar-tabular cross-stratification.	sharp, scoured base and high-relief margins	flood deposit in ephemeral stream channel
interbedded sand and silt	SFi	sand and silt with minor clay and granules	ribbon	alternating thin beds and laminae of sand and silt; rare horizontal lamination and ripple cross-lamination	sharp, scoured base and margins	slack-water and flood deposits in ephemeral stream channel
tabular sand, with gravel	SGt	dominantly medium to coarse sand, with common gravel and minor silt; poorly sorted	tabular	horizontal stratification, low-angle scour-and-fill stratification; rare trough and planar-tabular cross-stratification.	sharp, scoured base and low-relief margins	flood deposit in wide and/or laterally migrating ephemeral stream channel
stratified sand	Ss	v.f. sand	tabular	horizontal stratification and low-angle cross-stratification	—	proximal-overbank deposit
massive sand	Sm	dominantly v.f. sand, but ranging from silt to rare gravel	tabular	massive (bioturbated)	—	interchannel fluvial, and possibly admixed eolian, deposit
massive silty sand	SFm	v.f. sand and silt	tabular	massive (bioturbated)	—	interchannel fluvial, and possibly admixed eolian, deposit
nodular massive silty sand	SFn	v.f. sand and silt	tabular	massive (bioturbated)	abundant interspersed calcite nodules	interchannel fluvial, and possibly admixed eolian, deposit
well-sorted sand	Sw	v.f. sand; well sorted	tabular	mostly massive with very rare translatent wind-ripple laminations and trough cross-bedding.	—	interchannel eolian sand sheet
ash	A	dominantly fine ash, minor fine sand and silt	tabular	massive (bioturbated) or horizontal lamination	white to gray	primary ash fall and ash reworked with sand and silt by wind, sheet flow, and channelized flow
massive clayey silt	Fm	clay and silt	tabular	massive (bioturbated)	red and orange; common interspersed calcite nodules	Weakly developed paleosol
laminated silt and clay	Fl	clay and silt	tabular	horizontal laminations; alternating layers of clay and silt	—	interchannel fluvial deposit, possibly settled out of ponded water

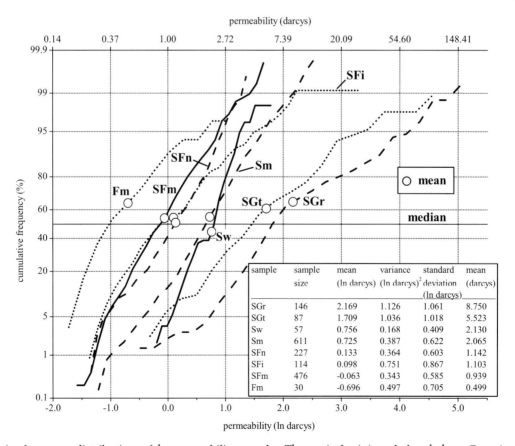

FIG. 3.—Cumulative frequency distributions of the permeability samples. The vertical axis is scaled such that a Gaussian distribution plots as a straight line.

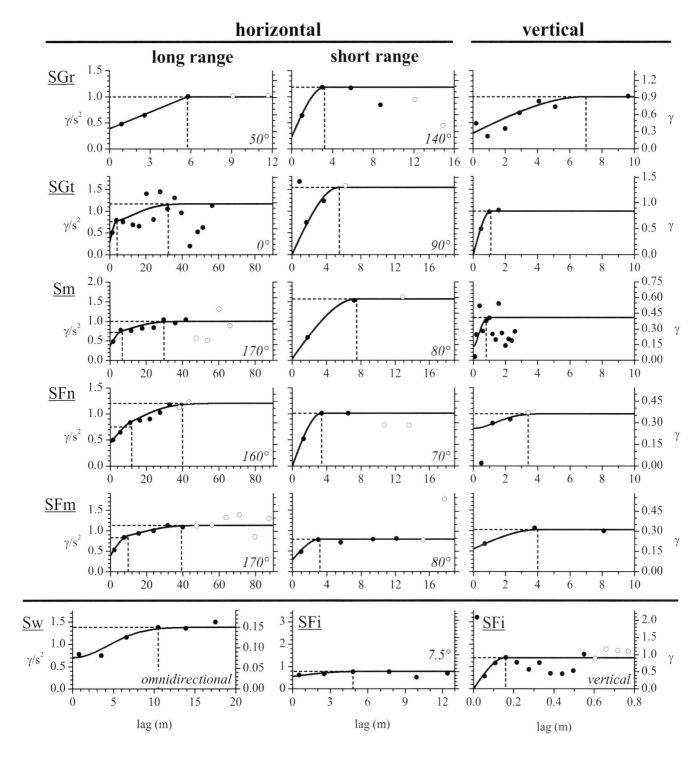

FIG. 4.—Variograms of permeability samples (ln darcys). Circles are experimental variogram values, excluding data outliers (see Table 2 for search-window parameters). Closed circles are for lags shorter than half the maximum lag, and open circles are for lags longer than half the maximum lag. Solid lines are model variograms, fitted manually to the experimental variograms. Dashed lines indicate the sills and ranges of the models (see Table 2 for details of the model variogram parameters). Both γ (right axes) and γ divided by the sample variances, s^2 (left axes), are depicted to facilitate interpretation of the sills (theoretical sill is $\gamma/s^2 = 1$). Sample variances are slightly less than the variances shown in Figure 3, because of exclusion of outlier values. Horizontal variograms, in directions of shortest and longest range, are parallel to the bedding planes and are oriented along indicated azimuths, where 0° is parallel to outcrop strike. Vertical variograms are perpendicular to the bedding planes (Fig. 2).

TABLE 2.—Variogram parameters.

Sample and direction	Experimental variogram search window				Nugget[**]	Model[#]					
	Angular tolerance (°)	Bandwidths[†]		Lag spacing[§] (m)		Model 1			Model 2		
		Azimuth (m)	Dip (m)			Type[††]	Sill[§§]	Range (m)	Type	Sill	Range (m)
SGr[##]											
50°	30	10.0	10.0	3.00	0.39	linear	1.00	5.75	N.A.	N.A.	N.A.
140°	15	5.0	5.0	3.00	0.23	spherical	1.18	3.20	N.A.	N.A.	N.A.
vertical	55	30.0	30.0	1.00	0.30	spherical	1.00	7.00	N.A.	N.A.	N.A.
SGt											
0°	20	15.0	15.0	4.00	0.30	spherical	0.76	4.00	Gaussian	1.17	32.50
90°	55	15.0	15.0	2.00	0.00	spherical	1.55	5.50	N.A.	N.A.	N.A.
vertical	60	10.0	10.0	0.50	0.00	spherical	1.00	1.10	N.A.	N.A.	N.A.
Sm											
170°	20	5.0	5.0	6.00	0.38	spherical	0.72	6.90	Gaussian	1.00	30.00
80°	30	10.0	10.0	6.50	0.04	spherical	1.57	7.50	N.A.	N.A.	N.A.
vertical	35	10.0	10.0	0.20	0.35	Gaussian	1.09	0.80	N.A.	N.A.	N.A.
SFn											
160°	20	15.0	15.0	5.50	0.45	spherical	0.75	12.00	Gaussian	1.20	40.00
70°	40	15.0	15.0	3.50	0.00	spherical	1.01	3.40	N.A.	N.A.	N.A.
vertical	40	10.0	10.0	1.20	0.72	Gaussian	1.00	3.40	N.A.	N.A.	N.A.
SFm											
170°	20	7.5	7.5	8.00	0.40	spherical	0.83	9.90	Gaussian	1.13	39.40
80°	40	15.0	15.0	3.00	0.29	spherical	0.79	3.17	N.A.	N.A.	N.A.
vertical	30	15.0	15.0	4.25	0.55	spherical	1.02	4.00	N.A.	N.A.	N.A.
Sw											
omnidi-rectional	90	65.0	2.0	3.50	0.70	Gaussian	1.38	10.50	N.A.	N.A.	N.A.
SFi											
7.5°	15	4.0	4.0	2.50	0.56	spherical	0.78	4.80	N.A.	N.A.	N.A.
vertical	40	1.0	1.0	0.05	0.00	spherical	1.40	0.16	N.A.	N.A.	N.A.

[*] parallel to the bedding-plane azimuth specified in degrees (0° is parallel to outcrop strike), perpendicular to the bedding plane ("vertical"), or omnidirectional (see Fig. 2).

[†] Azimuth bandwidth is the width of the search window in the x-y plane. Dip bandwidth is the thickness of the search window in the z direction.

[§] Lag tolerances are all 45% of the lag.

[#] Models were visually fitted to the experimental variograms (see Fig. 4). The complete model variogram equation for each direction is a linear combination of the nugget and all models. In some cases, two models were necessary to capture the shape of the experimental variogram.

[**] The values of the nugget and sill(s) are divided by the sample variance, s^2 (excluding outliers).

[††] Variogram models are calculated by these functions (modified from Pannatier, 1996, p. 48–51):

$\gamma(|h|) = C|h|/a$ for $|h| \leq a$, $\gamma(|h|) = C$ for $|h| > a$

spherical: $\gamma(|h|) = C(3|h|/2a - (|h|/a)^3/2)$ for $|h| \leq a$, $\gamma(|h|) = C$ for $|h| > a$

Gaussian: $\gamma(|h|) = C(1 - \exp(-3(|h|/a)^2))$

where γ = variogram value, $|h|$ = lag, C = variance contribution, a = range.

[§§] The sill is the variance contribution of the model plus the variance contribution of all lower structures (i.e., nugget and any lower model).

[##] Permeability is in ln darcys (Fig. 3).

N.A. = not applicable (variograms requiring only one model).

(sand and silt) and consists of alternating thin beds of contrasting grain size (Table 1).

These three channel lithofacies are set in a matrix of broad, tabular interchannel lithofacies (Fig. 2). The three most common of these interchannel lithofacies, Sm, SFm, and SFn, are massive, bioturbated deposits of mixed floodplain and eolian origin. The two silty sand lithofacies are texturally and structurally similar, and are distinguished only by interspersed calcite nodules of uncertain origin in SFn, but are not present in SFm. Two other significant interchannel lithofacies are Sw and Fm. Lithofacies Sw is well-sorted, tabular sand of probable eolian origin. Lithofacies Fm is the finest grained (clay and silt) and, although thin, forms remarkably laterally continuous beds (Fig. 2). This facies contains evidence of more advanced pedogenesis than other bioturbated facies and is interpreted to represent buried soil horizons. Lithofacies Ss and Fl (Table 1) occupy < 1% of the mapped outcrop, so we do not treat them as hydrogeologically significant. Distal-ashfall layers (Kuhle and Smith, 2001) comprising lithofacies A are also excluded from further analysis because they do not reflect sedimentary depositional processes.

Frequency Distributions of Permeability

The permeability sample means for the different lithofacies vary by about an order of magnitude between sample SGr (8.8 darcys) and sample SFm (0.9 darcys; Fig. 3). A one-order-of-magnitude difference in permeability between two aquifer units can strongly influence the flow of contaminants (Poeter and Gaylord, 1990). Permeability differences at the study site are, therefore, significant.

Hydrogeologically distinct lithofacies can also be recognized by differences in the variance or standard deviation of permeability. As shown by McKenna and Rautman (1996, p. 38–44) from groundwater simulations, groundwater travel times are more variable if the standard deviation of permeability is greater (mean permeability was kept constant in their simulations). In our study, permeability samples Sw and Sm have nearly the same mean but differ considerably in standard deviation (Fig. 3). The difference in standard deviation between these samples may be enough to hydrogeologically distinguish lithofacies Sw and Sm.

The frequency distributions of the permeability samples (Fig. 3) correlate well to the visually described sedimentary textures of the lithofacies (Table 1). The samples from the two coarsest-grained lithofacies (SGr and SGt) are the most permeable. The samples from the sandy lithofacies (Sw and Sm) are

less permeable, the silty sand lithofacies (SFn, SFi, and SFm) are even less permeable, and the finest-grained lithofacies (Fm) is the least permeable. The samples from the most poorly sorted and texturally heterogeneous lithofacies (SGr, SGt, and SFi) have the greatest permeability variance, whereas the sample from the best-sorted lithofacies (Sw) has the smallest variance.

The shapes of the permeability frequency distributions vary among samples. On the cumulative frequency plot (Fig. 3), the vertical axis is scaled such that a Gaussian (normal) distribution is a straight line. The natural-log-transformed frequency distributions of samples Sm and SFm appear to be closest to Gaussian distributions, but other permeability samples are distinctly not natural-log Gaussian. For instance, the break in slope for sample Sw, approximately at the mean, shows that the permeability frequency distribution is bimodal. For other samples, the means are greater than the medians, indicating positively skewed frequency distributions. In addition, for several samples (SGr, SGt, Sw, SFi, Fm) the change to a shallower slope at the very highest permeability values indicates a few remarkably high, but reproducible, permeability measurements.

Calculating and Modeling of Variograms

Variograms were calculated and modeled toward the goal of achieving statistical independence in the data sets compared with the Mann–Whitney test and the squared-ranks test for variances. These tests assume that the measurements are statistically independent, both within and between the data sets being compared (Conover, 1999, p. 272, 301). To use these tests correctly, each sample must be reduced to noncorrelated values, which requires analysis of variograms to establish the correlation lengths. The range of the variogram separates data points that are spatially correlated (variance is lower than the overall variance) and those that are not spatially correlated (variance is approximately equal to the overall variance) (Journel and Huijbregts, 1978, p. 36–37; Gringarten and Deutsch, 2001). Data points spaced closer than the variogram range are spatially correlated and, therefore, are not statistically independent (cf. Neuman, 1982; Sudicky, 1986).

Prior to calculating variograms we investigated the possibility of drift in the permeability measurements. Drift, an overall increase or decrease in a variable as a function of location in space, can preclude accurate calculation of the variogram range. We calculated linear regressions of permeability for each sample against the x, y, and z coordinates (Table 3). Coefficients of

TABLE 3.—Multiple linear regressions of permeability measurements on location in space (x, y, z).

| Sample | Estimated linear model[*] | | | | | | R^2 |
| | x | | y | | z | | |
	Coefficient	Error[†]	Coefficient	Error	Coefficient	Error	
SGr	-0.02671	0.02474	0.00023	0.00214	-0.02679	0.05688	0.06486
SGt	-0.03228	0.03643	0.00286	0.00211	-0.09244	0.11057	0.11230
Sw	0.01038	0.01066	-0.00216	0.00208	0.02704	0.01819	0.16622
Sm	0.00642	0.00592	-0.00017	0.00053	0.03111	0.01226	0.06428
SFn	-0.00186	0.01312	0.00029	0.00093	0.01813	0.02673	0.03482
SFi	0.02000	0.07363	-0.00580	0.01491	0.08995	0.17092	0.03613
SFm	0.00175	0.00595	-0.00092	0.00051	0.01509	0.01055	0.04158

Notes: Permeability is in ln darcys. Outlier values were excluded. See Figure 2 for orientation of axes.

[*] Intercept not included.

[†] The errors bracket 95% (± 47.5%) of the distribution about each estimated coefficient, assuming a t-distribution.

determination (R^2) are less than 0.10 for five of the seven samples, and for the other two samples are less than 0.20. That is, for most samples a linear model explains less than 10% of the variability in permeability, and for all samples a linear model explains less than 20% (Christensen, 1996, p. 170). Furthermore, the signs on the coefficients of the best-fit planes vary from sample to sample for different coordinates (Table 3). We consider the low R^2 values, plus the inconsistency of the signs of the coefficients, to indicate insignificant drift in the permeability measurements.

The permeability sample sizes vary (Fig. 3), so the quality and quantity of variograms also vary. Data for five samples (SGr, SGt, Sm, SFn, and SFm) are numerous enough to calculate and model variograms in three orthogonal directions (Fig. 4). Variograms were also calculated for samples Sw and SFi, but not in all orthogonal directions because data are too few. Specifically, for sample SFi the locations of permeability measurements are along primarily a single orientation (parallel to azimuth 7.5°), so the only possible horizontal variogram is in that orientation (Fig. 4). Measurements comprising sample Sw are sparse, and permit only an omnidirectional horizontal variogram (Fig. 4). To calculate an omnidirectional variogram assumes isotropy, which is arguably a reasonable assumption because lithofacies Sw is visually uniform in grain size (Table 1). We did not assume isotropy for the other data-poor sample, SFi, because of obvious outcrop-scale anisotropy in grain size of beds.

Outcrop orientation influences the quality of the experimental variograms even for samples with enough data to calculate variograms in all directions. The number of data pairs at each lag is greater for the variograms that are oriented parallel to the outcrop than for the variograms perpendicular to the outcrop (Gaud, 2002), because the extent of the outcrop is much less in the perpendicular direction. Furthermore, the horizontal variogram ranges tend to be longer in the outcrop-parallel direction than in the outcrop-perpendicular directions (Fig. 4, Table 2). The exception is sample SGr, where the longest range is oblique (50°) to the outcrop strike, probably because this lithofacies is narrow in the outcrop-parallel direction. Every horizontal variogram includes at least one model with a short range (3.17 m to 12.00 m). With the exception of sample SGr, however, the horizontal variograms for four of the samples exhibit an additional, nested model with a longer range (30 m and 40 m) parallel to the outcrop. Sills for all samples are as low as 75% and as high as 150% of the sample variance. There is also considerable variability in the nuggets, which are as low as 0.00 to more than 70% of the sample variance.

Nugget effects are the sum of measurement error (instrument error and operator error) and real variability at lag distances shorter than the measurement interval (Journel and Huijbregts, 1978, p. 148–153). Large nuggets can cause concern regarding the quality of the data. To identify the relative contributions of measurement error and short-scale variability, we calculated four supplemental experimental variograms (Fig. 5) using the measurements of permeability on cm- to dm-spaced grids. These variograms have very low γ values at the shortest lags, in contrast to the high nugget effects in some of the variograms of the meter-scale data (Fig. 4, Table 2). Because variance between data points is actually very low at very short lag distances (Fig. 5), the nugget effects (Fig. 4, Table 2) are probably due mostly to the relatively large distance between measurements, and only to a small degree to measurement error.

Removing Spatial Correlation

Variogram ranges were used to create data sets of statistically independent measurements for univariate statistical analy-

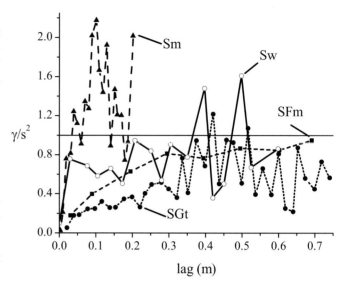

FIG. 5.—Experimental variograms of permeability (ln darcys) from the cm- to dm-scale data set. Compare nuggets with Figure 4. The orientation of all the variograms is parallel to the bedding planes and parallel to the local outcrop face. The horizontal solid line marks the theoretical sills (variances).

sis. A FORTRAN program (Gaud, 2002) was used to select a spatially uncorrelated *sub*sample from each permeability sample such that the data in the subsample are all spaced farther apart than the variogram range (Fig. 4, Table 2). For those samples requiring nested variogram models, we chose the smaller of the two ranges. The sills at these shorter ranges are 72% of the sample variance or greater, so using the shorter ranges associated with the lower sills will remove a considerable amount of spatial correlation from the samples and still leave enough data to perform statistical tests.

There is no unique spatially uncorrelated subsample for each sample. To illustrate, imagine a cluster of data more closely spaced than the range. Only one data point from that cluster can be included in any particular subsample. The decision as to which data point of that cluster to include is arbitrary, and is varied across the random sampling. We selected ten subsamples from each sample, randomly reordering the samples before each subsampling routine. We ran the subsampling program on all samples for which correlation length (range) could be defined in three orthogonal directions (Fig. 4, Table 2). Samples SFi and Fm, for which correlation lengths cannot be defined in all directions, were therefore excluded. We did, however, include sample Sw, for which we defined only the horizontal (omnidirectional), but not vertical, variogram. For the vertical direction of sample Sw, we assumed a range slightly greater than the average unit thickness, 0.5 m, of lithofacies Sw (Gaud, 2002). It is unlikely that the range is longer than that (Journel and Huijbregts, 1978, p. 38), so assuming a range of 1.0 m should be an overestimate and, if anything, exclude more data than necessary. Table 4 summarizes information regarding the spatially uncorrelated subsamples.

Mann–Whitney Tests

The Mann–Whitney test was used to compare the spatially uncorrelated permeability subsamples from the different lithofacies. The null hypothesis for this test is *the frequency distributions of permeability are the same for both lithofacies being compared* ("two-sided" test). We report the results of this test as p values; low p values indicate the sample data are inconsistent with the null hypothesis. Typical cutoff p values for accepting or rejecting this hypothesis are 0.1, 0.05, and 0.025 (e.g. Christensen, 1996, p. 32). The p-value results are reported as histograms (Fig. 6).

Spatially uncorrelated subsamples were created for only six of the full samples (Table 4), so there were just 15 sample comparisons possible using subsamples (Fig. 6). The p values are very low for 12 of these 15 comparisons (Fig. 6). The p values are relatively large for only two of the comparisons, Sw to Sm and SFn to SFm. Finally, for the comparison SGr to SGt the p values are a mixture of high and low values (Fig. 6). Most of the p values are less than typical cutoff levels for rejecting the null hypothesis, so the Mann–Whitney tests support the assertion that permeability frequency distributions tend to be distinct for different lithofacies.

Is the additional effort to remove spatial correlation really required, or would statistical comparisons of the full samples (i.e., without spatial correlation removed), though strictly invalid, give the same results anyway? The result of the Mann–Whitney test comparing the full samples of SGr to SGt is a low p value, 0.0011 (Gaud, 2002). When spatially uncorrelated subsamples are compared, however, the results are much higher p values (Fig. 6). Similarly, the result of the Mann–Whitney test comparing the full samples of SFn to SFm is a very low p value, < 0.0001 (Gaud, 2002). When spatially uncorrelated subsamples are compared, however, the p values are all greater than 0.1 (Fig. 6). These are critical observations, because if spatial correlation were ignored in these comparisons, the Mann–Whitney test would reveal the permeability frequency distributions as being distinct, whereas more rigorous analysis shows this not to be the case.

TABLE 4.—Summary of subsampling.

Sample	Full sample size[*]	Subsamples[†] Sizes	Subsamples[†] Average size	Subsamples[†] Average retention[§]
SGr	146	22 to 27	24.2	16.6%
SGt	87	18 to 22	20.3	23.3%
Sw	57	11 to 13	12.2	21.4%
Sm	611	89 to 103	96.7	15.8%
SFn	227	20 to 25	22.4	9.9%
SFm	476	48 to 54	51.0	10.7%

Note: See text for description of subsampling algorithm.

[*] Size = number of data.

[†] 10 subsamples were selected from each sample.

[§] Average retention = 100 x (Average size of subsamples) / (Full sample size).

Squared-Ranks Tests for Variances

The result of the Mann–Whitney tests (Fig. 6) indicates that most lithofacies permeability frequency distributions are distinct. The higher p values resulting from comparisons of samples Sw to Sm, SFn to SFm, and perhaps SGr to SGt (Fig. 6) does not necessarily negate the hypothesis that each lithofacies can be translated to a unique hydrofacies.

The Mann–Whitney test is sensitive to differences in means but not necessarily variances, so it is possible that this test would result in high p values for a test of two samples with similar means, even if the variances were dissimilar. The squared-ranks

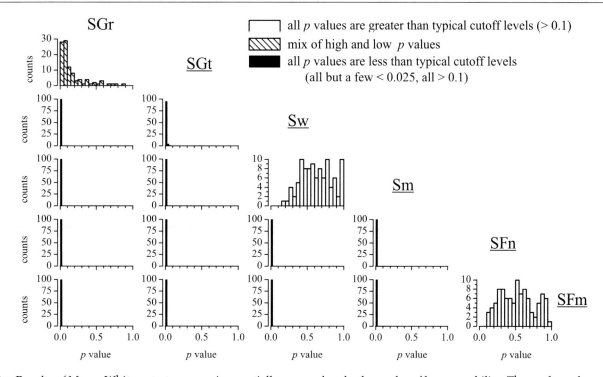

FIG. 6.—Results of Mann–Whitney tests comparing spatially uncorrelated subsamples of ln permeability. The total number of tests counted in each histogram is 10 x 10 = 100, because there are 10 subsamples for each full sample (Table 4). The histograms, therefore, represent all possible test results given these subsamples. Each subsample was, however, used in multiple tests, so the 100 tests in each histogram are not 100 statistically independent trials.

test for variances was used, therefore, to compare uncorrelated subsamples of SGr to SGt, Sw to Sm, and SFn to SFm (Fig. 7).

The null hypothesis for the squared-ranks test for variances, as for the Mann–Whitney test, is that *the frequency distributions of permeability are the same for both lithofacies being compared* ("two sided"). Similarly to the Mann–Whitney tests, we report the results of this test as *p* values (Fig. 7). Of the three sample comparisons, only the tests comparing Sw to Sm resulted in a large number of *p* values less than typical *p* value cutoff levels (Fig. 7). The *p* values of the tests comparing SGr to SGt, and SFn to SFm are mostly greater than the typical cutoff values (Fig. 7).

Comparing Permeability Samples for which Spatial Correlation Cannot Be Removed

For samples SFi and Fm, spatial correlation cannot be removed. Variograms cannot be modeled in all three orthogonal directions for these samples, so the limit of spatial correlation (variogram range), required for the algorithm that selects the spatially uncorrelated subsamples, cannot be defined. We can neither assume independence for statistical tests nor form uncorrelated subsamples.

Nevertheless, by qualitative observations of these samples, the permeability frequency distributions of lithofacies SFi and Fm can be distinguished from all the other lithofacies. The frequency distribution of sample SFi is bimodal, with the two modes separated by approximately one ln darcy (Fig. 8). This bimodality is present within single bodies of lithofacies SFi due to interbedding of finer- and coarser-grained sediment (Table 1). That is, this lithofacies is internally heterogeneous (*sensu* Freeze, 1975). No

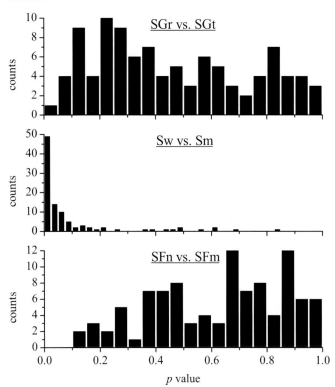

FIG. 7.—Results of squared-ranks tests for variances comparing spatially uncorrelated subsamples of permeability. The total number of tests counted in each histogram is 100 (see Fig. 6, Table 4). Permeability is in ln darcys.

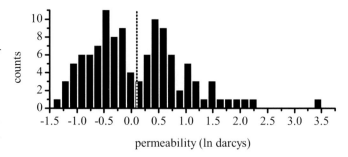

FIG. 8.—Frequency distribution of permeability sample SFi. This histogram is identical to the histogram used to calculate the cumulative frequency distribution of SFi (Fig. 3). The sample mean is marked by the dashed line. The total number of data is 114.

other lithofacies permeability-frequency distribution is heterogeneous at this small spatial scale. For sample Fm, the permeability frequency distribution is much lower than the frequency distributions of all other samples (Fig. 3). Lithofacies Fm, therefore, appears to be distinct as the least permeable lithofacies.

CONCLUSIONS

Only if lithofacies are distinct, either in permeability frequency distributions or in geometries, can the approach of translating lithofacies to hydrofacies be used effectively for characterizing aquifers. If not, aquifer characterization may be more efficiently accomplished with geologic units that are perhaps larger, smaller, or based on criteria other than grain size and geometry. In our study, most of the lithofacies are significantly distinct in either permeability or geometry.

The results of statistical tests comparing spatially uncorrelated permeability subsamples from the different lithofacies are, for most comparisons, low *p* values (Figs. 6, 7). The low *p* values indicate significant permeability differences between lithofacies. In addition, other lithofacies have distinct permeability frequency distributions because the distributions are uniquely bimodal (lithofacies Sfi, Fig. 8) or remarkably low (lithofacies Fm, Fig. 3).

Two lithofacies otherwise similar in grain size, sedimentary structures, and permeability (SGr and SGt) differ considerably in geometry (Table 1). Lithofacies SGr is ribbon form, and lithofacies SGt is tabular. These differences in shapes could impart differences in flow and transport characteristics in an analogous aquifer.

Facies SFn and SFm also have indistinguishable permeability distributions, but this is not surprising because the field descriptions of the facies are identical except for the presence of nodular cement in SFn, and permeability measurements were not made near visible cement. Furthermore, the extreme discontinuity of this nodular cement is unlikely to affect fluid flow. In a sense, then, the failure to translate SFn and SFm into distinct hydrofacies supports our initial hypothesis that grain size and geometry should be the most influential criteria in lithofacies designation.

The field-defined lithofacies, generally, have distinct permeability-frequency distributions or geometries, so we conclude that the one-for-one translation of lithofacies to hydrofacies is a useful method for characterizing aquifers. The correlation of grain size to permeability frequency distribution is a correlation of depositional process to permeability frequency distribution. Similar depositional processes deposit similar grain sizes with similar permeability distributions. In terms of permeability, lithofacies SGr and SGt are indistinguishable (Figs. 6, 7), and both are interpreted to be the flood deposits of ephemeral streams (Table 1). The permeability frequency distributions of lithofacies SFn and SFm are also statistically indistinguishable (Figs. 6, 7). These lithofacies are both interpreted to be interchannel fluvial, and possibly eolian, deposits that were mixed by bioturbation (Table 1).

The applicability of translating lithofacies to hydrofacies, as well as the opportunity to establish relationships between grain size and permeability, emphasizes the importance of outcrop-analogue studies for characterizing small-scale aquifer heterogeneity. Details can be observed at outcrops that are not otherwise resolved by borehole hydraulic tests or predicted by general lithofacies models. A simple bimodal view of channel deposits as coarse-grained ribbon-form lithofacies in an overall matrix of fine-grained interchannel deposits is not necessarily appropriate for characterizing small-scale aquifer heterogeneity. We found that channel deposits can be fine grained or tabular, and interchannel deposits are not uniformly fine-grained and of low permeability. The sedimentological controls on permeability are related to lithofacies, and it is at the outcrop where details of lithofacies are most apparent. Outcrop measurements of permeability can allow calculations of variograms in the horizontal direction at scales more detailed than can be done, for example, with borehole information. This can be particularly important for achieving independence for statistical tests. Outcrop-analogue studies, therefore, are valuable for aquifer characterization

ACKNOWLEDGMENTS

For assistance in data collection and manipulation we thank P. Florence, J. Ray, C. Dodson, M. Mikolas, E. Embid, A. Pantazis, D. Mitchell, S. Hollen, J. Schaer, J. Preston, J. Armour, W. Roberts, K. Wegmann, and D. Koning. We appreciate useful discussions with F. Pazzaglia, D. Gutzler, C. Shaw, K. Steffen, J. Degnan, and S. Huestis. For assistance with the permeameter we thank M. Davis, R. Macy, D. Henderson, and M. Petronis. We benefited from helpful reviews by David Dominic, Robert Ritzi, Brian Willis, and John Bridge. This research was funded by a National Science Foundation grant (EAR-9706116) and a Petroleum Research Fund (American Chemical Society) grant (29123-AC8) to Smith, and a UNM Kelly-Silver Graduate Fellowship to Gaud. The Bureau of Land Management (Taos District) and C. Robinson provided access to the field site.

REFERENCES

ANDERSON, M.P., 1989, Hydrogeologic facies models to delineate large-scale spatial trends in glacial and glaciofluvial sediments: Geological Society of America, Bulletin, v. 101, p. 501–511.

ANDERSON, O.J., JONES, G.E., AND GREEN, G.N., 1996, Geologic Map of New Mexico: New Mexico Bureau of Mines.

ANDERTON, R., 1985, Clastic facies models and facies analysis, in Benchley, P.J., and Williams, B.P.J., eds., Sedimentology; Recent Developments and Applied Aspects: Oxford, U.K., Blackwell Scientific Publications, p. 31–47.

BEARD, D.C., AND WEYL, P.K., 1973, Influence of texture on porosity and permeability of unconsolidated sand: American Association of Petroleum Geologists, Bulletin, v. 57, p. 349–369.

BYERS, E., AND STEPHENS, D.B., 1983, Statistical and stochastic analyses of hydraulic conductivity and particle-size in a fluvial sand: Soil Science Society of America, Journal, v. 47, p. 1072–1081.

CAVAZZA, W., 1986, Miocene sediment dispersal in the central Española Basin, Rio Grande Rift, New Mexico, U.S.A.: Sedimentary Geology, v. 51, p. 119–135.

CAVAZZA, W., 1989, Sedimentation pattern of a rift-filling unit, Tesuque Formation (Miocene), Española Basin, Rio Grande rift, New Mexico: Journal of Sedimentary Petrology, v. 59, p. 287–296.

CHILINGAR, G.V., 1964, Relationship between porosity, permeability, and grain-size distribution of sands and sandstones, in van Straaten, L.M.J.U., ed., Deltaic and Shallow Marine Deposits: Proceedings of the Sixth International Sedimentological Congress, The Netherlands and Belgium, 1963: Amsterdam, Elsevier, Developments in Sedimentology, v. 1, p. 71–75.

CHRISTENSEN, R., 1996, Analysis of Variance, Design and Regression; Applied Statistical Methods: London, Chapman & Hall, 587 p.

Conover, W.J., 1999, Practical Nonparametric Statistics, Third Edition: New York, John Wiley & Sons, 584 p.

DAVIS, J.M., LOHMANN, R.C., PHILLIPS, F.M., WILSON, J.L., AND LOVE, D.W., 1993, Architecture of the Sierra Ladrones Formation, central New Mexico: Depositional controls on the permeability correlation structure: Geological Society of America, Bulletin, v. 105, p. 998–1007.

DAVIS, J.M., WILSON, J.L., AND PHILLIPS, F.M., 1994, A portable air-minipermeameter for rapid in-situ field measurements: Ground Water, v. 32, p. 258–266.

DETMER, D.M., 1995, Permeability, porosity, and grain-size distribution of selected Pliocene and Quaternary sediments in the Albuquerque Basin: New Mexico Geology, v. 17, p. 79–87.

DREYER, T., SCHEIE, Å., AND WALDERHAUG, O., 1990, Minipermeameter-based study of permeability trends in channel sand bodies: American Association of Petroleum Geologists, Bulletin, v. 74, p. 359–374.

FREEZE, R.A., 1975, A stochastic-conceptual analysis of one-dimensional groundwater flow in nonuniform homogeneous media: Water Resources Research, v. 11, p. 725–741.

FRIEND, P.F., SLATER, M.J., AND WILLIAMS, R.C., 1979, Vertical and lateral building of river sandstone bodies, Ebro Basin, Spain: Geological Society of London, Journal, v. 136, p. 39–46.

GAUD, M.N., 2002, Outcrop investigation of the permeability and spatial distributions of alluvial-slope lithofacies, near Española, New Mexico: unpublished M.S. Thesis, University of New Mexico, Albuquerque, 100 p.

GOGGIN, D.J., CHANDLER, M.A., KOCUREK, G., AND LAKE, L.W., 1992, Permeability transects of eolian sands and their use in generating random permeability fields: Society of Petroleum Engineers, Formation Evaluation, v. 7, p. 7–16.

GRINGARTEN, E., AND DEUTSCH, C.V., 2001, Teacher's aide: Variogram interpretation and modeling: Mathematical Geology, v. 33, p. 507–534.

JOHNSON, N.M., AND DREISS, S.J., 1989, Hydrostratigraphic interpretation using indicator geostatistics: Water Resources Research, v. 25, p. 2501–2510.

JOURNEL, A.G., AND HUIJBREGTS, C.J., 1978, Mining Geostatistics: London, Academic Press, 600 p.

KITTRIDGE, M.G., LAKE, L.W., LUCIA, F.J., AND FOGG, G.E., 1990, Outcrop/subsurface comparisons of heterogeneity in the San Andres Formation: Society of Petroleum Engineers, Formation Evaluation, v. 5, p. 233–240.

KLINGBEIL, R., KLEINEIDAM, S., ASPRION, U., AIGNER, T., AND TEUTSCH, G., 1999, Relating lithofacies to hydrofacies: Outcrop-based hydrogeological characterisation of Quaternary gravel deposits: Sedimentary Geology, v. 129, p. 299–310.

KOLTERMANN, C.E., AND GORELICK, S.M., 1995, Fractional packing model for hydraulic conductivity derived from sediment mixtures: Water Resources Research, v. 31, p. 3283–3297.

KOLTERMANN, C.E., AND GORELICK, S.M., 1996, Heterogeneity in sedimentary deposits: A review of structure-imitating, process-imitating, and descriptive approaches: Water Resources Research, v. 32, p. 2617–2658.

KUHLE, A.J., AND SMITH, G.A., 2001, Alluvial-slope deposition of the Skull Ridge Member of the Tesuque Formation, Española Basin, New Mexico: New Mexico Geology, v. 23, p. 30–37.

McKenna, S.A., and Poeter, E.P., 1995, Field example of data fusion in site characterization: Water Resources Research, v. 31, p. 3229–3240.

McKenna, S.A., and Rautman, C.A., 1996, Scaling of Material Properties for Yucca Mountain: Literature Review and Numerical Experiments on Saturated Hydraulic Conductivity: Sandia Report, SAND95-2338, 131 p.

Miall, A.D., 1985, Architectural-element analysis: A new method of facies analysis applied to fluvial deposits: Earth-Science Reviews, v. 22, p. 261–308.

Neuman, S.P., 1982, Statistical characterization of aquifer heterogeneities: An overview, *in* Narasimhan, T.N., ed., Recent Trends in Hydrology: Geological Society of America, Special Paper 189, p. 81–102.

North, C.P., and Taylor, K.S., 1996, Ephemeral-fluvial deposits: Integrated outcrop and simulation studies reveal complexity: American Association of Petroleum Geologists, Bulletin, v. 80, p. 811–830.

Olea, R.A., 1994, Fundamentals of semivariogram estimation, modeling, and usage, *in* Yarus, J.M., and Chambers, R.L., eds., Stochastic Modeling and Geostatistics: Principles, Methods, and Case Studies: American Association of Petroleum Geologists, Computer Applications in Geology, v. 3, p. 27–35.

Pannatier, Y., 1996, Variowin: Software for Spatial Data Analysis in 2D: New York, Springer, 91 p.

Poeter, E., and Gaylord, D.R., 1990, Influence of aquifer heterogeneity on contaminant transport at the Hanford Site: Ground Water, v. 28, p. 900–909.

Ritzi, R.W., Jr., Dominic, D.F., Brown, N.R., Kausch, K.W., McAlenny, P.J., and Basial, M.J., 1995, Hydrofacies distribution and correlation in the Miami Valley aquifer system: Water Resources Research, v. 31, p. 3271–3281.

Ritzi, R.W., Jr., Dominic, D.F., Slesers, A.J., Greer, C.B., Reboulet, E.C., Telford, J.A., Masters, R.W., Klohe, C.A., Bogle, J.L., and Means, B.P., 2000, Comparing statistical models of physical heterogeneity in buried-valley aquifers: Water Resources Research, v. 36, p. 3179–3192.

Robinson, J.W., and McCabe, P.J., 1997, Sandstone-body and shale-body dimensions in a braided fluvial system: Salt Wash Sandstone Member (Morrison Formation), Garfield County, Utah: American Association of Petroleum Geologists, Bulletin, v. 81, p. 1267–1291.

Shepherd, R.G., 1989, Correlations of permeability and grain size: Ground Water, v. 27, p. 633–638.

Smith, G.A., 2000, Recognition and significance of streamflow-dominated piedmont facies in extensional basins: Basin Research, v. 12, p. 399–412.

Sudicky, E.A., 1986, A natural gradient experiment on solute transport in a sand aquifer: Spatial variability of hydraulic conductivity and its role in the dispersion process: Water Resources Research, v. 22, p. 2069–2082.

Vukovic, M., and Soro, A., 1992, Determination of Hydraulic Conductivity of Porous Media from Grain-Size Composition: Littleton, Colorado, Water Resources Publications, 83 p.

Willis, B.J., and White, C.D., 2000, Quantitative outcrop data for flow simulation: Journal of Sedimentary Research, v. 70, p. 788–802.

HIGH-RESOLUTION STRATIGRAPHIC CHARACTERIZATION OF UNCONSOLIDATED DEPOSITS USING DIRECT-PUSH ELECTRICAL CONDUCTIVITY LOGGING: A FLOODPLAIN-MARGIN EXAMPLE

MARCIA K. SCHULMEISTER*, JAMES J. BUTLER, Jr., AND EVAN K. FRANSEEN
Kansas Geological Survey, 1930 Constant Ave., Campus West, The University of Kansas, Lawrence, Kansas 66047, U.S.A.
Present address: Earth Science Department, Emporia State University, 1200 Commercial St., Emporia, Kansas 66801, U.S.A.
e-mail: schulmem@emporia.edu

DOUGLAS A. WYSOCKI
National Resource Conservation Service, U.S. Department of Agriculture, National Soil Survey Center Building, 100 Centennial Mall North, Lincoln, Nebraska 68508-3866, U.S.A.

AND

JAMES A. DOOLITTLE
National Resource Conservation Service, U.S. Department of Agriculture, 11 Campus Blvd. Suite 200, Newtown Square, Pennsylvania 19073, U.S.A.

ABSTRACT: Electrical logs of various types have been used for decades in a wide variety of geoscience applications. Except for studies within a few meters of the land surface, these logs have been obtained using existing wells or boreholes. Recently, electrical conductivity (EC) sensors have been incorporated into direct-push equipment to obtain sedimentologic information in unconsolidated deposits without the need for existing wells and at a resolution (0.02 m) that has not been possible using conventional logging tools. The high resolution of this information, coupled with the speed at which it can be obtained, makes direct-push EC logging a valuable new tool for a wide variety of hydrostratigraphic studies. We document the utility of this approach in a detailed stratigraphic evaluation of a floodplain margin in a major river valley in the United States. Throughout the central United States, unconsolidated sequences underlying floodplains are typically composed of fining-upward glaciofluvial or Holocene sediments in which silt and clay overbank deposits cap coarser materials that serve as regionally significant aquifers. EC transects at a field site on the Kansas River floodplain show that this fine-grained cap may be truncated by, or interfingered with, coarser sediments at the floodplain margin. This increased stratigraphic complexity suggests that the depositional settings assumed for the more central portions of the floodplain may not be appropriate in the margin areas. The replacement of fine-grained sediments with coarser-grained materials at the margin of the floodplain has significant implications for groundwater recharge and solute movement. Interpretations made using the EC transects are consistent with results from an electromagnetic survey, as well as head and chemistry data. This work shows that direct-push EC logging can provide information about site stratigraphy at a level of detail that would be difficult to obtain with conventional approaches. This unprecedented level of detail enables important insights to be obtained regarding stratigraphic controls on groundwater flow and solute transport.

INTRODUCTION

Field and modeling studies in a wide variety of geologic settings have shown the importance of detailed descriptions of aquifer heterogeneity for applications ranging from the prediction of contaminant transport (e.g., Sudicky and Huyakorn, 1991) to the design of effective remediation schemes (e.g., National Research Council, 1994; Hyndman et al., 2000; Bilbrey and Shafer, 2001) to the assessment of stream–aquifer interactions (e.g., Butler et al., 2001). These studies have demonstrated clearly that fine-scale hydrostratigraphic features can significantly influence the movement of groundwater and accompanying solutes in many situations. However, few approaches for subsurface characterization can provide information about site hydrostratigraphy at the level of detail that such studies have found is needed. Currently, most hydrostratigraphic information is obtained through the collection of drill cuttings and continuous cores, and use of wellbore or surface geophysics. Time and cost limitations, however, often restrict the number of cores or wells to a spacing that is inadequate for investigations in heterogeneous systems. In addition, the sampling volume of geophysical methods is commonly too large to resolve small-scale features. Thus, new approaches are needed if such details are to be incorporated in hydrogeologic investigations on a routine basis. In this paper, we discuss one such approach and demonstrate the relevance of the information that it can provide.

Over the last two decades, a variety of direct-push-based methods have been developed for use in investigations at sites of groundwater contamination. These approaches overcome many limitations of traditional field methods and show considerable potential for detailed subsurface characterization in unconsolidated formations (e.g., Tillman and Leonard, 1993). Direct-push electrical conductivity (EC) logging, which was developed in the mid-1990s (Christy et al., 1994), holds particular promise in this regard. Recent work has demonstrated the utility of direct-push EC logging for investigations of ground-water contamination (e.g., McCall, 1996; Beck et al., 2000; McCall and Zimmerman, 2000; Einarson et al., 2000; U.S. Environmental Protection Agency, 2000) and saline–freshwater interfaces (Johnson et al., 1999; Fenstemaker et al., 2001). Schulmeister et al. (2003a) assessed the quality and resolution of information obtained from direct-push EC logging, and demonstrated the potential of the approach for hydrostratigraphic studies. That potential is explored in detail in this paper.

The utility of direct-push EC logging for hydrostratigraphic studies is demonstrated here in an investigation of stratigraphic relationships in alluvial sediments that lie beneath the floodplain of a major river valley. Although floodplain margins have not

Aquifer Characterization
SEPM Special Publication No. 80, Copyright © 2004
SEPM (Society for Sedimentary Geology), ISBN 1-56576-107-3, p. 67–78.

received a great deal of attention in the hydrologic literature, the sedimentary framework in these areas may play an important role in determining the groundwater quality of the aquifer underlying the floodplain (henceforth, floodplain aquifer). Throughout the central portions of the United States, unconsolidated glaciofluvial and fluvial sequences typically display a fining-upward character as a result of Pleistocene and Holocene changes in climate or base level (e.g., Sharp, 1988; Larkin and Sharp, 1992). The uppermost sediments in these sequences are typically composed of clay and silt overbank deposits that serve as an important barrier to the transport of contaminants to the underlying aquifer. However, at the margins of the floodplains, this low-permeability cap does not always exist. Instead, it may be replaced by coarse-grained or poorly sorted materials, such as mass-movement deposits and alluvial fans, thus creating recharge areas for the aquifer. In several studies, the groundwater chemistry near the margins of floodplains bounded by terraces has been shown to differ from that in the interior of the floodplains (Haycock and Burt, 1993; Lucey et al., 1995), further suggesting that the valley margins may be important recharge areas. In this paper, direct-push EC logging is used to investigate the stratigraphy in the floodplain to floodplain-margin setting to assess the potential for significant recharge in the margin areas.

BACKGROUND

Electrical Conductivity in Unconsolidated Sediments

The electrical conductivity of sedimentary material is a function of the moisture content of the material and the conducting properties of its pore fluid and matrix (Schon, 1996). In the saturated zone, where variations in moisture content are relatively small, fluid and matrix properties are the dominant con-

trols on electrical conductivity. When variations in groundwater chemistry are small, differences in sediment size and type are the major factors affecting electrical conductivity (Keys, 1989). Silt- and sand-size particles of covalently bonded minerals, such as quartz, mica, and feldspar, are relatively nonconductive. For this reason, electrical conductivity in coarse-grained aquifers primarily reflects the concentration of dissolved constituents. Clay-size particles, such as phyllosilicates, humic substances, and iron and manganese oxides and oxyhydroxides, tend to be highly conductive, because of their small size, relatively high surface area per unit volume, and charge characteristics (Langmuir, 1997). Thus, in formations where fine-grained materials occur and dissolved solids concentrations are low, variations in electrical conductivity are primarily a function of the vertical and lateral distribution of clay-bearing units. In such settings, EC logging is an excellent means of delineating stratigraphic controls on groundwater flow and transport.

Direct-Push EC Logging

Direct-push EC logging is an extremely versatile method for obtaining information about vertical and lateral variations in electrical conductivity (Christy et al., 1994; Butler et al., 1999; Schulmeister et al., 2003a). This approach utilizes a sensor that is attached to the end of a string of small-diameter pipe and driven into the subsurface using a percussion hammer and a hydraulic slide (Fig. 1). The sensor configuration used in this work consists of a four-electrode Wenner array with an inner-electrode spacing of 0.02 m. As the EC probe is advanced, a current is applied to the two outer electrodes and voltage is measured across the two inner electrodes. Given the applied current and the measured voltage, electrical conductivity is calculated to produce a real-time log of electrical conductivity versus depth. Data are collected every

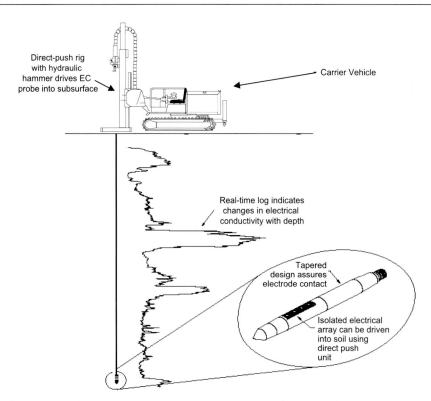

Direct-push rig with hydraulic hammer drives EC probe into subsurface

Carrier Vehicle

Real-time log indicates changes in electrical conductivity with depth

Tapered design assures electrode contact

Isolated electrical array can be driven into soil using direct push unit

FIG. 1.—A schematic of the direct-push electrical conductivity logging approach used in this study (after Geoprobe Systems, 1998).

0.015 m as the probe is advanced and a potentiometer mounted on the mast of the direct-push unit tracks the depth and speed of that advance. The vertical resolution of the sensor (0.015 m), coupled with its small depth of investigation (5 to 10 cm; Beck et al., 2000), enables hydrostratigraphic features to be recognized at a level of detail formerly possible only with continuous cores (McCall, 1996; Schulmeister et al., 2003a). Moreover, because the probe is in direct contact with the formation and no drilling fluids are used, the approach is not subject to the bias produced by irregular borehole diameters and drilling fluids, as is the case for most wellbore-geophysical methods. Logs can be completed relatively rapidly (e.g., 45 minutes for a 22 meter log; Butler et al., 1999; Kram et al., 2000) and there are few limitations on placement location. Thus, numerous logs can be obtained at a lateral spacing that is rarely feasible using other approaches in a time- and cost-efficient manner. The enhanced understanding of site hydrostratigraphy that can result is demonstrated in this paper.

STUDY AREA

The Geohydrologic Experimental and Monitoring Site

The work described in this paper was conducted at a Kansas Geological Survey (KGS) research site where hydrostratigraphic features are known to exert a significant influence on ground-water flow and solute transport (e.g., Butler et al., 1998; Butler et al., 2002; Bohling, 1999; Davis et al., 2002; Schulmeister et al., 2003b). The Geohydrologic Experimental and Monitoring Site (GEMS) is located along the northern margin of the Kansas River valley (Fig. 2) on approximately 22 m of late Pleistocene and Holocene sediments that overlie Pennsylvanian bedrock (Johnson and Martin, 1987; Kettle and Whittemore, 1991) and form the Newman terrace. The unconsolidated sequence consists of fluvial deposits, which can be divided into two major units. The lower 11 m of the sequence (henceforth, Unit 1) consists of fining-upward deposits of pebbles and fine sand with local discontinuous lenses of finer-grained material. The upper 11 m of the sequence (henceforth, Unit 2) consists of predominantly silt and clay with interlayered or discontinuous lenses of fine to medium sand. The distinct boundary between Unit 1 and Unit 2 represents a transition from braided-stream to meandering-stream depositional processes associated with a late Wisconsinan–early Holocene climatic change, and is observed in alluvial fills throughout the United States (Sharp, 1988). The margin of the modern floodplain near GEMS is marked on the land surface by an escarpment that rises to an older Pleistocene terrace, and, in the subsurface, by an abrupt rise in the Pennsylvanian bedrock (O'Connor, 1960).

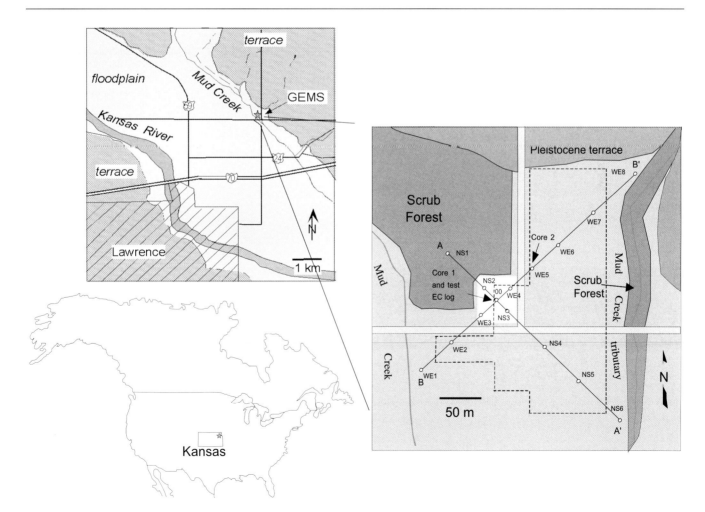

FIG. 2.—Location of GEMS (stars and white stippled area) and surrounding hydrologic and geologic features. Locations of EC logs are denoted by white circles along transects A–A' and B–B'. Boundaries of the EM survey area are indicated by dashed lines.

For the last decade, GEMS has been the site of extensive research on groundwater flow and solute transport in heterogeneous formations. A number of studies have found significant spatial variation in the hydraulic properties and groundwater chemistry of the alluvium. For example, hydraulic testing in Unit 1 has revealed variations in hydraulic conductivity of over two orders of magnitude (Sellwood, 2001; Butler et al., 2002; Davis et al., 2002), whereas chemical profiles have provided strong evidence for chemical evolution of groundwater along lateral flow paths separated by fine-grained sedimentary layers (Schulmeister, 2000; Schulmeister et al., 2003b). The considerable degree of lateral and vertical variability demonstrated in this previous work suggests that the heterogeneity of the alluvium plays an important role in controlling flow and transport in the vicinity of GEMS.

Recently, a component of the work at GEMS has been directed at assessing the value of the information that is obtained from direct-push EC logging. An initial EC log placed at the center of the site (henceforth, test EC log) was in good agreement with previous geologic interpretations based on core materials from the same location (Fig. 3). Continuous cores were obtained adjacent to EC logs at two locations. Very thin (< 2.5 cm) clay-rich layers in the cores coincided with spikes in electrical conductivity in the adjacent EC logs (Fig. 4). A strong correlation (correlation coefficient of 0.72) was found between the magnitude of the direct-push EC value and clay content in 50 sampled layers from these cores, demonstrating that EC logs can be used as semiquantitative indicators of clay content (Schulmeister et al., 2003a). The occurrence of prominent EC spikes and thin clay layers at similar depths in the two cores (e.g., 3 m and 6 m depths in Figure 4) suggests that EC logs can be used to assess the lateral continuity of sedimentary units. In addition, a slightly higher overall clay content in Core 1 and correspondingly higher EC values in the adjacent log suggest that EC logs can also be used for identifying lateral facies

variations. Although the ability of EC logging to resolve vertical contrasts in sedimentary sequences has been demonstrated in previous work (e.g., Butler et al., 1999; Schulmeister et al., 2003a), the use of this approach for resolving lateral variations has not been fully assessed. A demonstration of the utility of the approach for evaluating lateral variations in sedimentary sequences is a primary focus of this paper.

METHODS OF INVESTIGATION

Paleosol Identification

Buried soils (paleosols) mark periods of landscape stability in sedimentary sequences and are extremely useful for bracketing units in which facies changes occur (e.g., Weissmann and Fogg, 1999). Buried soils within alluvial Holocene fills of the Kansas River valley are extensively documented (Holien, 1982; Logan, 1985; Johnson and Martin, 1987; Mandel, 1987) and have been used as major stratigraphic markers for correlations (Johnson and Logan, 1990). Five prominent paleosols have been identified in outcrops of sediments beneath the Newman terrace throughout the eastern part of the Kansas River valley and are likely to occur in the vicinity of GEMS. Because the materials that typically make up paleosols are electrically conductive, these layers should be recognizable in EC logs and therefore could be useful as marker beds for correlations based on those logs.

Weathering and composition changes that occur during soil formation result in the accumulation of organic materials and formation of clay minerals. Compositional features (such as organic materials) and macroscopic structural and color characteristics observed in the cores were used here as indicators of possible paleosols (U.S.D.A. nomenclature (Schoeneberger et al., 1998) used for all descriptions). Additional chemical indicators of soil development were utilized as supporting evidence. Carbon and nitrogen are usually present in elevated amounts in organic-

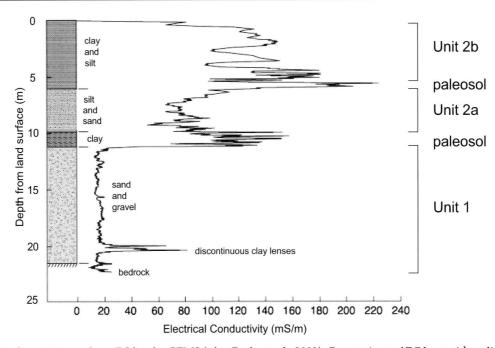

Fig. 3.—Lithologic description and test EC log for GEMS (after Butler et al., 2002). Comparison of EC logs with sediment cores from the site demonstrates that higher EC values represent fine-grained material and lower EC values indicate coarser sediments. Labels on right side of figure designate the major stratigraphic units identified in this work, as discussed in the text.

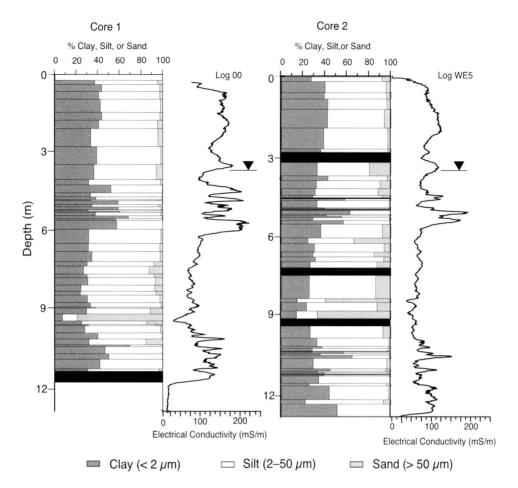

Fig. 4.—Comparisons of particle size and electrical conductivity in continuous cores and adjacent EC logs, respectively (after Schulmeister et al., 2003a). Core and adjacent EC log separated by less than 1 m; distance between two core locations is about 50 m (Fig. 2). Blackened layers represent intervals for which particle-size analyses were not conducted. Position of water table is indicated by inverted triangles.

rich A horizon materials (Brady, 1984) and thus can provide supporting evidence of soil development. Carbon and nitrogen abundances were determined on 72 samples from both cores using dry combustion methods (U.S. Department of Agriculture, 1996) and an Elementar Vario Carbon–Nitrogen–Sulfur Analyzer at the National Soil Science Center Laboratory of the Natural Resource Conservation Services.

Direct-Push EC Logging

Direct-push EC logs were obtained at fifteen locations along two approximately perpendicular transects at GEMS (Fig. 2). Seven logs (NS labels) were collected along a 275 m transect (A–A') that is oriented roughly parallel to the floodplain margin, and nine logs (WE labels) were obtained along a 350 m transect (B–B') that is oriented roughly perpendicular to the margin. One log (00) was obtained at the intersection of the two transects.

EM Survey

An electromagnetic induction (EM) survey was used to support interpretations made from the EC logs. Although an EM survey does not allow the depths and thicknesses of individual layers to be determined, it does enable a relatively continuous

record of lateral variations in depth-averaged electrical conductivity to be obtained. The EM meter is noninvasive and requires only one person to operate, making it a versatile tool for rapid evaluation of areas between EC logs to assess if additional logs are needed. An EM survey was conducted at GEMS using a Geonics EM31 meter (frequency 9,810 Hz) operating in a station-to-station mode. A total of 164 survey points were established in an irregularly shaped grid (interval 15.2 m) that encompassed most of the EC transect area (Fig. 2). Measurements in both the horizontal- and vertical-dipole orientations were obtained at each grid point. Measurements were taken with the meter held at hip height (about 1 meter above the surface) in both orientations. At hip height, the depth of penetration is about 2 m and 5 m in the horizontal- and vertical-dipole orientations, respectively (McNeill, 1980). The lateral resolution of the EM31 is approximately equal to the intercoil spacing (about 3.7 m).

RESULTS AND DISCUSSION

Identification of Paleosols

The presence of fine blocky structure in clay layers and charcoal and wood fragments suggests that at least two paleosols exist in the study area (Fig. 5). Elevated concentrations of carbon

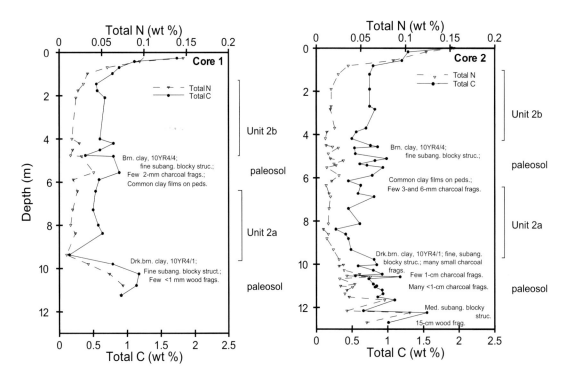

FIG. 5.—Total (wt %) carbon (C) and nitrogen (N) and brief morphologic description for Cores 1 and 2. Organic materials, soil structure, and clay films on vertical faces indicate soil development (paleosols) at 4–6 m and 10–12.5 m, respectively. Generally higher C and N levels in samples from these intervals support the paleosol interpretations. Labels on the right side of each plot designate major stratigraphic units identified in this work, as discussed in the text.

and nitrogen coincide with some of these features and are consistent with a paleosol interpretation. Most of the organic material and the highest carbon and nitrogen levels are in a clay-rich interval near the bottom of both cores (depths of 10–12.5 m; Figure 5). The thickness of this interval and the abundance of organic material suggest that it is a well-developed paleosol. Thick paleosols have been documented at approximately this same elevation elsewhere in the Kansas River basin (Johnson and Martin, 1987). Less developed soil morphologic features and slightly elevated levels of carbon and nitrogen occur at depths between 4 and 6 m (Fig. 5), suggesting the presence of a weakly developed paleosol in this interval. Weakly developed, but laterally continuous, paleosols have also been documented elsewhere on the floodplain at several depths within this portion of the sequence (Johnson and Martin, 1987; Johnson and Logan, 1990). Both paleosol intervals are coincident with high EC values, which allows these horizons to serve as marker beds for lateral correlation using EC log signatures, as illustrated in the following section.

EC Logs–Lateral Correlations and Facies Changes

Data from the two EC transects were used to construct cross sections to assess lateral continuity and facies changes in the vicinity of the floodplain margin. Cross sections were prepared in two formats: (1) as stratigraphic cross sections (Figs. 6A, 7A) based on the visual interpretation of the EC logs by a sedimentologist; and (2) as machine-contoured cross sections (Figs. 6B, 7B) created with the Surfer software package (Golden Software, 1997). Although little significance should be attached to the details of the interpolation between EC logs in the machine-contoured cross sections, these cross sections do provide useful

visualizations of relative variations in the clay content of the alluvium.

The recognition and correlation of paleosols on EC logs in both transects, as well as of patterns in EC logs in the strata above and below the paleosols, allowed a more detailed stratigraphic framework to be defined than had previously been possible at GEMS. This stratigraphic framework, along with the lateral patterns within its major units, is discussed below.

The two paleosols are recognizable in most of the EC logs. In transect A–A' (Fig. 6), the two paleosols are present in all logs except NS6 and are laterally traceable at relatively constant elevations. In transect B–B' (Fig. 7), the paleosol layers appear to be present in most logs but are less prominent at the northeast end of the transect (WE7–WE8). As traced from the southwest, the base of the lower paleosol decreases in elevation from WE3 to WE5 before increasing towards the floodplain margin. The lower paleosol appears to be significantly thicker between WE3 and WE5 than elsewhere in the transect. The elevation of the upper paleosol is relatively constant from WE1 to WE5, before also increasing towards the floodplain margin. Little change in thickness is observed in the upper paleosol.

As stated previously, the unconsolidated sequence at GEMS can be subdivided into two major units. Unit 1, which comprises the floodplain aquifer, is characterized by relatively low EC values with thin, discontinuous zones of high EC, suggesting deposits that consist of sand and gravel with discontinuous clay lenses. This is consistent with the test EC log and accompanying core information (Figs. 3, 4), and previous work (e.g., Butler et al., 1998; Butler et al., 2002). Changes in the thickness of Unit 1 are primarily associated with changes in the elevation of the bedrock surface. In transect A–A', the bedrock surface increases in elevation in the

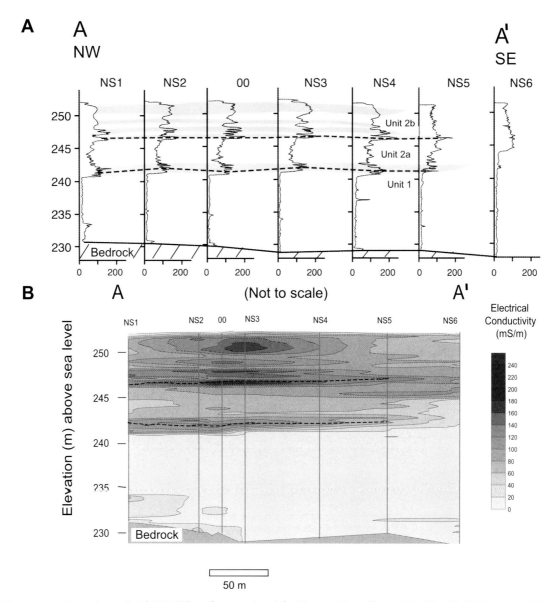

FIG. 6.—EC transect oriented parallel (NW–SE) to the margin of the Kansas River floodplain (Fig. 2). **A)** Stratigraphic cross section showing interpreted lateral correlations and facies patterns based on EC logs. Clay-rich intervals are shown in gray. Note that the spacing of EC logs does not reflect actual lateral distances between logs but was instead chosen to optimize the visual comparison of log patterns. **B)** Machine-contoured representation of electrical conductivity for visual display of relative variations in clay content. The spacing of EC logs reflects the actual lateral distance between logs. The two paleosols are shown as dashed lines in both diagrams.

northwesternmost logs (00, NS2, and NS1). This rise in bedrock elevation and the fining of sediments in Unit 1 in its vicinity suggest that log NS1 is closer to the margin of the floodplain than the other logs in that transect. In transect B–B', the presence of the floodplain margin is more strongly indicated. The elevation of the bedrock surface increases significantly between logs WE5 and WE6, and continues to rise gradually to the northeast. This rise in the bedrock surface is accompanied by the fining of sediments in Unit 1.

Unit 2 can be divided into two subunits (2a and 2b). Unit 2a is characterized by mostly intermediate EC values with thin, discontinuous zones of both high and low EC. The thin peaks and troughs in the EC logs suggest that there are discontinuous clay and sand intervals, respectively, in Unit 2a. This is consistent with the test EC

log and accompanying core, which indicate that the unit consists primarily of silt and clay, with some thin sand layers. Although lateral variations within Unit 2a in transect A–A' are not pronounced, the EC data suggest that sediments in Unit 2a are slightly coarser towards the northwest and that minor clay intervals are more common to the southeast. Unit 2a does not appear to be traceable to NS6, an issue that is discussed further in the following section. Transect B–B' indicates that the unit coarsens significantly in the direction of the floodplain margin, with minor discontinuous clay intervals more common at the southwest end of the transect.

Unit 2b is characterized by intermediate and high EC values, which is consistent with the predominantly clay and silt compo-

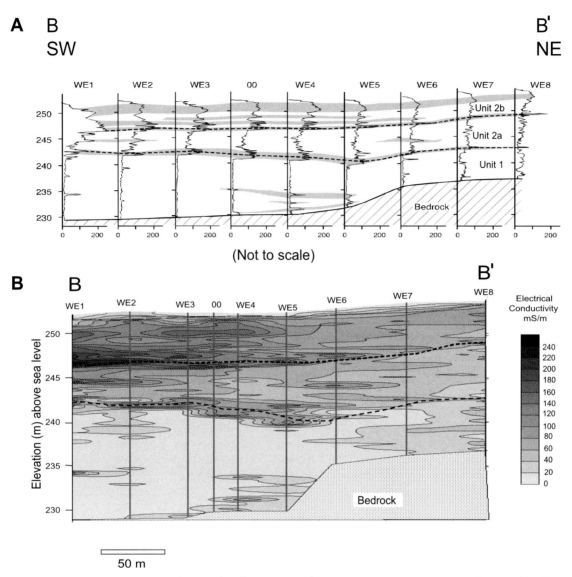

FIG. 7.—EC transect oriented perpendicular (SW–NE) to the margin of the Kansas River floodplain near the mouth of the Mud Creek tributary (Fig. 2). **A)** Stratigraphic cross section showing interpreted lateral correlations and facies patterns based on EC logs. Clay-rich intervals are shown in gray. Note that the spacing of EC logs does not reflect actual lateral distances between logs but was instead chosen to optimize the visual comparison of log patterns. **B)** Machine-contoured representation of electrical conductivity for visual display of relative variations in clay content. The spacing of EC logs reflects actual lateral distance between logs. The two paleosols are shown as dashed lines in both diagrams.

sition indicated by the test EC log and accompanying core. Both transects indicate that there are up to three clay-rich intervals in Unit 2b. In transect A–A', the three intervals are traceable from northwest to southeast from NS1 to NS4, with the highest clay content observed in the areas of NS2, 00, and NS3. In transect B–B', the lower clay-rich interval is traceable to WE6, the middle interval to WE5, and the upper interval across the entire transect. The EC logs indicate that the highest clay concentrations occur in the southwestern and middle portions of transect B–B' and that the materials become coarser towards the northeast.

EC Logs—Interpretations

The occurrence of thin, discontinuous clay lenses at several depths in Unit 1 is consistent with previous interpretations of

stratified sediments in the aquifer (Jiang, 1991). The finer-grained materials in Unit 1 are generally located near the floodplain margins in both transects, implying a colluvial origin for this material (slumping and sloughing of debris from the nearby terrace or valley wall).

The nature of the paleosols and facies in Unit 2 appears to be related to the distance from the floodplain margin. The relative continuity and constant elevations and thicknesses of the paleosols and individual layers (particularly in Unit 2b) away from the margin suggests that relatively uniform depositional processes occurred in that area. In contrast, changes in geometry and facies appear much more significant as the floodplain margin and tributary stream valley (Mud Creek tributary) are approached. The coarsening of sediments in Units 2a and 2b near the margin of the floodplain in transects A–A' (NS1) and B–B' (WE5–WE8) is consistent with current geomorphic interpretations of this setting. Modern terrace–slope deposits in many river valleys consist of different materials than are found elsewhere on the floodplain (Bowman, 1986). These poorly sorted, coarse-grained colluvial sediments originate as slope wash and soil creep on terrace slopes or as alluvial-fan deposits from ephemeral streams that enter larger river valleys (Kehew and Boettger, 1986). Mass-movement deposits, such as earthflow debris and landslide materials, are commonly intermixed with valley-margin colluvium elsewhere along the margins of the Kansas River valley (Bowman, 1986; Sorenson et al., 1987), and the Holocene alluvial-fan deposits of small tributaries have been documented on the floodplain (Mandel, 1998, 1999; Douglas County N.R.C.S. Field Office, personal communication, 2001). Thus, one would expect a coarsening of sediments in Units 2a and 2b near the margin of the Kansas River floodplain, especially in the vicinity of a tributary stream.

The distinct transition in character between logs NS4 and NS6 (apparent truncation of paleosols and significant coarsening of Unit 2a) suggests that the sediments in this area may have originated from different depositional processes. Log NS6 is located close to the course of the modern Mud Creek tributary channel (Fig. 2), so one possible explanation is that the sediments in the vicinity of this log represent more recent fluvial activity in the Mud Creek tributary and the dissection of the older sediments encountered at locations NS1–NS4. Alternatively, these sediments may represent older channel deposits emplaced during formation of the Newman terrace. In any case, the EC logs identify this transition, which has important implications for groundwater flow and solute transport, and can be used to guide further data collection.

The apparent increase in elevation and the thinning of the two paleosols to the northeast on transect B–B' suggests that the paleosols reflect the rise in topography that occurs along the alluvial-fan deposits in the direction of the mouth of the tributary valley. This is not unusual for this setting, because alluvial-fan soils have been mapped previously in tributary valleys and buried alluvial-fan surfaces along the Kansas River floodplain margin (Johnson and Logan, 1990; Douglas County N.R.C.S. Field Office, personal communication, 2001). Paleosols are often absent from, or thinner in, the tributary valleys, presumably because of the valleys' smaller sediment-storage capacities and propensity for frequent sediment flushing. The apparent thinning of the paleosols in the vicinity of the transition from the floodplain to the floodplain margin may be a reflection of these mechanisms. The persistence of the paleosols across this portion of the study area suggests that downcutting and aggradation near the mouth of the tributary were interrupted by periods of stability and soil development, which has important implications for paleoclimate studies.

EM survey

EM survey data are presented for both the horizontal-dipole (Fig. 8A) and vertical-dipole (Fig. 8B) orientations. Higher conductivities were obtained in the vertical orientation than in the shallower-sensing, horizontal orientation. This was expected because of the higher moisture contents below the water table, and the sequence of fine-grained sediments between depths of 2 and 5 m (e.g., Figure 4).

In general, the EM data are in good agreement with the EC logs. The EC-based interpretation of sediments coarsening near the floodplain margin and the Mud Creek tributary is supported by conductivity patterns shown in the EM surveys. Although the EM survey does not extend to the southwest end of transect B–B', higher depth-averaged conductivity in the southwesternmost EM survey points suggests a fining of materials in the southwest direction, and is in agreement with similar interpretations made from the EC logs. In addition to supporting interpretations made using the EC logs, the EM survey provides information about conditions in areas not sampled by the logs. The lower EM values

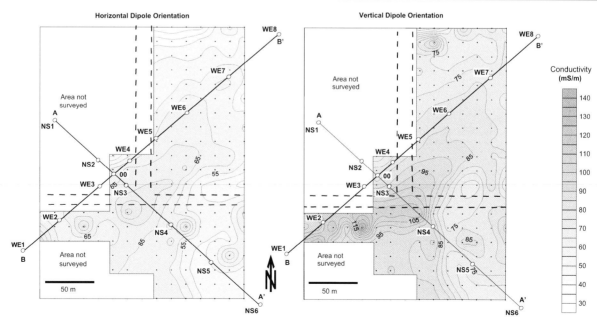

Fig. 8.—EM survey data collected in horizontal- and vertical-dipole configurations (after Doolittle, 2001). Horizontal-dipole and vertical-dipole orientations represent 2 m and 5 m depth-weighted averages, respectively. The high-conductivity data peak in the north-central part of the vertical survey is believed to indicate an underground gas line, and was ignored in interpretations based on these data.

along the eastern boundary of the survey area are consistent with the presence of colluvial sediments along the margin of the terrace, or they could indicate recent stream cutting activity along the Mud Creek tributary. In addition, a zone of relatively high-conductivity material is revealed in both EM orientations between EC logs NS3 and NS4. This zone appears to indicate the presence of a previously unrecognized feature, and it demonstrates the potential of surface geophysical surveys to identify locations where additional EC logs are needed. Clearly, the overall agreement between the two methods shows the advantage of combining EC logging and surface geophysical methods when detailed three-dimensional evaluations of subsurface stratigraphy are required.

Implications for Groundwater Flow and Solute Transport

Floodplain aquifers are generally thought to receive recharge by seepage through river channels, infiltration of precipitation through overlying sediments, leakage from adjacent bedrock aquifers, and infiltration of terrace runoff along floodplain margins (Sharp, 1988). In many mid-continent floodplain aquifers in the United States, fine-grained sediments overlie the sands and gravels of the aquifer and greatly restrict the amount of recharge due to infiltrating precipitation (Fisk, 1944; Sharp, 1988). In this situation, other sources can potentially make up a significant component of the aquifer recharge.

The results of the EC logging and EM survey provide some insight into the relative importance of terrace-runoff infiltration as a recharge mechanism. Terrace runoff can bring significant volumes of water to the margins of floodplains (Burt and Haycock, 1996). In the presence of the fine-grained sediments that cap the unconsolidated sequence in the interior of the floodplain, relatively little of this water would actually recharge the aquifer. However, the EC transects and EM survey data show clearly that the clay content of Unit 2b decreases in the vicinity of the margin of the floodplain near GEMS (Figs. 7, 8). This apparent truncation or interfingering of clay-rich horizons near the margin has important implications for recharge. One would expect that the decreasing clay content in the near-surface sediments would result in greater recharge into the underlying aquifer. Although we are unaware of previous studies that have examined the importance of floodplain-margin recharge, other authors have observed that heads near floodplain margins bounded by terraces tend to be slightly elevated with respect to those in the floodplain interior and have invoked infiltration of terrace runoff as an explanation for that head difference (Sharp, 1988). Head data from wells completed in the upper 11 m of the unconsolidated sequence at GEMS indicate that higher water levels exist near the floodplain margin and that the flow direction is roughly perpendicular to the margin (Schulmeister, 2000). Data on groundwater chemistry also provide insight into the relative importance of recharge along the floodplain margin. Significant variations in groundwater chemistry across the transition from the floodplain to the floodplain margin have been observed at GEMS. For example, concentrations of total dissolved solids in groundwater collected from the near-margin regions were less than half the concentrations measured in the more interior parts of the floodplain (Schulmeister et al., 2003b). Enhanced recharge along the margins is the most plausible explanation for these differences in head and concentration. Such gradients in hydraulic and geochemical conditions have important implications for the movement and fate of contaminants that may enter floodplain aquifers via recharge along the margins.

The stratification observed on the EC transects suggests that groundwater at GEMS should primarily flow in a series of laterally continuous zones of relatively high permeability (e.g.,

Pryor, 1973; Sharp, 1988). The movement of solutes at different velocities and the different rates of reactions in such zones can often lead to chemical stratification (e.g., Hoyle, 1989). Previously reported vertical variations in hydraulic head and NO_3 at GEMS (Schulmeister, 2000) and trends in total dissolved solids (Schulmeister et al., 2003b) support an interpretation of flow along the laterally continuous units inferred by the EC transects. Patterns in groundwater chemistry could easily be misinterpreted if sedimentary controls such as those identified in the EC transects are not recognized.

CONCLUSIONS

This work demonstrates that direct-push EC logging is a powerful tool for the delineation of fine-scale stratigraphic features in saturated unconsolidated sequences with clay-bearing units and groundwater of a relatively uniform salinity. The detailed view of vertical and lateral variations in site stratigraphy that can result from this approach would be extremely difficult to obtain with conventional drilling- and geophysics-based methods. A series of direct-push EC logs can be completed rapidly at a lateral spacing that is rarely feasible using other approaches. Such logs can yield a greatly enhanced understanding of site-specific stratigraphic controls on groundwater flow and solute transport. In addition, these logs can provide valuable information for stratigraphic studies, particularly those for which an understanding of the relative timing and spatial extent of depositional events is important.

The utility of direct-push EC logging was demonstrated here through an investigation of stratigraphic relationships in the vicinity of a floodplain margin. In this investigation, EC logs were obtained along two transects, perpendicular and parallel, respectively, to the floodplain margin. The correlation of paleosols and patterns of EC logs in strata above and below those paleosols allowed a more detailed stratigraphic framework to be defined for the unconsolidated sequence than had previously been possible. This framework consists of a basal sand and gravel unit with discontinuous clay lenses, a middle unit consisting primarily of silt and clay with discontinuous clay- and sand-rich intervals, and an upper unit consisting almost entirely of clay and silt. The EC traverses indicate an increase in clay in the basal unit and a coarsening of sediments in the upper two units as the floodplain margin is approached. These lateral changes in sediment type are attributed to colluvial, mass-movement, and alluvial-fan processes that are common at the bases of terraces along floodplain margins. The change from fine-grained sediments to coarse-grained sediments in the upper two units at the margin of the floodplain has significant implications for groundwater recharge and solute movement. Because colluvial, mass-movement, and alluvial-fan deposits similar to those found in the Kansas River floodplain have also been documented near the bases of terrace slopes on other floodplains in the Mississippi River valley, the findings and methodologies used in this study may be relevant for a large class of floodplain aquifers in the United States and elsewhere.

Despite the extremely high resolution of the information that can be obtained in the vertical direction, interpretations made from traverses of direct-push EC logs will always be accompanied by uncertainty regarding conditions between individual logs. As shown in this study, the combination of direct-push EC logging and surface geophysics can help reduce that uncertainty. The EM survey method used in this study enables lateral patterns in depth-averaged conductivity to be rapidly identified. EM results were used here to support interpretations developed from the EC traverses and identify areas where additional EC logs would be helpful. Other surface-geophysical methods, such as shallow seismic reflection, ground-penetrating radar, and electrical resistivity ground imaging (Baines et. al., 2002), can provide much greater detail than this depth-averaged EM approach. When such methods are used in conjunction with direct-push EC logs, the uncertainty in the subsurface characterization should be significantly less than would be possible with any single method. Clearly, the combination of direct-push EC logging and surface geophysics represents an important new approach for the three-dimensional characterization of the stratigraphic framework of unconsolidated sequences.

This study reiterates the importance of a detailed description of site stratigraphy for investigations of groundwater flow and transport. However, a complete hydrostratigraphic characterization of a sedimentary sequence requires that information from the EC logs be supplemented by high-resolution data on the chemical and hydraulic properties of the sequence. Recently, direct-push-based methods have been developed for obtaining high-resolution records of hydraulic conductivity (McCall et al., 2002) and pore-fluid geochemistry (Schulmeister et al., 2003a) in a single direct-push probehole. These approaches can be combined by using EC logging to construct a stratigraphic framework for a site, after which the hydraulic and geochemical methods can be used for investigations of zones of particular interest. This integration of high-resolution methods should allow significant new insights to be developed into site hydrostratigraphy. Such insights could be extremely important for guiding and constraining future modeling investigations and for refining hydrostratigraphic concepts.

ACKNOWLEDGMENTS

This research was supported in part by the Kansas Water Resources Research Institute under grant HQ96GR02671 Modif. 008 (subaward S01044; JJB PI). The project was initiated prior to, but was guided by, a Memorandum of Understanding between the American Association of State Geologists and the Natural Resources Conservation Service (NRCS). We gratefully acknowledge John Healey (KGS) for operation of the direct-push unit, Wes McCall (Geoprobe Systems) and Bruce Evans (NRCS) for advice on soil sampling/description, and Margaret Townsend (KGS) for her assistance in conducting the EM survey. This manuscript benefited from reviews by Rolfe Mandel (KGS) and SEPM reviewers (David Hyndman (Editor), Gary Weissmann, and an anonymous reviewer).

REFERENCES

BAINES, D., SMITH, D.G., FROESE, D.G., BAUMAN, P., AND NIMECK, G., 2002, Electrical resistivity ground imaging (ERGI): A new tool for mapping the lithology and geometry of channel-belts and valley-fills: Sedimentology, v. 49, p. 441–449.

BECK, F.P., CLARK, P.J., AND PULS, R.W., 2000, Location and characterization of subsurface anomalies using a soil conductivity probe: Groundwater Monitoring and Remediation, v. 20, no. 2, p. 55–59.

BILBREY, L.C., AND SHAFER, J.M., 2001, Funnel and gate performance in a moderately heterogeneous flow domain: Ground Water Monitoring and Remediation, v. 21, no. 3, p. 144–151.

BOHLING, G.C., 1999, Evaluation of an induced gradient tracer test: Ph.D. Dissertation, The University of Kansas, Lawrence, Kansas, 224 p.

BOWMAN, M.W., 1986, A disparity in the rate of lateral channel cutting between two reaches of the Kansas River: M.S. Thesis, The University of Kansas, Lawrence, Kansas, 247 p.

BRADY, N.C., 1984, The Nature and Properties of Soils, 9th Edition: New York, Macmillan Publishing Co., 750 p.

BURT, T.P., AND HAYCOCK, N.E., 1996, Linking hillslopes to floodplains, in Anderson, M.G., Walling, D.E., and Bates, P.D., eds., Floodplain Processes: Chichester, England, John Wiley & Sons Ltd., 496 p.

BUTLER, J.J., JR., HEALEY, J.M., ZLOTNIK, V.A., AND ZURBUCHEN., B.R., 1998, The dipole flow test for site characterization: Some practical considerations (abstract): EOS, Transactions, American Geophysical Union, v. 79, no. 17, p. S153 (Also at www.kgs. ukans.edu/Hydro/publication/OFR98_20/index.html).

BUTLER, J.J., JR., HEALEY, J.M., ZHENG, L., McCALL, W., AND SCHULMEISTER, M.K., 1999, Hydrostratigraphic characterization of unconsolidated alluvium with direct-push sensor technology (abstract): Geological Society of America, Abstracts with Program, v. 31, no. 7, p. A350 (Also at www.kgs.ukans.edu/Hydro/Publications/OFR99_40/index. html).

BUTLER, J.J., JR., ZLOTNIK, V.A., AND TSOU, M.-S., 2001, Drawdown and stream depletion produced by pumping in the vicinity of a partially penetrating stream: Ground Water, v. 39, p. 651–659.

BUTLER, J.J., JR., HEALEY, J.M., McCALL, G.W., GARNETT, E.J., AND LOHEIDE, S.P., II, 2002, Hydraulic tests with direct-push equipment: Ground Water, v. 40, p. 25–36.

CHRISTY, C.D., CHRISTY, T.M., AND WITTING, V., 1994, A percussion probing tool for the direct sensing of soil conductivity: Proceedings of the 8th National Outdoor Action Conference, Minneapolis, Minnesota, National Ground Water Association, p. 381–394.

DAVIS, G.A., CAIN, S.F., BUTLER, J.J., JR., ZHAN, X., HEALEY, J.M., AND BOHLING, G.C., 2002, A field assessment of hydraulic tomography: A new approach for characterizing spatial variations in hydraulic conductivity (abstract): Geological Society of America, Annual Meeting, Abstracts with Program, vol. 34, p. 23.

DOOLITTLE, J.A., 2001, Trip report #330-20-7, U.S. Department of Agriculture, National Resource Conservation Service, NRCS, Newton, Pennsylvania, 10 p.

EINARSON, M.D., SCHIRMER, M., PEZESHKPOUR, P., MACKAY, D.M., AND WILSON, R.D., 2000, Comparison of eight innovative site characterization tools used to investigate an MTBE plume at Site 60, Vandenberg Air Force Base, California: Proceedings of the 1999 Petroleum Hydrocarbons and Organic Chemicals in Ground Water: Prevention, Detection and Remediation Conference, p. 147–157.

FENSTEMAKER, T., HALIHAN T., AND SHARP, J.M., 2001, Using resistivity to detect movement of salinity fluids in the barrier island sediments of Padre Island (abstract): Geological Society of America, Abstracts with Programs, v. 33, no. 6, p. A-46.

FISK, N.H., 1944, Geologic Investigation of the Alluvial Valley of the Lower Mississippi River: U.S. Army Corps of Engineers, Mississippi River Commission, 78 p.

GEOPROBE SYSTEMS, 1998, Tools and Equipment Catalog, Salina, Kansas.

GOLDEN SOFTWARE, INC., 1997, Surfer, ver. 6.04: Golden, Colorado.

HAYCOCK, N.E., AND BURT, T.P., 1993, Role of floodplain sediments in reducing the nitrate concentration of subsurface run-off: A case study in Cotswolds: U.K. Hydrological Processes, v. 7, p. 287–295.

HOLIEN, C.W., 1982, Origin and geomorphic significance of channel-bar gravel of the lower Kansas River: M.S. Thesis, The University of Kansas, Lawrence, Kansas, 128 p.

HOYLE, B., 1989, Ground-water quality variations in a silty alluvial soil aquifer, Oklahoma: Ground Water, v. 27, p. 540–549.

HYNDMAN, D.W., DYBAS, M.J., FORNEY, L., HEINE, R., MAYOTTE, T., PHANIKUMAR, M.S., TATARA, G., TIEDJE, J., VOICE, T., WALLACE, R., WIGGERT, D., ZHAO, X., AND CRIDDLE, C.S., 2000, Hydraulic characterization and design of a full-scale biocurtain: Ground Water, v. 38, p. 462–474.

JIANG, X., 1991, A field and laboratory study of the scale dependence of hydraulic conductivity: M.S. Thesis, The University of Kansas, Lawrence, Kansas, 149 p.

JOHNSON, B., HOPKINS, B.W., AND McCALL, W., 1999, Direct-push electrical logging for rapid site assessment and definition of brine plumes (abstract), in Sublette, K.L., Thoma, G., and Ward, T.J., eds., Proceedings of the 6th International Petroleum Environmental Conference, Houston, Texas, Integrated Petroleum Environmental Consortium.

JOHNSON, W.C., AND LOGAN, B., 1990, Geoarchaeology of the Kansas River basin, in Lasca, N.P., ed., Archaeological geology of North America: Geological Society of America, Centennial Guidebook, v. 4, p 267–299.

JOHNSON, W.C., AND MARTIN, C.W., 1987, Holocene alluvial-stratigraphic studies from Kansas and adjoining states of the east-central Plains, in Johnson, W.C., ed., Quaternary Environments of Kansas: Kansas Geological Guidebook Series 5, p. 109–122.

KEHEW, A.E., AND BOETTGER, W.M., 1986, Depositional environments of buried-valley aquifers in North Dakota: Ground Water, v. 24, p. 728–734.

KETTLE, W.D., AND WHITTEMORE, D.O., 1991, Ecology and hydrogeology of the Kansas Ecological Reserves and the Baker University wetlands, in Kettle, W.D., and Whittemore, D.O., eds., Kansas Academy of Science Multidisciplinary Guidebook 4: Kansas Geological Survey, Open-File Report 91-35, 125 p.

KEYS, W.S., 1989, Borehole geophysics applied to groundwater investigations: USGS Techniques of Water-Resources Investigations, Book 2, Chapter E2: U.S. Geological Survey, Denver, Colorado.

KRAM, M., LIEBERMAN, S., AND JACOBS, J.A., 2000, Direct sensing of soils and groundwater, in Lehr, J., ed., Standard Handbook of Environmental Science, Health, and Technology: New York, McGraw Hill, p. 11.124–11.150.

LANGMUIR, D., 1997, Aqueous Environmental Geochemistry: Upper Saddle River, New Jersey, Prentice Hall, 561 p.

LARKIN, G.L., AND SHARP, J.M., 1992, On the relationship between river-basin geomorphology, alluvial aquifer hydraulics and ground-water flow direction in alluvial aquifers: Geological Society of America, Bulletin, v. 104, p. 1608–1620.

LOGAN, B., 1985, O-Keet-Sha; culture history and its environmental context; The archaeology of Stranger Creek basin, northeastern Kansas: Ph.D. Dissertation, University of Kansas, Lawrence, Kansas, 434 p.

LUCEY, K.J., KUZNIAR, R.L., AND CALDWELL, J.P., 1995, Hydrogeology and water quality of the Mississippi River alluvium near Muscatine, Iowa, June 1992 through June 1994: U.S. Geological Survey, Water Resource Investigations Report 95-4049, 74 p.

MANDEL, R., 1987, Geomorphology of the Wakarusa River valley, northeastern Kansas, in Logan, B., ed., Archaeological Investigations in the Clinton Lake Project Area, Northeastern Kansas: National Register Evaluation of 27 Prehistoric Sites: Kansas City, U.S. Army Corps of Engineers, p. 20–34.

MANDEL, R., 1998, The effects of Holocene climatic change on river systems in the central Great Plains (Abstract): Geological Society of America, Abstracts with Program, v. 30, p. 169.

MANDEL, R., 1999, Geomorphological Investigation of the Proposed Veterans Administration Cemetery, Fort Riley, Kansas. Prepared for Parsons Infrastructure and Technology, St. Louis, Missouri. Report submitted to Cultural Resources Division, U.S. Army Corps of Engineers, Kansas City District, Kansas City, Missouri.

McCALL, W., 1996, Electrical conductivity logging to determine control of hydrocarbon flow paths in alluvial sediments: Proceedings of the 10th National Outdoor Action Conference, Las Vegas, Nevada: National Ground Water Association, p. 461–477.

McCALL, W., AND ZIMMERMAN, P., 2000, Direct push electrical and CPT logging: An introduction: Proceedings of the Seventh International Symposium on Borehole Geophysics for Minerals, Geotechnical, and Groundwater Applications, Houston, Texas: The Minerals and Geotechnical Logging Society–Society of Professional Well Log Analysts, p. 103–114.

McCALL, W., BUTLER, J.J, JR., HEALEY, J.M., LANIER, A.A., SELLWOOD, S.M., AND GARNETT, E.J., 2002, A dual-tube method for vertical profiling of hydraulic conductivity in unconsolidated formations: Environmental and Engineering Geoscience, v. 8, no. 2, p. 75–84.

McNEILL, J.D., 1980, Electromagnetic terrain conductivity measurements at low induction numbers: Geonics Ltd., Mississauga, Ontario, Technical Note TN-6, 15 p.

NATIONAL RESEARCH COUNCIL, 1994, Alternatives for Ground Water Cleanup: National Academy Press, 315 p.

O'CONNOR, H.G., 1960, Geology and ground-water resources of Douglas County, Kansas: Kansas Geological Survey, Bulletin 148, 200 p.

PRYOR, W.A., 1973, Permeability–porosity patterns and variations in some Holocene sand bodies: American Association of Petroleum Geologists, Bulletin, v. 57, p. 162–189.

SCHOENEBERGER, P.J., WYSOCKI, D.A., BENHAM, E.C., AND BRODERSON, W.D., 1998, Field Book for Describing and Sampling Soils. Ver 1.1: Natural Resources Conservation Service, U.S.D.A., National Soil Survey Center, Lincoln, Nebraska.

SCHON, J.H., 1996, Physical properties of rocks: Fundamentals and principles of petrophysics, in Helbig, K., and Treitel, S, eds., Handbook of Geophysical Exploration 18: White Plains, New York, Elsevier Science, Inc., 529 p.

SCHULMEISTER, M.K., 2000, Hydrology and geochemistry of a floodplain margin: Ph.D. Dissertation, The University of Kansas, Lawrence, Kansas, 132 p.

SCHULMEISTER, M.K., BUTLER, J.J., JR., HEALEY, J.M, ZHENG, L., WYSOCKI, D.A., AND McCALL, G.W., 2003a, Direct-push electrical conductivity for high-resolution hydrostratigraphic characterization: Ground Water Monitoring & Remediation, v. 23, no. 3, p. 52–63.

SCHULMEISTER, M.K, HEALEY, J.M., McCALL, G.W., BIRK, S., AND BUTLER, J.J., JR., 2003b, High-resolution characterization of chemical heterogeneity in an alluvial aquifer, in Kovar, K., ed., Modelcare 2002: Calibration and Reliability in Groundwater Modelling: A Few Steps Closer to Reality: Wallingford, UK, International Association of Hydrological Sciences, Publication 277, p. 419–423.

SELLWOOD, S.M., 2001, A direct-push method of hydrostratigraphic characterization: M.S. Thesis, The University of Kansas, Lawrence, Kansas, 87 p.

SHARP, J.M., 1988, Hydrogeology of alluvial aquifers, in Back, W., Rosenshein J.S., and Seaber, P.R., eds., Hydrogeology: Geological Society of America, Geology of North America, v. O–2, p. 273–282.

SORENSON, C.J., SALLEE, K.H., AND MANDEL, R.D., 1987, Holocene and Pleistocene soils and geomorphic surfaces of the Kansas River valley, in Johnson, W.C., ed., Quaternary Environments of Kansas: Kansas Geological Survey, Guidebook Series 5, 208 p.

SUDICKY, E.A., AND HUYAKORN, P.S., 1991, Contaminant migration in imperfectly known heterogeneous groundwater systems, U.S. National Report of the International Union of Geologists and Geophysicists, 1987–1990: Reviews in Geophysics, v. 29, p. 240–253.

TILLMAN, N., AND LEONARD, L., 1993, Vehicle mounted direct push systems, sampling tools and case histories: An overview of an emerging technology, in Proceedings of the 1993 Meeting on Petroleum Hydrocarbons and Organic Chemicals in Ground Water: Prevention, Detection, and Restoration: Ground Water Management, v. 17, p. 177–188.

U.S. DEPARTMENT OF AGRICULTURE, 1996, Soil Survey Laboratory Methods Manual: Soil Survey Investigations Report 32, Version 3, 693 p.

U.S. ENVIRONMENTAL PROTECTION AGENCY, 2000, Innovations in site characterization: Geophysical investigations at hazardous waste sites: EPA-542-R-00-003. Washington D.C: U.S. EPA Technology Innovation Office.

WEISSMANN, G.S., AND FOGG, G.E., 1999, Multi-scale alluvial fan heterogeneity modeled with transition probability geostatistics in a sequence stratigraphic framework: Journal of Hydrology, v. 226, p. 48–65.

PRESENCE OF PREFERENTIAL FLOW PATHS IN SHALLOW GROUNDWATER SYSTEMS AS INDICATED BY TRACER EXPERIMENTS AND GEOPHYSICAL SURVEYS

MURRAY E. CLOSE

Institute of Environmental Science and Research, P.O. Box 29181, Christchurch, New Zealand
e-mail: murray.close@esr.cri.nz

DAVID C. NOBES

Department of Geological Sciences, University of Canterbury, Private Bag 4800, Christchurch, New Zealand
e-mail: david.nobes@canterbury.ac.nz

AND

LIPING PANG

Institute of Environmental Science and Research, P.O. Box 29181, Christchurch, New Zealand
e-mail: liping.pang@esr.cri.nz

ABSTRACT: Preferential flow paths in shallow groundwater systems can be characterized by intensive tracer experiments, but these are expensive and time consuming to carry out. Geophysical surveys, such as ground-penetrating radar (GPR), have also been used to detect the presence of preferential flow paths in these systems, but the results have rarely been compared. Tracer experiments and GPR surveys were combined in two shallow alluvial gravel aquifer systems to better detect the presence of, and characterize, shallow groundwater. The two groundwater systems had differing hydraulic conductivities, dispersivities, and degrees of heterogeneity.

Aquifer parameters (flow velocity, hydraulic conductivity, dispersivity) were derived from the tracer data using the method of temporal moments. Preferential flow paths were inferred using data on tracers and pesticide concentrations. The radar image showed preferential flow paths with trends similar to those identified from the tracer experiments and pesticide leaching trials. The combination of these techniques increased the confidence in the final interpretation.

INTRODUCTION AND BACKGROUND

Preferential flow paths in groundwater systems are often associated with heterogeneous media, such as fractures, old river channels, and layers or lenses of media having contrasting permeabilities. Water and contaminants are transported much more rapidly in these zones, sometimes causing unexpectedly rapid arrival of contamination down-gradient. They may also cause significant divergence of the flow direction on a local scale if the preferential flow paths are orientated differently than the regional flow direction, resulting in breakthrough at unexpected locations. As a reflection of the important role that preferential flow can play in the transport of contaminants, the characterization of preferential flow paths has been the subject of increasing research interest.

A number of studies have been reported on the characterization of preferential flow paths for groundwater systems (for example, Ptak and Teutsch, 1994; Donovan and Frysinger, 1997; Pang et al., 1998). A number of methods can be used in characterization of the effects of preferential flow paths in groundwater systems, such as multi-level slug tests (Melville et al., 1991), multi-level borehole dilution tests (Freeze and Cherry, 1979), borehole flow meters (Molz et al., 1989; Young, 1995), and natural- and forced-gradient tracer experiments (Ptak and Teutsch, 1994; Pang et al., 1998). Except for tracer experiments, the above methods are limited to being used in single wells and hence give information for a limited aquifer volume. They are used mostly for vertical characterization of variability in permeability. Tracer tests give good information on spatial variability of permeability over a larger scale but require multiple monitoring wells and hence are very expensive and time consuming to carry out.

Many geophysical surveys do not require the installation of arrays of monitoring wells and hence have the potential to assess the presence and orientation of preferential flow paths in shallow groundwater systems in a rapid, non-invasive and cost-effective manner. Traditionally, variations in the electrical properties, as measured using electrical resistivity and electromagnetic (EM) methods, have been used to delineate changes in the water content and water quality, and thus have been used in tracer experiments (e.g., White, 1988). However, electrical and electromagnetic methods yield only approximate estimates of the depths of the tracers, as inferred from the particular resistivity electrode or EM coil separations and frequencies. Ground-penetrating radar (GPR), on the other hand, yields an image of the variations in subsurface physical properties both as a function of surface location and as a function of depth (Davis and Annan, 1989). GPR has been used as a tool in characterization of preferential flow paths (Steenhuis et al., 1990; Rea and Knight, 1998). It does not measure hydraulic properties but rather responds to changes in the dielectric properties of the subsurface. Conceptually, one could transform dielectric properties to hydraulic properties because they can in some instances be related (Rea and Knight, 1998). On the basis of this concept, we strive herein to use the information extracted from the GPR data to describe spatial heterogeneity and preferential flow paths of the subsurface.

Preferential flow paths are particularly important in fractured-rock, karst, and alluvial-gravel groundwater systems. Flow velocities can vary by an order of magnitude within such systems. This study focuses on alluvial-gravel systems, which are widespread in many parts of New Zealand, and constitute a major aquifer type in the country. They are a valuable source of water supply, but they are vulnerable to groundwater contamination because they are highly conductive and are often overlain only by thin layers of recent soils. The variations in permeability which result in the formation of these preferential flow channels arise from the sorting and deposition patterns associated with meandering gravel-bed rivers. Tracer studies carried out in alluvial-gravel systems in New Zealand have shown flow divergence from the regional piezometric flow direction on a local scale (10–100 m). Thorpe et al. (1982), in a study of the Heretaunga Plains aquifers, observed sharp curvature (greater than 30 degrees) over 10–20 m and divergence from the direction indicated by the regional piezometric maps of about 30 degrees over a distance of about 120 m. They observed gentle curvature of flow lines at this scale, consistent with buried river channels. Pang et al. (1988), in an intensive tracer study on the Central Plains aquifer in Canterbury, observed similar curvature of preferential flow paths over a scale of 20–90 m.

In this study, we selected two alluvial-gravel aquifer systems of contrasting hydraulic conductivities and dispersivities to conduct our investigation into the existence of preferential flow paths using multiple data types. The sites were associated with field trials of pesticide leaching (Close et al., 1999). This paper reports on the use of natural-gradient tracer experiments, data from the pesticide-leaching trials, and GPR surveys to identify and characterize preferential flow paths in these two groundwater systems, and to assess the usefulness of geophysical surveys in these investigations.

CHARACTERIZATION AND EXPERIMENTS

Field Sites

Two field sites, Te Awa and Twyford, are located about 11 km apart in Hawkes Bay, North Island of New Zealand. Alluvial gravels appear at the Te Awa site at 1 m depth, overlain by free-draining coarse sand and sandy gravels, whereas alluvial gravels appear at the Twyford site at 3 m depth overlain by mainly fine sandy loam with layers of fine sands and silt loam. Gravels were derived from graywacke sandstone. The Te Awa site is part of the main Heretaunga Unconfined Aquifer, which consists of heterogeneous mixture of coarse gravels and sands with occasional lenses of silt and clay binding the gravels, and extends to a depth of 30 m below ground surface (Thorpe et al., 1982). The aquifer of the Twyford site is a local perched unconfined system, with more fine materials. Borelogs from the monitoring wells were obtained during installation to give more detailed information at each site.

The location and layout of wells are shown in Figure 1A for the Te Awa site and in Figure 1B for the Twyford site. Each site consisted of 10 monitoring wells, with one well located up-gradient of the area used for pesticide application at each site (N1, T1; not shown in Fig. 1), one well located within the application area (N2, T2), and the rest down-gradient. All the wells were constructed of PVC and had a diameter of 50 mm. Wells N3, N7, and N8 at the Te Awa site and T5, T7, and T8 at the Twyford site were 8 m deep and were screened between 4 and 8 m. The rest of the wells were 7 m deep and were screened between 3 and 7 m. Groundwater levels varied between 3.5 to 5.2 m below ground levels. The local flow direction was approximately northeast-ward at the Te Awa site and northward at the Twyford site.

Tracer Experiments

In order to determine groundwater flow direction and to characterize the groundwater dispersion process, groundwater tracer experiments were carried out at both sites during August–September 1993 and January–March 1995. At the time of the 1993 experiment, N9, N10, T9, and T10 had not been installed, and these wells were located on the basis of the results from the 1993 tracer experiments. A few liters (5 and 3 liters in the 1993 and 1995 experiments, respectively) of 20% rhodamine WT (RWT) were injected into wells T2 and N2, which were located in the center of the pesticide plots. RWT was used as a nonretarded tracer to

indicate groundwater flow, because experiments in a similar alluvial-gravel aquifer near Christchurch, New Zealand, had indicated that it is not retarded in these systems (Pang et al., 1998). The injection interval for the tracer solution was from 0.5 m below water table to the bottom of the screen (7 m bgl), and the tracer was injected using a perforated hose along this length. The injection took several minutes. The groundwater levels at the injection wells of both sites were about 4.5 m and 4.84 m below ground level for the 1993 and 1995 experiment, respectively.

All the down-gradient wells were sampled at approximately 0.5 m below water table. Samples were collected using either a 12 V Amazon submersible pump or Manning automatic samplers. The RWT samples were analyzed using a spectrofluorimeter with an excitation wavelength of 543 nm and an emission wavelength of 573 nm.

Groundwater velocity (v) and longitudinal dispersivity (α_x) at each well were estimated from the concentration breakthrough curve (BTC) of RWT, based on a modified method of time moments for a three-dimensional problem (Goltz and Roberts, 1987):

$$v = \frac{\left(x^2 + \frac{\alpha_x y^2}{\alpha_y} + \frac{\alpha_x z^2}{\alpha_z} \right)^{\frac{1}{2}}}{\mu_1} \tag{1}$$

$$\alpha_x = \frac{\left(\mu_2 - \mu_1^2 \right) v}{2\mu_1} \tag{2}$$

in which

$$\mu_1 = \frac{\int_0^\infty t\, c(x, y, z, t)\, dt}{\int_0^\infty c(x, y, z, t)\, dt} \tag{3}$$

$$\mu_2 = \frac{\int_0^\infty t^2\, c(x, y, z, t)\, dt}{\int_0^\infty c(x, y, z, t)\, dt} \tag{4}$$

where x is the longitudinal distance along the flowline; y and z are the horizontal and vertical offsets from the main flowline, respectively; α_x, α_y, and α_z are the dispersivities in the x, y, and z directions, respectively; μ_1 and μ_2 are the standardized first and second moments, respectively; c is the concentration; and t is the time since injection.

The main flowline (and consequently the y offset values) was defined from the maximum dye concentrations through each array. The z value was set as zero, because wells were sampled at a depth similar to the injection depth. Values of μ_1 and μ_2 were estimated from the numerical integration of the BTC using the trapezoidal rule. The α_x/α_y ratios were taken as 4 for the Te Awa site (Heretaunga Unconfined Aquifer) and 20 for the Twyford site (perched aquifer) from Pang and Close (2000). They determined these ratios with a curve-fitting approach using a three-dimensional solute transport model, AT123D (Yeh, 1981).

If v is known, the hydraulic conductivity (K) of the aquifer media can then be calculated from aquifer hydraulic gradient (I) and effective porosity (η) using the Darcy equation:

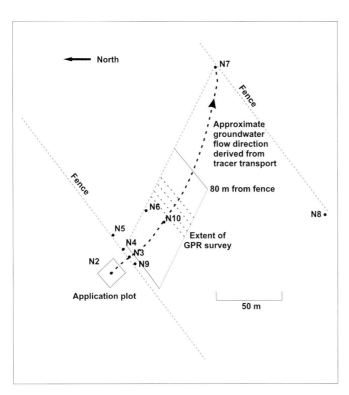
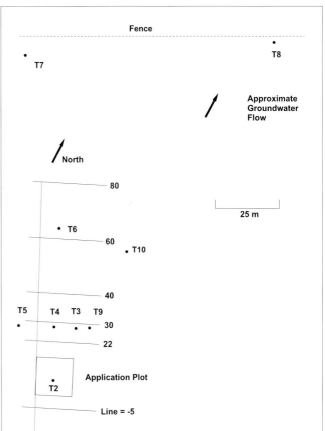

FIG. 1.—**A)** Location of wells at the Te Awa experimental site. The preferential flowline (bold dashed line) was inferred using the maximum RWT concentrations from the tracer experiments. Profiles were acquired parallel to the fence, with one end of each 30 m line on the N4-N6-N7 baseline. The extent of the GPR survey is shown as a parallelogram. The locations of the profiles at 45, 50, 55, and 60 m from the fence, shown in Figure 9, are indicated. **B)** Location of wells at the Twyford experimental site. The approximate flowline is indicated using the maximum RWT concentrations from the tracer experiments. The labeled lines were used for the GPR surveys. The survey origin is at the SW corner of the application plot.

$$K = \frac{vI}{\eta} \qquad (5)$$

An η value of 0.25 was adopted from Thorpe et al. (1982) as typical of the alluvial gravel aquifers at the study sites.

Pesticide Leaching Trials

Bromide, as a conservative tracer, and several pesticides, including picloram, were applied at the ground surface to an area 15 m by 15 m at each site (Figure 1) in November 1993. Their movement was monitored at each site through the soil profile using suction cups, and into the groundwater using the monitoring wells. At the end of the study period at each site (January 1996 for the Te Awa site and February 1997 for the Twyford site), irrigation was intensively applied over several days to create a pulse of leaching. The wells were monitored intensively to establish the relationship between the unsaturated zone and the groundwater for use in model calibration. This relationship was modeled and discussed by Pang et al. (2000). These data on groundwater concentration of bromide and picloram were used for this study in combination with tracer experimental data to indicate the

existence of preferential flow paths. There were only a small number of down-gradient wells, and therefore the precision of the flow direction down-gradient is low. However, the relative concentrations observed in the wells, particularly N3 and N7 for the groundwater tracer experiments, can be used to assist in the determination of flow direction. Further details of the pesticide leaching study are given in Close et al. (1999) and Pang et al. (2000).

Acquisition and Processing of Geophysical Data

Two complementary geophysical methods were used at both sites to assist the detection of the spatial patterns of preferential flow paths: a shallow horizontal-loop EM (HLEM) survey using a Geonics EM31™, and a GPR survey using a Sensors & Software pulseEKKO IV™ system. The geophysics surveys were carried out in 1996, after the dye-tracing experiments, and while the pesticide leaching trial was still in progress. Because the electrical properties are a major influence on the attenuation of GPR signals, electrical or EM surveys should be carried out in advance of GPR surveys so that potential problems in near-surface signal attenuation can be identified (Theimer et al., 1994). The EM surveys indicated that no conductive attenuation problems for GPR were likely. The EM responses (Nobes, 1996) were primarily from the vadose zone, and thus are not reported or discussed here.

GPR records were acquired in common-offset mode every 20 cm along each 100 MHz GPR survey line (Fig. 1). In this mode, the transmitting and receiving antennas were fixed at a constant separation, in this case 1 m, and were stepped along the survey line at fixed increments of 20 cm. The radar record consists of three components (Fig. 2): the direct air wave arrives first, traveling at 300 m/μs (30 cm/ns), and provides a timing reference for the record, what is called the "time zero"; the direct ground wave arrives next, traveling at a velocity that is characteristic of the ground immediately in contact with the antennas, thus providing a ground surface reference; and then any reflections (subsurface or otherwise) arrive at later travel times. The radar records are gathered into profiles, and the radar echoes returned are plotted as a function of the two-way travel time (TWT).

The GPR record spacing is governed by the resolution of the signal in the near-surface, which in turn depends on the velocity of the radar signal in the ground and the central frequency of the radar pulse. At the Te Awa site, the lateral variations in the physical properties were difficult to correlate between survey lines, and a second suite of GPR survey lines was completed the next day, placed every 10 m starting 5 m out from the edge of the tracer injection location. The two suites of GPR lines were then merged to form a set of survey lines spaced 5 m apart. A suite of more detailed 200 MHz survey lines were also acquired near the injection wells for both experiments, but the radar signals did not penetrate past the water table and provided little information except for data on shallow stratigraphy. Thus at the Twyford site the GPR survey lines extended from 5 m up-gradient from the application area to 80 m down-gradient (Fig. 1B), and at the Te Awa site, GPR survey lines extended from 5 to 80 m from the fence at 5 m intervals. Only the orientation of the survey lines and the 80 m line are shown in Fig. 1A, to avoid unnecessary clutter.

In addition to the common-offset survey mode, common mid-point (CMP) surveys were carried out near the test plots (where the corelogs were obtained) in order to estimate the variations in the radar velocity with depth. This allowed us both to convert the TWT to an approximate depth, and also to determine what subsurface layering was apparent in the velocity analysis. An average velocity is also used to migrate the profiles, which collapses subsurface scattering events and places dipping reflectors in their correct positions. Radar migration is fairly robust to minor changes in the subsurface velocity, of the order of 10–15% (Jol, personal communication, 2003), and thus using the average velocity in this study was appropriate.

CMPs were carried out for two antenna frequencies, 100 and 200 MHz, at each site. In this mode, the transmitting and receiving antennas were stepped out at regular increments from a central point along a survey line. The travel time for both direct air and ground waves and for subsurface reflections increases, and the rate of increase in travel time with antenna separation is used to give an estimate of the subsurface radar velocity (Fig. 3). In addition, there are a number of air-wave refractions, which occur when energy from the ground can critically refract in the air along the surface of the ground (Bohidar and Hermance, 2002). These refractions do not provide any additional information about the stratigraphy and are not used in the velocity analysis. Individual reflectors were evaluated in Gradix™ using both semblance analysis (Hatton et al., 1986; Sheriff, 1991), which is a measure of the power of a reflection event as a function of the velocity, and curve fitting. The results are similar, but the curve fitting, which is illustrated schematically in Figure 3, yields results with less uncertainty. The common-offset profiles also provide stratigraphic information, in the sense that the phase of the event (a positive or negative echo) is indicative of a change in the radar velocity, which in turn is indicative of a change in lithology and an associated change in water content. The nature of the change in lithology or water content is determined in relation to the known site lithology. The CMPs can also be correlated with the radar

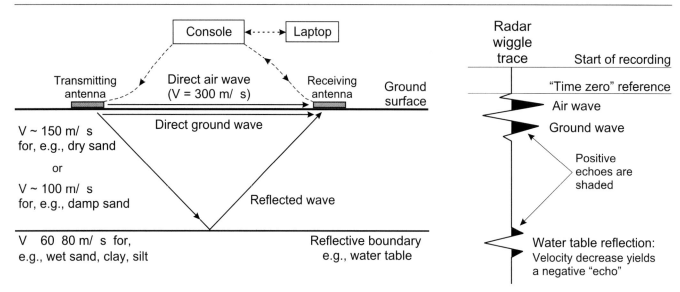

FIG. 2.—The basic aspects of ground-penetrating radar are illustrated. A console (top, center left) connects a laptop and the radar antennas. A transmitting antenna (top left) sends out a radar pulse. A receiving antenna (top center) detects the direct air and ground waves, and any subsurface echoes, such as from the water table. Received signals are stored in the laptop. Each record is displayed as a "wiggle trace" (right), containing direct and reflected waves. Normally, positive echoes are shaded and negative echoes are not. The air wave arrives first, acting as a time reference ("time zero"). The ground wave provides a "ground surface" reference.

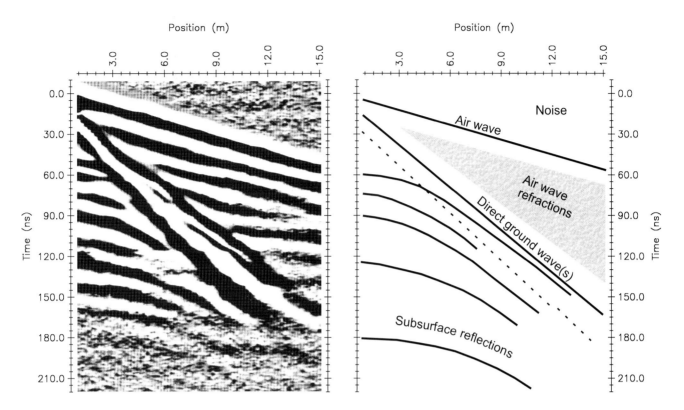

FIG. 3.—As part of a central mid-point (CMP) survey, transmitting and receiving radar antennas are stepped out from a central point. We obtain the velocity structure with depth from the curved subsurface reflections. The change in radar velocity is correlated primarily with water content but also with changes in lithology, especially grain-size variations. The main components of the CMP in the left-hand panel are identified in the right-hand panel. The velocities are obtained primarily from curve fitting and by correlation with the common-offset profiles, as described in the text.

profiles, so that CMP events can be assigned to events in the radar profiles. This helps isolate multiples and confirm velocity increases and decreases using the phases of the reflections in the common-offset record.

The GPR results were stored as individual profiles and can be either displayed in that fashion or gathered into a three-dimensional (3D) data cube (e.g., Fig. 4, for the Te Awa data set). Such a data cube can then be viewed from a variety of angles, and the continuity of a reflector or of a particular target, e.g., the water table or a subsurface channel, can be followed from line to line across the site. Before the GPR data are collated in the 3D data cube, each profile must be corrected for any drift in the time reference, the "time zero"; the time references must be aligned from profile to profile; noise reduction can be carried out; and the data are migrated, as described earlier. The dominant "noise" in GPR records is due to the interaction of the transmitting and receiving antennas. The receiving antenna tends to saturate with signal over time, which results in a low-frequency (long-period) increase in the background radar energy with time, which is called "wow". Thus, our steps in processing are: 1, dewow; 2, time zero adjustment for each profile; 3, alignment of the time zero from profile to profile; and 4, migration of the profiles, which was useful only for the Te Awa profiles, because of the absence of subsurface channels or diffractions in the Twyford profiles. Finally, gain functions are applied to the profiles to enhance the presentation of the radar reflectors and thus aid the analysis and interpretation of the GPR data. In our case, the features of interest, subsurface preferential flow paths, lie below the water table. The

water table is a strong event, and the radar energy reflected from beds above the water table is much stronger than the energy reflected from beds below the water table. Thus, a special gain function was designed to amplify the reflections from below the water table. The gain (amplification factor) increases slowly with time (depth) down to the water table, at which point the gain increases in a large step to allow for the significant reflection of energy from the water table and the consequent decrease in reflection strength below the water table. The processed profiles were then gathered into the 3D radar cube shown in Figure 4. This last step was not done for the Twyford data, because the profiles revealed simple layered sequences, with little lateral variation that would benefit from such an approach.

RESULTS AND DISCUSSION

Tracer Experiments and Leaching Trials

During the 1993 experiments, significant concentrations of RWT were detected in N3, N6, and N7 at the Te Awa site, and T3 and T8 at the Twyford site (Fig. 5A, Table 1). Only traces of RWT were found in other wells. The contrasting dye concentrations in adjacent wells indicate very low dispersivities and possibly the presence of preferred flowpaths. On the basis of the experimental results, N9, N10, T9, and T10 were installed.

During the 1995 experiments, RWT was detected in N3, N7, N10, T3, T8, T9, and T10 (Fig. 5B, Table 1). Traces of the dye were detected in N4, N5, and N6, and no dye was found in the rest of

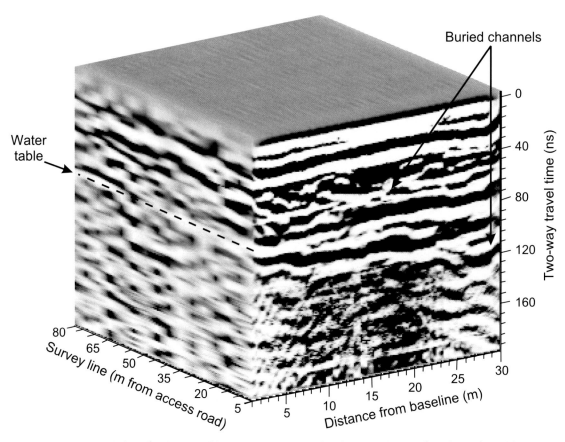

Fɪɢ. 4.—Te Awa GPR 3D Data Cube. The GPR profiles at Te Awa were closely spaced enough to be gathered into a coarse three-dimensional (3D) data cube for additional interpretation and analysis.

the wells. The dye concentrations were highest in N3, N10, and N7 at the Te Awa site, and T3, T9, T10, and T8 at the Twyford site. On the basis of the tracer arrivals, we interpret that these wells are along or close to the main flowline. Note that N3 is slightly off the main flowline, because dye concentrations in N3 and N10 were similar (Fig. 5B) but N10 is much farther downgradient. However, there was insufficient information to determine the offset accurately. In 1993 the maximum observed concentration in N7 (19.6 µg/l) was greater than that observed in N3 (15.8 µg/l), although N7 was 130 m farther down-gradient (Table 1). Modeling of the concentrations observed in the wells in 1993 indicated that N7 is on or very close to the flowline. This indicates that the flowline curved around towards N7 after flowing towards N10 (in 1995 there was an incomplete BTC for N7; Fig. 5B). The curvature in the flowline (Fig. 1A) indicates that there were zones of preferential flow at the Te Awa site. The sharp rise in RWT concentration in T3 in 1995 (Fig. 5B) was probably because the sampling tube was lowered by 0.4 m 10 days after the RWT injection. This was because the water level had fallen by 0.2 m over the 10 day period and the sampling tube in this well had been positioned too close to the water table. The dye had been injected from 0.5 to about 2 m below the water table, as noted earlier.

The maximum concentrations of bromide and picloram observed in each well from the pesticide leaching trials are also given in Table 1. There is a good relationship between the concentrations observed in N2, at the center of the application area, and N10, approximately 50 m down-gradient. The frequency of sampling for N3 and N9 was not sufficient, and the peak concentration was missed in these wells. Relatively low bromide concentrations were observed relative to picloram because most of the bromide had leached from the profile at the time of the intensive irrigation at the end of the study, whereas significant picloram was still present in the profile. The results of intensive irrigation from the Twyford are consistent with the results of the groundwater tracing experiment, with a steady decrease in concentrations down-gradient. Both the intensive-irrigation results and the tracer experiments indicate that T10 is slightly off the flowline because concentrations were less in T10 than in T8, which is 80 m farther down-gradient.

Aquifer parameters estimated from the method of moments (Equations 1–5) for the well-defined BTCs are listed in Table 2. The velocity estimated from the method of moments considers the whole distribution of a BTC. Aquifer parameters estimated from tracer data are generally consistent between experiments. An exception is the dispersivity values for T3. Some of the difference may be because the sampling for T3 was stopped too soon after the peak for the 1995, which truncated the BTC, and the sharpness of the BTC for 1995 was affected by the lowering of the sampling tube. Thus the dispersivity for 1993 of 2.8 m would be more reliable. The estimated overall groundwater velocities through the wells range from 3.9 to 11.0 m/day (median = 8.5 m/day) for the Te Awa site and from 1.4 to 4.9 m/day (median = 3.1 m/day) for the Twyford site. The estimates of v and K for N3 are lower than the rest of the estimates for the Te Awa site; this is probably because the well was assumed to be on the flowline

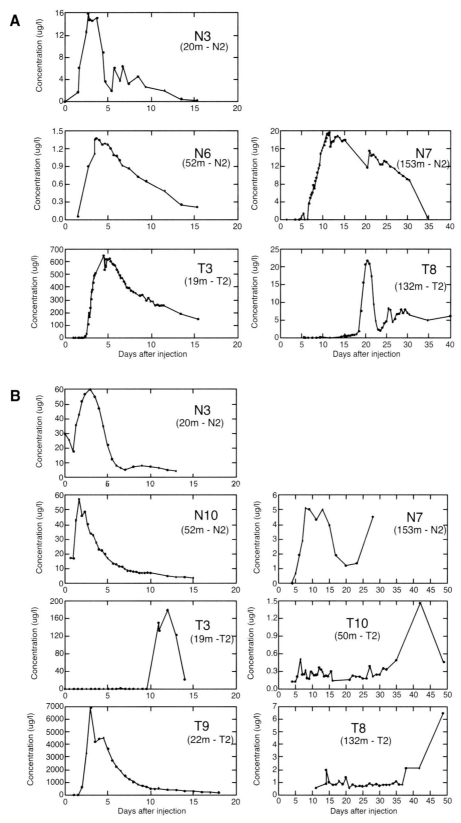

FIG. 5.—**A)** Observed concentrations of RWT in monitoring wells during the tracer experiments in 1993. Wells N3, N6, and N7 are from the Te Awa site, and wells T3 and T8 are from the Twyford site. **B)** Observed concentrations of RWT in monitoring wells during the tracer experiments in 1995. Wells N3, N10 and N7 are from the Te Awa site, and wells T3, T9, T10, and T8 are from the Twyford site.

TABLE 1.—Maximum concentrations of tracers and pesticides observed in each well for tracing experiments and for the intensive irrigation in the pesticide leaching trial.

Te Awa Site

Well	Distance from well 2 (m)	RWT Tracer – 1993 (mg/l)	RWT Tracer – 1995 (mg/l)	Intensive irrigation – Br (mg/l)	Intensive irrigation – picloram (mg/l)
N2	0	na	na	0.4	76
N9	20	na	< 0.01	0.1	0.4
N3	20	15.8	60	0*	0.3*
N4	22	< 0.02	0.05	0	0
N5	27	< 0.02	0.03	na	na
N10	52	na	57	0.1	28
N6	52	1.4	0.4	na	na
N8	161	< 0.02	na	na	na
N7	153	19.6	5.1*	na	na

Twyford Site

Well	Distance from well 2 (m)	RWT Tracer – 1993 (mg/l)	RWT Tracer – 1995 (mg/l)	Intensive irrigation – Br (mg/l)	Intensive irrigation – picloram (mg/l)
T2	0	na	na	4.4	250
T9	22	na	6936	1.7	68
T3	19	650	179	1.2	49
T4	17	< 0.2	< 0.2	0.1	na
T5	21	< 0.2	< 0.2	na	na
T10	50	na	1.5*	0.1	0
T6	50	< 0.15	< 0.2	na	na
T8	132	21.8	> 6.5*	0.2	2
T7	108	< 0.15	na	na	na

Note: na = not analyzed.   * peak concentration missed

---

when it was not, as discussed above. The groundwater velocities were slightly higher in 1995 compared to 1993 at the Te Awa site, consistent with the change in hydraulic gradient. At the Twyford site the hydraulic gradient was lower in 1995 than in 1993, and the groundwater velocities were also lower. The values for the Te Awa site are similar to the typical velocity range of 5–20 m/day reported by Thorpe et al. (1982) for the Heretaunga Unconfined Aquifer.

Multiple peaks were observed in the BTCs associated with wells T3, T8, N3, and N7 (Fig. 5), indicating multiple pathways of different permeabilities in the groundwater systems. Travel times for the peak concentrations were used to estimate velocities of the individual pathways. Table 3 shows that flow velocities through individual flow paths for a well can vary by a factor of between 1.3 and > 3.7. Approximately the same velocity ratio for N3 was observed for similar peaks between experiments (Table 3), which

---

TABLE 2.—Hydraulic conductivity and dispersivity estimated from the method of moments.

Parameter	Symbol	Units	Year	Te Awa site					Twyford site				
				N3	N10	N6	N7	Median	T3	T9	T10	T8	Median
Distance from injection well	x	m		20	53	49	161		19	22	51	138	
Offset from mean flowline	y	m		0.0*	0.0	15.8	0.0		4.5	0.0	0.0	0.0	
Hydraulic gradient	I		1993				0.0011					0.0018	
			1995				0.0013					0.0015	
Groundwater velocity	v	m/day	1993	3.9		8.4	8.6		3.5			4.9	
			1995	4.9	11.0		9.3	8.5	2.3	2.8	1.4	3.4	3.1
Hydraulic conductivity	K	m/day	1993	890		1910	1950		490			675	
			1995	935	2110		1790	1850	385	460	240	560	475
Dispersivity	a$_x$	m	1993	3.7			7.8	10.8		2.8			5.5	
			1995	5.0	14.6		16.5	9.3	0.1	10.5	3.2	5.3	4.3

Note: Median values are obtained from data of both tracer experiments
* - y offset for N3 may not be accurate as described in text
Hydraulic gradient is calculated between wells N2 and N7 for Te Awa and between T2 and T8 for Twyford.

TABLE 3.—Groundwater velocities through flow paths indicated by the multiple peaks in tracing experiments.

Well	Time to Peak (days)	Peak Concentration (mg/l)	Distance (m)	Velocity (m/day)	Velocity ratio
1 – Te Awa site					
N3-1993 experiment	2.7	15.8	20.2	7.5	
	6.7	6.3	20.2	3.0	2.5
N3-1995 experiment	3.0	60.0	20.2	6.7	
	9.0	8.3	20.2	2.2	3.0
N7- 1995 experiment	8.0	5.1	161.4	20.2	
	> 28.0	> 4.5	161.4	< 5.5	> 3.7
2 – Twyford site					
T8-1993 experiment	20.0	20.7	137.5	6.9	
	25.5	8.3	137.5	5.4	1.3
	29.5	8.1	137.5	4.7	1.5

indicates that the same pattern of multiple pathways was encountered in both experiments. The more permeable flow path had the higher observed tracer concentration on both occasions. Breaks in sampling patterns for some wells (e.g., N7) meant that more multiple peaks might have been distinguishable had sampling been more continuous. Multiple tracer peaks in wells have been observed in similar hydrogeological settings by Pang et al. (1998) and were associated with highly preferential flow paths that were also significantly curved at the 20–40 m scale.

Because the tracer experiments involved injection from a well (point source), it was not surprising that the tracer plume was detected in only one of the wells located approximately 20 m downgradient, because the nearest wells in the direction perpendicular to the flow at that distance were 5–10 m away. However, for the pesticide trial, the source area was 15 m by 15 m and yet the plume was still detected only in wells N3 and N9, and was not detected at all in N4, which was only 10 m away. The breakthrough pattern indicates that the flow line was both quite restricted and curved, moving first in a south-southeastward direction and then in a more southeastward direction, as schematically indicated in Figure 1A. Thus the groundwater observations from the pesticide trial emphasize the presence of preferential flow paths at the Te Awa site. At the Twyford site the higher concentrations were observed in T9, which was the easternmost well, and thus indicates only direction of flow and not restriction of the flow path. The indicated flow direction is approximately linear and not curved as it is at the Te Awa site.

Geophysical Data Interpretation

As noted earlier, both 100 and 200 MHz CMPs were acquired, and the results were combined. The 200 MHz CMP results provide the detailed shallow stratigraphy when correlated with corelog records. The Te Awa and Twyford radar stratigraphies (Fig. 6) correlate in general with core results and with observations of the water table made during the period of the geophysical surveys. The water table was different when the core logging was done. The Te Awa CMP results indicate the presence of a lower-velocity sequence down to about 1 m, which correlates with the pumice sand alluvium found from coring. Below this are gravels, which from the CMP results have varying amounts of finer material and varying degrees of saturation, as discussed earlier.

The water table appears to have coincided at the time of the survey with a change in lithology to more consolidated sands and gravels, so that the velocity does not decrease significantly, as would have been expected. The Twyford velocities, of the order of 80 m/µs (8 cm/ns), are generally lower than at Te Awa, where the average velocity is approximately 90–92 m/µs (9.0 to 9.2 cm/ns) down to the target depths, consistent with the higher silt content observed at Twyford. The transition from silts to gravels observed in the CMP results correlates well with the transition from layered silt loams and sandy loams to gravels observed in the cores.

The CMP results represent the broad layering present at the Te Awa and Twyford sites. Single profiles from Te Awa (Fig. 7) and Twyford (Fig. 8) also show this general layering but also indicate the presence or absence of lateral subsurface variability. The Te Awa profile, taken 80 m from the access road, has some indications of buried channels at a number of depths, whereas the Twyford profile is strongly layered, with little lateral variability. This single Twyford profile is representative of all of the Twyford profiles, which suggests that there is little lateral variability except over a large scale, of the order of tens to hundreds of meters. There are reflections from the boundary fence on the western margin of the site and from one of the sampling wells. There is also a layer at about 45 ns TWT (about 2 m depth) which contains numerous diffractions that are characteristic of this layer, but the changes in depth and thickness are small, of the order of tens of centimeters or less over a lateral extent of tens of meters, and are not significant. The Twyford profile is dominated by the water-table reflection, and also has a subtle banding that may be due to multiple reflections between the water table and deeper layers, but the overall result shows layering with little lateral variation. This is consistent with the tracer test results that indicate simple diffusive flow.

If we focus on a set of four profiles from Te Awa, gathered over a range of 15 m and migrated using an average velocity of 9 cm/ns, we can see the presence of a buried channel, or set of channels, just below the water table (Fig. 9). The channel is present in all profiles, but in these four we can track a portion of the movement where the channel bifurcates. It lies initially to the northern (left-hand) end of the surveys (Fig. 9A, 45 m from access road) but has broadened and shifted slightly southward (to the center, Fig. 9B, 50 m). At 55 m (Fig. 9C) the channel appears to be developing

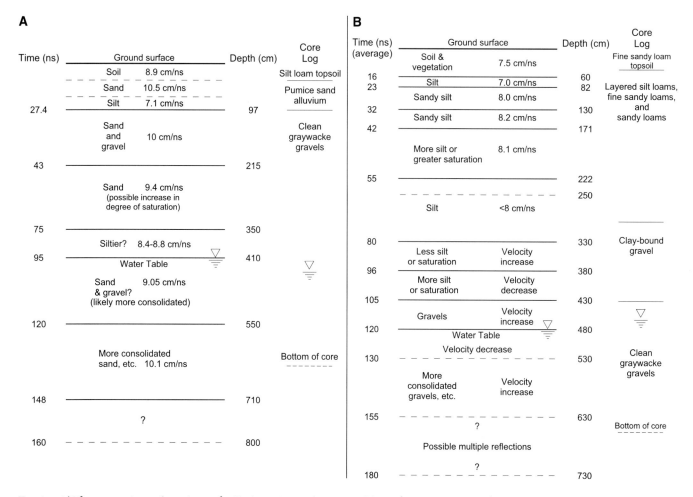

FIG. 6.—**A**) The approximate layering at the Te Awa site, as determined from the CMP survey. The velocity structure is generally well correlated with the lithology observed in the core log (shown at the right), but the GPR velocity structure, which is a combination of 100 MHz and more detailed shallow 200 MHz CMPs, has more detail than the core log. **B**) The layering at the Twyford site, as determined from the CMP survey. As for the Te Awa site, the layering is generally well correlated with the core log but has more detail.

subsidiary channels, and at 60 m (Fig. 9D) it has clearly bifurcated into a main channel (to the south, right) and a secondary channel to the north (left). The main channel eventually swings back around to the north, where we observe it in the profile at 80 m (Fig. 7). This pattern of channel position is consistent with the observed tracer flow.

The GPR profiles were used to determine or infer the location of possible channels just below the water table. In most cases, the channel edge was clear. In some cases, the edge was partly obscured by signal noise or by multiples, and was less well defined. In a few cases, the edge is inferred from more subtle disruptions in the subsurface responses, and these are labeled "Possible channel edge". The channel locations, and the possible flow direction inferred from these channel locations, are overlaid on the approximate groundwater flow direction derived from the tracer experiment (Fig. 10). Where there is good borehole control, the results agree well.

CONCLUSIONS

Preferential flow paths in groundwater are difficult to characterize with well-to-well tracing experiments, because the charac-

terization requires a high density of wells and detailed sampling. Geophysical techniques can provide much more continuous spatial data but require a lot more interpretation and usually some independent data for correlation. The tracer tests, observations of groundwater concentrations from the pesticide trials, and the geophysical results all give a consistent interpretation for the two study sites. Each technique by itself was too sparse or the interpretation was insufficiently constrained to permit full confidence in the interpretation. The combination of these techniques increased the confidence in the final interpretation. At the Te Awa site there were significant preferential flow paths or channels that gave rise to restricted flow in curved pathways. At the Twyford site the geology appeared to be more uniform, with little evidence for preferential flow paths.

ACKNOWLEDGMENTS

This study was funded by a contract from the Foundation for Science, Research and Technology, New Zealand. Thanks to Jim Watt and Keith Vincent of Landcare Research for their assistance with the tracer experiments, and to the staff of the Hawkes Bay Regional Council, particularly Dr. D. Dravid, for assistance with

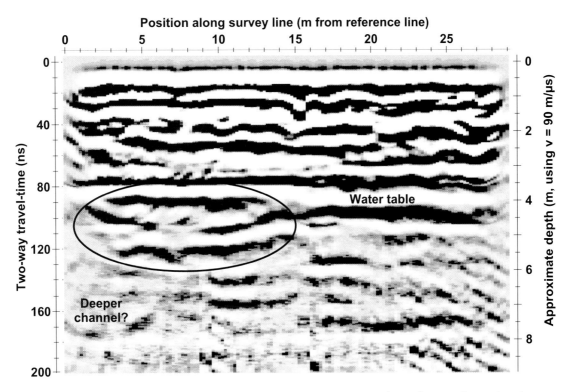

FIG. 7.—Te Awa GPR profile, 80 m from access road. The Te Awa radar profiles, as shown here by the oval in the example for the migrated profile acquired 80 m from the access road, contain features indicative of buried channels.

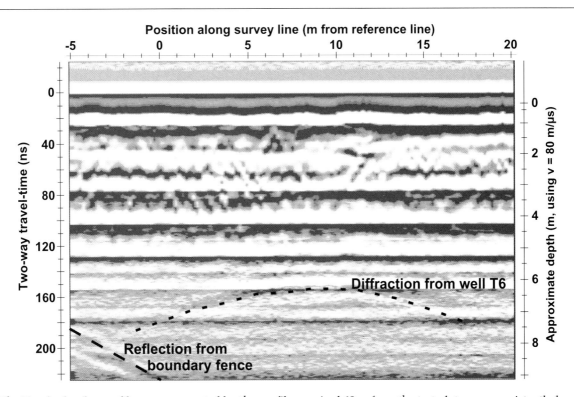

FIG. 8.—The Twyford radar profiles, as represented by the profile acquired 60 m from the test plot, were consistently layered and relatively undisturbed, except by interference from nearby sampling wells, specifically T6, and the boundary fence at the western edge of the site. The banding apparent in the profile is a combination of the layering with multiple reflections between the water table and the sediment layers. The profile is unmigrated to better show the diffraction-rich layer at 45 ns TWT (approximately 2 m depth).

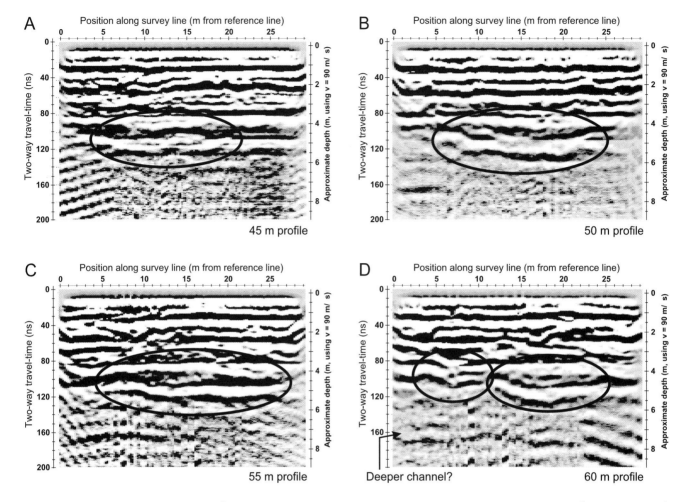

Fig. 9.—A sequence of four profiles for the Te Awa site at : **A)** 45 m; **B)** 50 m; **C)** 55 m; and **D)** 60 m, illustrate the variation in the subsurface channels which can give rise to the preferential flow paths observed in the tracer tests. At 45 m, we see a broad shallow channel, as indicated by the oval; at 50 m, the channel was broadened and deepened; at 55 m, the channel is broader still; and at 60 m the channel has bifurcated, providing alternate flow paths. The profiles were all migrated using an average subsurface radar velocity of 9 cm/ns (90 m/μs).

the study and for funding and installation of the monitoring wells. Thanks also to A. Binley and an anonymous reviewer, whose comments improved the manuscript.

REFERENCES

BOHIDAR, R.N., AND HERMANCE, J.F., 2002, The GPR refraction method: Geophysics v. 67, p. 1474–1485.

CLOSE, M.E., WATT, J.P.C., AND VINCENT, K.W., 1999, Simulation of picloram, atrazine and simazine transport through two New Zealand soils using LEACHM: Australian Journal of Soil Research, v. 37, p. 53–74.

DAVIS, J.L., AND ANNAN, A.P., 1989, Ground-penetrating radar for high resolution mapping of soil and rock stratigraphy: Geophysical Prospecting, v. 37, p. 531–551.

DONOVAN, J.J., AND FRYSINGER, K.W., 1997, Delineation of preferred-flow paths by response to transient lagoon exfiltration: Ground Water, v. 35, p. 990–996.

FREEZE, R.A., AND CHERRY, J.A., 1979, Groundwater: Englewood Cliffs, New Jersey, Prentice Hall, 792 p.

GOLTZ, M.N., AND ROBERTS, P.V, 1987, Using the method of moments to analyze three-dimensional diffusion-limited solute transport from

temporal and spatial perspectives: Water Resources Research, v. 23, p. 1575–1585.

HATTON, L., WORTHINGTON, M.H., AND MAKIN, J., 1986, Seismic Data Processing; Theory and Practice. Oxford, U.K., Blackwell Scientific Publications, 177 p.

MELVILLE, J.G., MOLZ, F.J., AND GÜVEN, O., 1991, Multilevel slug tests with comparison to tracer data: Ground Water, v. 29, p. 897–907.

MOLZ, F.J., MORIN, R.H., HESS, A.E., MELVILLE, J.G., AND GÜVEN, O., 1989, The impeller meter for measuring aquifer permeability variations: evaluation and comparison with other tests: Water Resources Research, v. 25, p. 1677–1683.

NOBES, D.C., 1996, Report on Geophysical Surveys of the Watson Rd and Ngatarawa Rd test sites, Hawkes Bay Region, 20–23 April 1996: University of Canterbury, Canterprise Report for Landcare Research and ESR.

PANG, L., CLOSE, M.E., AND NOONAN, M., 1998, Rhodamine WT and *Bacillus subtilis* transport through an alluvial gravel aquifer: Ground Water, v. 36, p. 112–122.

PANG, L., CLOSE, M.E., WATT, J.P.C., AND VINCENT, K.W., 2000, Simulation of picloram, atrazine and simazine leaching through two New Zealand soils and into groundwater using HYDRUS-2D: Journal of Contaminant Hydrology, v. 44, p. 19–26.

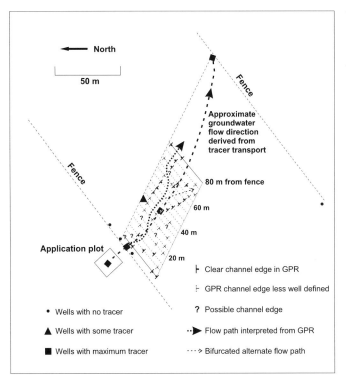

FIG. 10.—Summary of locations of channels below the water table at the Te Awa site as determined from the GPR profiles, superimposed on the approximate groundwater flow direction as derived from the tracer experiment. The symbols for the wells are derived from the results presented in Table 2. The GPR channel locations are used to estimate a possible flow path, as shown.

PANG, L., AND CLOSE, M.E., 2000, Simulation of the linkage between solute transport in the unsaturated zone and groundwater: Institute of Environmental Science and Research Technical Report no. TR0001, 11 p.

PTAK, T., AND TEUTSCH, G., 1994, Forced and natural gradient tracer tests in a highly heterogeneous porous aquifer: Instrumentation and measurements: Journal of Hydrology, v. 159, p. 79–104.

REA, J., AND KNIGHT, R., 1998, Geostatistical analysis of ground-penetrating radar data: a means of describing spatial variation in the subsurface: Water Resources Research, v. 34, p. 329–339.

SHERIFF, R.E., 1991, Encyclopedic Dictionary of Exploration Geophysics: Tulsa, Oklahoma, Society of Exploration Geophysicists, 376 p.

STEENHUIS, T.S., KUNG, K.J.S., AND CATHLES, L.W., 1990, Finding layers in the soil: Ground-penetrating radar as a tool in studies of groundwater contamination: Engineering: Cornell Quarterly, v. 25, p. 15–19.

THEIMER, B.D., NOBES, D.C., AND WARNER, B.G., 1994, A study of the geoelectric properties of peatlands and their influence on ground-penetrating radar surveying: Geophysical Prospecting, v. 42, p. 179–209.

THORPE, H.R., BURDEN, R.J., AND SCOTT, D.M., 1982, Potential for contamination of the Heretaunga Plains Aquifers: Ministry of Works and Development, Christchurch, New Zealand, Water & Soil Technical Publication 24, 148 p.

WHITE, P.A., 1988, Measurement of ground-water parameters using saltwater injection and surface resistivity: Ground Water, v. 26, p. 179–186.

YEH, G.T., 1981, AT123D: Analytical transient one-, two-, and three-dimensional simulation of waste transport in the aquifer system. ORNL-5602: Oak Ridge National Laboratory, Oak Ridge, Tennessee, Environmental Sciences Division Publication no. 1439, 88 p.

YOUNG, S.C., 1995, Characterization of high-K pathways by borehole flowmeter and tracer tests: Ground Water, v. 33, p. 311–318.

TIME-LAPSE GEOPHYSICS FOR MAPPING FLUID FLOW IN NEAR REAL TIME: RESULTS FROM A CONTROLLED MESOSCALE EXPERIMENT

ROELOF VERSTEEG

Idaho National Engineering and Environmental Laboratory, P.O. Box 1625, MS 2025,
Idaho Falls, Idaho 83415-2107, U.S.A.
e-mail: versrj@inel.gov

ABSTRACT: Accurate modeling of subsurface processes requires densely spaced values of hydrological properties, biological activity, and geochemical conditions, as well as the changes in these values. Obtaining these high-resolution property values invasively is cost prohibitive and likely infeasible. The only practical way to obtain these values is through geophysical imaging tools (e.g., Sauck et al., 1998). While the best we can do with single geophysical surveys is obtain a map of physical properties, time-lapse 3D geophysical surveys can provide access to processes in near real time—information that can be used in making decisions on a range of subsurface environmental mitigation efforts.

While the use of time-lapse geophysics has become well accepted, especially in near-surface geophysics, the processing of this data in real time for optimal use of the information is still in its infancy. A controlled mesoscale experimental setting was created at Columbia University and used for an implementation of an approach in which geophysical data are processed to automatically provide near-real-time images that provide insight into ongoing processes. A controlled injection of canola oil in a large sand tank yielded a suite of 162 3D datasets that were processed in near real time, demonstrating the practicality of this approach to yield information on fluid flow in real time.

INTRODUCTION AND MOTIVATION: THE USE OF GEOPHYSICS TO IMAGE PROCESSES

The development of time-lapse 3D or 4D geophysics is one of the main innovations in the world of geophysics in the last ten years. It has found applications both in global seismic (Song and Richards, 1996; Creager, 1997), oil industry (Anderson et al., 1993; Anderson et al., 1994; Fanchi et al., 1999) and near-surface geophysics (Birken and Versteeg, 2000; LaBrecque and Yang, 2000). The main benefit of 4D surveys over 3D surveys is that they can be interpreted more easily in regard to flow and transport processes—something that for many cases is much more of interest than the pure "static" state of the earth. The basic notion underlying 4D geophysics is simple: collect multiple datasets with the same acquisition configuration and parameters at different times, remove the complexity of the background by "subtracting" the initial dataset, and come up with a time-dependent change in physical properties, which can be interpreted as either hydrological or chemical processes. It should be noted that an added benefit of 4D data is the ability to identify and remove noise because of the redundancy of information implicit in 4D datasets. While the approach of extracting processes from 4D data works in concept, in practice the interpretation of 4D data in terms of processes is far from ideal (see Versteeg and Birken, 2001b, and Versteeg, 2000). However, for applications in near-surface geophysics there are added challenges: first, collecting data at high enough frequencies so that one avoids temporal aliasing, and second, processing the data at such a rate that the information extracted from the data can be used in a timely manner.

THE NEED FOR RAPID SAMPLING: AVOIDING TEMPORAL AND SPATIAL ALIASING OF PROCESSES

A consideration of oil-industry 4D data shows that processing and interpretations are often done on only two or three datasets. In near-surface geophysics the situation is somewhat better, but even there we often have only a small (5–10) number of 3D datasets. To understand why this could be a problem we only have to think back to the well known sampling theorem which states that, in order to capture a signal adequately, the sampling rate should be at least twice that of the highest frequency in the signal. Considering this makes it immediately clear that, although we can interpret sets of two, three, or four datasets as parts of an unaliased dataseries, the probability that this is true—without having a fundamental insight into the processes—is low. In geophysical time-lapse imaging this problem was encountered in work done by Lane et al. (1998) in a tracer experiment in fractured bedrock. Because the time for a GPR acquisition took longer than substantial movement of the tracer, their approach was to employ a so-called sequential injection and scanning procedure (essentially repeating the experiment several times, and taking different subsets of the dataset every time).

In the work done by Lane et al. (1998) the required sampling rate was known from previous similar experiments. In field applications, knowing the required sampling rate (both temporal and spatial) for our datasets would require information both on the processes that occur and the change in the data caused by the process. Our sampling strategy is governed by whichever one of these imposes the "strictest" demands. Determining this parameter requires us to have insight into the geophysical signature of processes. While one can try to observe this signature in the field, there are a number of problems with this approach. First of all, in the field we currently have little control over flow and transport processes. Second, the change in the data due to the processes is often of second order, and is on the same scale as that which could be caused by small changes in instrument deployment. Thus, while the field is where we need to apply our methods, it is probably not the best place to develop an observational and interpretational strategy. Note that one example of a 4D field study in which acquisition parameters were barely sufficient is the Borden dataset (Brewster et al., 1995), in which both the spatial and temporal sampling rates were insufficient to capture the full detail of the DNAPL movement (Birken and Versteeg, 2000).

The approach to this problem pursued by the writer was to create a location for high-resolution collection of 4D geophysical data to study processes. This approach resulted in Columbia's subsurface imaging laboratory An in-depth discussion of this laboratory can be found in Versteeg and Birken (2001a), and a summary of this discussion is given in the next section. This laboratory allows the collection of 4D datasets with spatial sampling distances of 2 cm and temporal sampling rates of 20 minutes per dataset for each 3D dataset.

COLUMBIA'S SUBSURFACE IMAGING LABORATORY

Columbia's subsurface imaging laboratory consists of the following components:

1. An 8 ft x 6 ft x 6 ft (2.4 m x 1.8 m x 1.8 m) tank, constructed from Extren®, a high strength poltruded fiberglass;
2. An automated gantry system, mounted on the tank, allowing automated movement of a radar antenna over the tank (Fig. 1);
3. Infrastructure for material emplacement. The setting of the tank (in a former swimming pool) allows filling the tank from above, and emptying it using a compressed-air-driven vacuum; and
4. Infrastructure for automated data collection, processing, and visualization (Fig. 2).

This laboratory has two related goals. The first was to have a setting in which dense, high-quality 4D geophysical data sets could be collected so that approaches for automated processing and interpretation could be developed. The second goal was to study the geophysical signature of subsurface processes.

The Need for Real-Time Data Processing

As mentioned in the introduction, one of the challenges in near-surface geophysics is the need for near-real-time data processing, because the value of information is related to its timeliness. A second challenge is how to make the information accessible to end users. Thus, as geophysicists move towards a situation where there are continuous monitoring systems in place that collect multiple datasets a day, two fundamental questions will have to be addressed:

• How do we process the data?

• How do we deliver the results in near real time?

The questions of how to process and deliver results are of course related, and they both pose significant challenges. There are two main constraints on both of these: first, processing and result delivery has to be done **automatically**, because there is no way human processors can keep up with the stream of data provided by real-time systems, and second, dataset processing has to happen in less time than it takes to collect a new dataset, to allow results to be delivered in near real time. Note that the definition of near real time is actually related to the measurement frequency (which is of course defined by the frequency of the process under observation).

• Finding an approach to data processing that yields information on processes is a first challenge, and one that is only partly resolved here. However, a more significant challenge was finding a way to provide results in near real time.

The first big experiment in the subsurface imaging lab (Versteeg et al., 2000) demonstrated the need for complete automation of acquisition and processing. At that time, no infrastructure was available for real-time processing, so processing flows had to be created and run manually, taking several months of personnel time and weeks of processor time. As an aside, manual data acquisition invariably introduces errors in naming conventions and documentation (especially when done at 3 am). Similarly, it took several years before the

FIG. 1.—Extren tank with automated gantry system. The radar antenna (a 1 Ghz antenna from Mala Geosciences) is controlled through an automated acquisition program written in Labview, which controls the gantry.

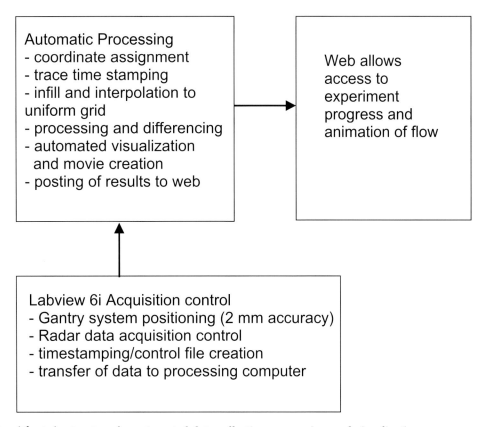

FIG. 2.—Schematic of the infrastructure for automated data collection, processing, and visualization.

data from the Borden experiment (which occurred over a period of a week) were analyzed.

The challenge for automated acquisition, processing, visualizing, and reporting is that each of these steps traditionally involves multiple manual steps, all of which have to be automated. While data acquisition was relatively easy to automate (using the gantry system), data processing and visualization were more difficult to resolve. In fact, for some processes (e.g., velocity analysis and inversion), fully automated processing is virtually impossible.

The first step toward automatic processing is automated acquisition. This allows one to generate all relevant information on the data automatically and in a standard, uniform way. The relevant information includes (among others)

- time of data acquisition
- instrument location
- acquisition parameters (number of stacks, acquisition frequency, number of samples)

All this information is collected and managed by the acquisition program.

Once the data are collected and available for processing, the next step is to apply a processing and imaging flow. As with oil-industry data, this requires equalization, i.e., making sure that we have the "same" datacube every time, meaning a cube for which the dimensions of the cube and the location of the traces are identical. In theory this should be the case with our acquisition system, because this positions the radar system with high (sub-centimeter) accuracy. In practice we were faced with three problems for our specific setup:

- Our radar system occasionally drops a trace (in general one in about 4000 traces) so that while our control system has a position for the radar trace there is no corresponding data point.

- There is a small but noticeable shift between radar profiles collected in opposite directions (in order to save time our acquisition system goes back and forth instead of always having the same profile direction). This is because the acquisition system triggers on the basis of position, but this position is where the acquisition of a trace starts. Because the acquisition of a trace takes about 200 milliseconds (during which our radar moves approximately 6 mm), the radar traces in adjacent profiles is shifted by about 1 cm. This results in a noticeable zigzag pattern in the data cubes, which complicates interpretation.

- Because of the finite response time of our system the exact trigger location of traces between different 3D runs can change by as much as 5 mm. This is of course noted in the position file, but it means that, in our raw field records, trace 20 of profile 1 of run 2 may be shifted compared to trace 20 of profile 1 of run 7.

These issues can be dealt with **if** we have information on when each trace was collected and was supposed to be collected (which allows synchronization of position and data information, and insertion of missing traces at the correct location), on acquisition velocity (which allows us to deal with trace shifting) and if we have a sufficient data density to interpolate traces—all conditions that are met through our automated acquisition system. We can thus implement a suite of processing steps that yield data cubes that have identical dimensions and trace locations and thus lend themselves to automated processing.

As part of these processing operations we assign header information for each trace (in standard SEGY format), which includes 4D run number, time at which the trace was taken, location information, and trace and profile number. Once this is done, the data are ready for automated differencing and visualization. Details on the data differencing are discussed in a following section. Because the data cubes are identical in size and location, the data differencing (using the attribute calculation and differencing described subsequently) can be done automatically, to provide a data-difference cube.

Automated Processing of 4D Data

There are four different approaches to processing 4D GPR data (details can be found in Versteeg and Birken, 2001b):

1. Difference (migrated) data: this is simple, but unstable because of the oscillatory nature of GPR data.

2. Invert 3D data and compare inversion results: this approach is most commonly used in oil industry 4D (Burkhart et al., 2000), but has also been used in near-surface geophysics (Lane et al., 1999). While this is a good first step, it has fundamental problems because of the effect of the change in the data on the result of the inversions, and consequentially on our ability to interpret the differences. For example, a change in velocity might mean that a certain part of the subsurface is more or less illuminated between different data sets, and consequentially that the confidence in the information on this part of the subsurface is different between different inversions. For radar data there is the added complexity that currently the problem of full-waveform GPR inversion has not been solved: while we can model GPR data fairly well, full-waveform inversion would require knowing the antenna radiation pattern in detail. Because this is strongly dependent on the near-surface properties (Arcone, 1981, 1995) (which are the ones we are inverting for) the problem of full-waveform inversion remains open.

3. Inversion of 4D data: this is most likely the best solution. While it has seen some implementations in, e.g., 4D resistivity inversion (LaBrecque and Yang, 2000), it has many computational and fundamental challenges (including the one of GPR inversion mentioned above). One of the core problems is that the changes in our data are of second order: traveltime changes are usually in the order of 1% of the total traveltime and reflection amplitude changes are in the order of a few percent compared to the original reflections. One possible approach is to focus on the inversion of the differences—which brings up the questions on how to take our differences and which differences we should take (which is far from trivial, because the number of ways in which we can difference data increases nearly exponentially with the number of datasets),

4. Calculation of smooth data attributes and differencing of data attributes: while this is simple, it does give some interpretable results, as is shown in the subsequent sections. Because this

can be done in near real time and is the only approach that can be done automatically, it is the approach taken for the data from the subsurface imaging laboratory. In our current processing approach we calculate the average energy of the background dataset for each point in the data using a simple running-average window of variable length (optimized by trial and error) and then calculate a normalized difference between the energy in our background data and our subsequent datasets. The advantage of this approach is that it shows localized changes and that this calculation can be done in near real time.

Automated Visualization and Data Presentation

While there are multiple packages available that allow interactive visualization of 3D or 4D data, the challenge faced here was to do automated visualization. While this can to some extent be addressed using predefined visualization settings, it does require a visualization package that allows scripting and shell-based execution. We decided to use Data Explorer (aka DX, originally from IBM, currently open source (www.opendx.org)) for visualization purposes in conjunction with a simple automated mpg movie generator script (mpeg2encode) that can be used to animate the image files of the individual 3D runs.

A challenge encountered when collecting and visualizing large amounts of data is that of how one extracts and presents the maximum amount of information from the data. While this is already a problem for 3D datasets, the problem becomes even larger for 4D datasets, especially in an automated environment. One solution could be to make data available in a web-based viewing format (e.g., the netcdf format, which can be viewed with programs such as Webwinds; Elson et al., 2001). While this is feasible with small datasets, this is not a viable solution for larger datasets such as those collected in our environments (several hundreds to thousands of MB) because of limitations on network traffic and machine performance. Some of the datasets we are currently collecting even strain local visualization packages. One solution could be to create a "movies on demand" approach in which the data are stored in a database and a user requests visualization parameters through a local or web interface, resulting in generation of a specified movie. This is feasible but it does not address the question of which data contain the most information.

Automated Processing and Visualization Summary

Our complete processing system (shown schematically in Fig. 2) works the following way:

After setup of a 4D run, the acquisition system (controlled by Labview) starts collecting data. The acquisition system controls the radar acquisition system. At completion of each 3D survey the data are transferred by ftp to a dedicated processing platform (a Sun Ultra 30). On this platform a processing shell runs, which periodically checks for data. Once new data arrive, they are processed into a uniform data cube by a suite of scripts and shells that make extensive use of Seismic Unix (Cohen and Stockwell, 2000). A separate script takes this data cube and calculates an attributes cube and differences the appropriate cubes. Dataexplorer then produces gif files of both the raw and attribute cube data based on scripts. The raw-data gif files are posted to the website and all the gif files are merged into two quicktime movies. A script places the gifs and movies (both of the raw and the differenced data) on the public website and an updated html page is automatically generated. This whole process takes about 2–15 minutes (depending on data size) but in general happens about twice as fast as the acquisition time for a new run, so that the data are available near real time.

EXAMPLE OF NEAR-REAL-TIME 4D IMAGING OF FLUID FLOW: IMAGING AN OIL INJECTION IN COLUMBIA'S SUBSURFACE IMAGING LABORATORY

In order to study how we can use 4D data in real time, an experiment was designed to observe the changes in geophysical signature resulting from injection of canola oil in water-saturated sand and to extract near-real-time information on fluid flow by use of the approach described previously.

For this experiment the tank was filled with sand in which a constant water table was established. In order to allow the injection of oil without having any preferential pathways, an injection system was installed that could deliver oil to the center of the tank (using simple pressure-head-driven injection) (Fig. 3). This system allows the injection of oil (or any other fluid) using a flexible tube. Because the inlet of our tube was above the tank, the injection was gravity driven.

Radar Acquisition Parameters

Our radar acquisition parameters were based on a perceived need for high temporal resolution, because we expected oil to migrate quickly. This expectation was based on a small-scale experiment in which we injected canola oil at the bottom of a small container filled with saturated sand. The oil migrated rapidly (~ten minutes to migrate ten centimeters upward). On the basis of this and on previous experiments, we limited our spatial area of acquisition to about 50% of the maximum area. Our data-acquisition area is a square with cornerpoints at 27.0 cm and 182.0 cm in x, and 20 cm and 136.0 cm in y. Note that these coordinates are relative to the corner of the tank (Figure 3, top). In this area, 30 profiles with 4 cm spacing between profiles are collected. Each profile has 160 traces at 1 cm spacing with 800 samples. Sampling frequency is 12.4 GHz and we use a 16-fold stack. The ends of each profile are removed to give 156 traces/profile for a total of 4680 traces per 3D run. Each run takes about 23 minutes and 50 seconds, with an additional ten seconds needed for the repositioning of the system and data-transfer procedures. 162 3D datacubes were collected over a period of 66 hours and 41 minutes, with the experiment starting at 13:58:10 on 15 August 2000.

Oil Injection

During the experiment, canola oil was injected at two times: during the acquisition of the sixth 3D run (2 hours, 7 minutes, and 37 seconds after the beginning of the experiment) 5 liters of canola oil was injected from 4:15:47 until 4:31:44. A second 10 liter injection started at 23:57:45 on 15 August 2000 during the acquisition of the 25th run, and was completed on 16 August 2000 at 00:30:32 during the acquisition of the 26th run. Canola oil was chosen based on the fact that the contrast of the oil with the water-saturated sand would result in a significant change in reflection coefficient. Thus, we expect to be able to see the injection quite well. The injection tube has an inner diameter of 1/4 inch (7 mm), and although some oil remained in this tube this should be limited to about 50 ml.

Real-Time Data Processing, Assessment, and Visualization

After acquisition, the data were preprocessed and automatically visualized as described previously. This resulted in data as

shown in Figure 4, which shows a cutout of four of the 162 data cubes with an automatic gain control (AGC) applied to enhance the later data. While these figures show the change in geophysical data caused by the oil injection as well as the similarity between radar cubes, they do not show the reproducibility between surveys or the exact magnitude of the oil injection. Reproducibility is important because we look at differences in the data, thus if differences occur in regions where they should not occur (e.g., the edges of our cube) it would invalidate our approach.

To get an appreciation of both the reproducibility between surveys and the changes caused by the oil injection, consider Figures 5 and 6, which show the same trace at six instances from the 4D cube at two different locations: one location at the edge of our observational area (Fig. 5; trace 50) and one location at approximately the center of our observational area (Fig. 6; trace 2418). The six instances are from surveys 1, 33, 65, 97, 129, and 161.

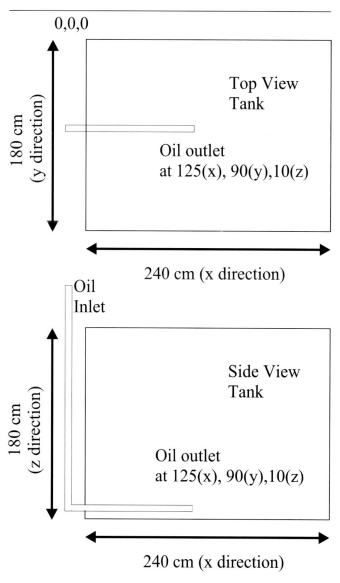

FIG. 3.—Setup of the oil experiment. A 0.5 inch (1.27 cm) PVC pipe goes to the center of the tank. Oil is injected into the tank from the inlet. The inlet is approximately 2 meters above the top of the tank.

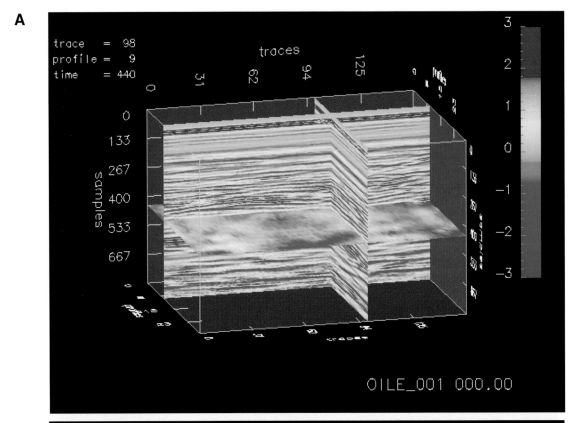

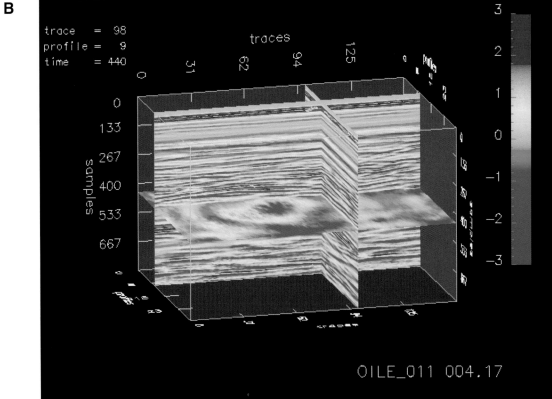

FIG. 4.—Visualization of four of the 162 cubes of data. The data have been autogained. All figures show a cutout of the data cube The name in the right-hand bottom corner indicates the number of the experiment in the 4D run and the time at which the acquisition was started (relative to the first run). **A)** run 01; **B)** run 11; **C)** run 31; **D)** run 162.

C

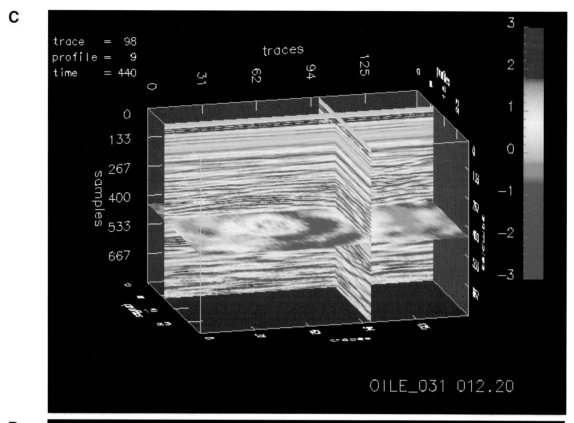

D

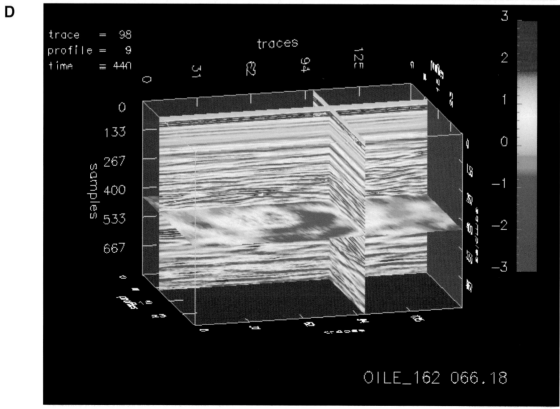

F<small>IG</small>. 4.—(Continued).

Figures 5 and 6 show that there is virtually no change between the beginning and the end of the experiment for the edge trace, but there is a clear change occurring at the center. This observation is important in the data processing because it (1) tells us how reproducible our data are and (2) gives us a notion of the amplitude of the change. Knowing the data reproducibility is of utmost importance in 4D data processing. If our data is reproducible to only 3%, and we see changes of 3.5%, we should be very cautious in interpreting these changes—if we interpret them at all. It is interesting that this reproducibility assessment is often completely neglected in near-surface time-lapse studies, where all too often the implicit assumption is that all observed changes are due to processes.

Data Differencing and Flow Visualization

Figures 4 and 6 show the change in the data resulting from the oil injection. However, to get a better (and real-time) appreciation of the change in the data, consider the results from the data-differencing process (Fig. 7). As described previously, the data differencing is done on a smooth data attribute (the average smoothed trace energy, obtained by smoothing the data using a 20-sample window). The smoothing results in a corresponding datacube, which can be differenced with the similarly treated background data (for which we use the first data cube)

The differenced data cubes show the area of the oil intrusion and movement of the oil much more clearly than does the raw data. Note that the visualization settings are the same as for the original datacubes, and the data-differencing operation creates a dataset with the same size as the original one. As an aside, one of the challenges in 4D data is how to abstract the results so that they are accessible: we have a four-dimensional data cube that contains more information than can easily be represented in simple static images. Figure 8 shows another way to look at the data: a comparison between the same depth slice at different times.

The images shown in Figures 4 and 7 are produced in near real time. After a complete data run (which takes about 23 minutes),

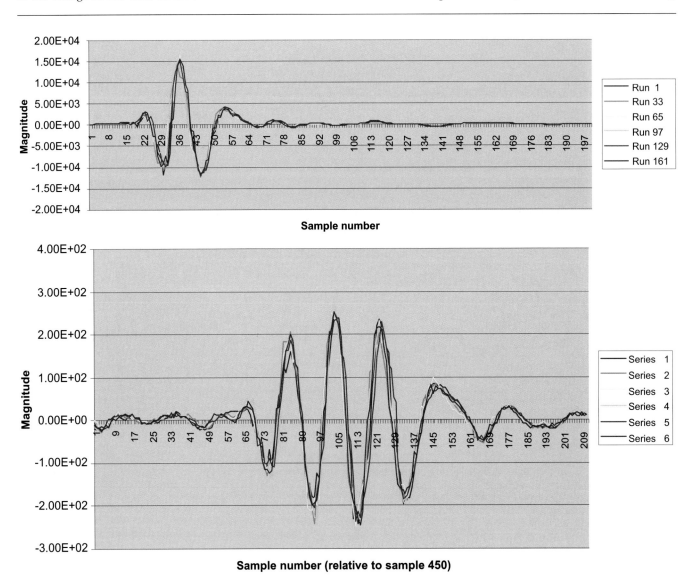

Fig. 5.—Data from six runs for trace 50 (at the edge of our data cubes). Top: samples 1-200, bottom, samples 450-650. Note different amplitudes, and note that the data between different runs are virtually identical.

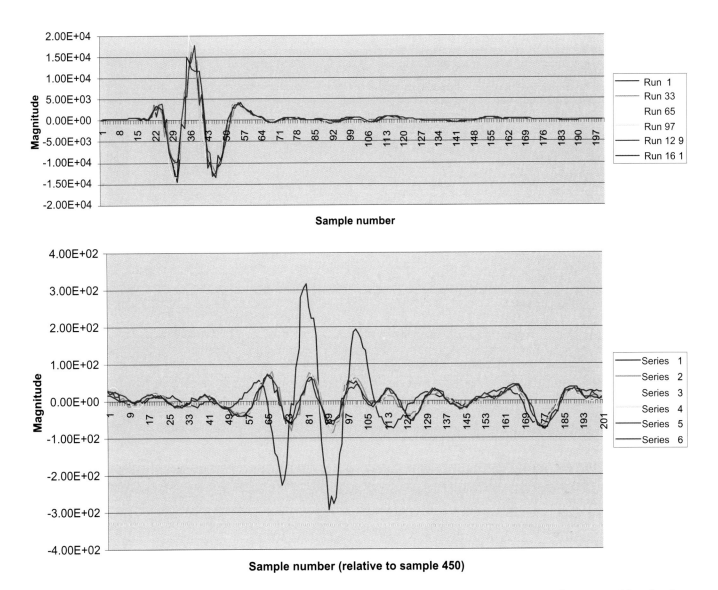

F$_{IG}$. 6.—Data from six runs for trace 2418 (at the center of our data cube). Top, samples 1–200; bottom, samples 450–650. Note the clear difference in data from run 1 with the other runs, but also that there is little difference between runs 33 and 161.

it takes about 12 minutes to process the data and produce images (which include animations of the previous runs). The processed data and the images are posted on a website once this processing is complete. Figure 7 (and in the animations which are created from a sequence of the different differenced figures) provides access to the movement of the oil in real time, and thus our original goal is met.

CONCLUSION, DISCUSSION, AND FURTHER WORK

The results presented here show unequivocally that we can both observe and image fluid flow using GPR in our tank in near real time using an automated setup. This can be done even though the magnitudes of the changes in our data are quite small (significantly smaller than those in the Borden data (Brewster et al., 1995)). The processing that was done to image this fluid flow is relatively simple and exploits the fact that we have only an isolated event with relatively little change in arrival time. How-

ever, even with these assumptions we can clearly delineate flow and obtain significant detail on oil movement.

While the fact that this method works in the lab is encouraging, one of the fundamental questions that can be asked is how portable this approach is to field sites and other methods. Changes in the subsurface due to a range of processes have been observed in numerous repeated field studies for a range of different methods: shallow seismic (West and Menke, 2000), GPR, resistivity, induction EM. None of these efforts have yielded results comparable to those presented here. Our contention is that we could obtain similar results in the field by following the lessons we have learned in the laboratory. This includes using sampling efforts which allow us to collect precisely positioned field data at temporal densities comparable to the density used in the laboratory (i.e., at intervals in the order of hours rather than days). While this is a challenging task, 4D data provide more information about aquifer properties than 3D data, and if we have enough data the 4D data can be

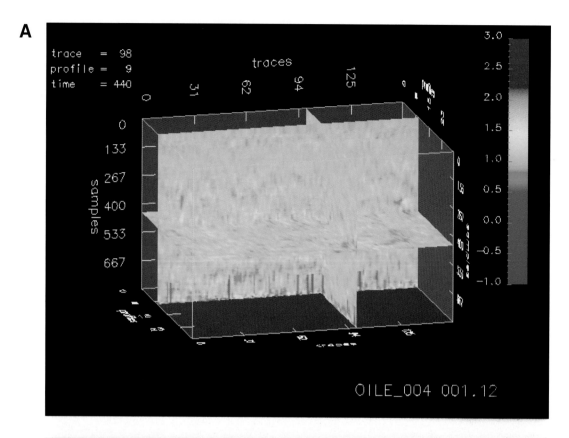

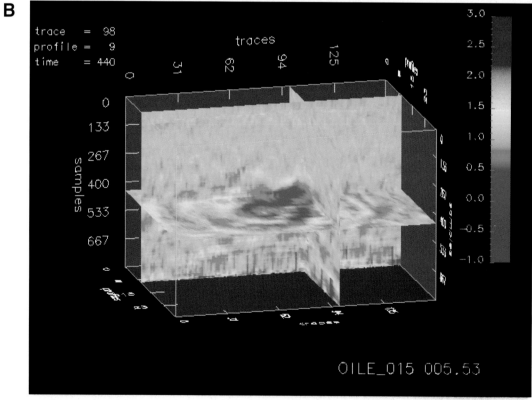

Fig. 7.—Difference cubes resulting from processing. **A)** Cube showing difference between initial data and data at 1 hour and 12 minutes shows that no change has occurred **B)** Cube showing difference between initial data and data at 5 hours and 53 minutes shows the extent of the oil just after injection **C)** Cube showing difference between initial data and data at 45 hours and 25 minutes shows final extent of the oil.

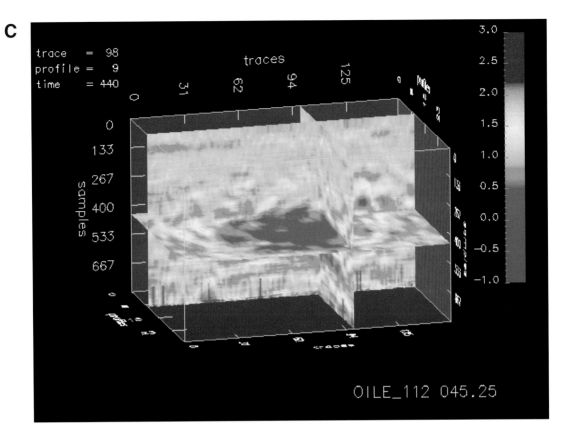

Fig. 7.—(Continued).

processed automatically to estimate the flow. Finally, 4D geophysical data contain significantly more information than has been extracted by the relatively simple processing flow used in this paper. In theory we can use geophysics to estimate differential temporal and spatial rates of flow in our medium. If we measure the forcing functions (hydraulic head) at the same time, we should be able to get some sense of hydrologic properties. However, the results obtained in this experiment did not allow us to make estimates of this kind.

While the processing flows outlined here can provide information on flow in this case, many challenges remain before time-lapse geophysics can provide real-time information on flow in the field. Acquisition and processing need to be carefully controlled and need to integrate geophysical with hydrological and geochemical measurements. Integrated geophysical–hydrogeological–geochemical modeling and inversion codes are needed to translate signal amplitudes into concentrations, and from this, estimate the solute mass balance and flow vectors for the subsurface. Although this is challenging, it is likely possible and is a topic of ongoing work by the writer and others in the hydrogeophysics community.

ACKNOWLEDGMENTS

Infrastructure collection and data collection for this effort while the author was at Columbia were supported by Environmental Protection Agency grant #GR825209-01-0: *Four dimensional (4D) visualization and analysis of Ground Penetrating Radar data for the determination of three dimensional hydrological conductivity and time-dependent fluid flow*. In addition to the author, many people participated in building the tank and running experiments. Their support is gratefully acknowledged, specifically that of Ralf Birken, Justin Kuczynski, Steve Lee, Davide Gei, Jandyr Travassos, Ted Koczynski, Koray Ergun, and Shan Wei. The research on this effort at Idaho National Engineering and Environmental Laboratory (INEEL) was supported by the Laboratory Directed Research and Development Program. The INEEL is operated for the Department of Energy by Bechtel BWXT Idaho, CLC under the DOE's Idaho Operations Office contract DE-AC07-99ID13727.

REFERENCES

ANDERSON, R., CATHLES, L.M., AND NELSON, H.R., 1993, Data Cube depicting fluid flow history in Gulf Coast Sediments: Oil and Gas Journal, v. 91, no. 16, p. 85–93.

ANDERSON, R., FLEMINGS, P., LOSH, S., AUSTIN, J., AND WOODHAMS, R., 1994. Gulf of Mexico growth fault drilled, seen as oil, gas migration pathway: Oil and Gas Journal, v. 92, no. 21, p. 97–104.

ARCONE, S.A., 1981, Distortion of model subsurface radar pulses in complex dielectrics: Radio Science, v. 16, p. 855–864.

ARCONE, S.A., 1995, Numerical studies of the radiation patterns of resistively loaded dipoles: Journal of Applied Geophysics, v. 33, p. 27–38.

BIRKEN, R., AND VERSTEEG, R., 2000, Use of four dimensional ground penetrating radar and advanced visualization methods to determine subsurface fluid migration: Journal of Applied Geophysics, v. 43, p. 215–226.

BREWSTER, M.L., ANNAN, A.P., GREENHOUSE, J.P., KUEPER, B.H., OLHOEFT, G.R., REDMAN, J.D., AND SANDER, K.A., 1995, Observed migration of a

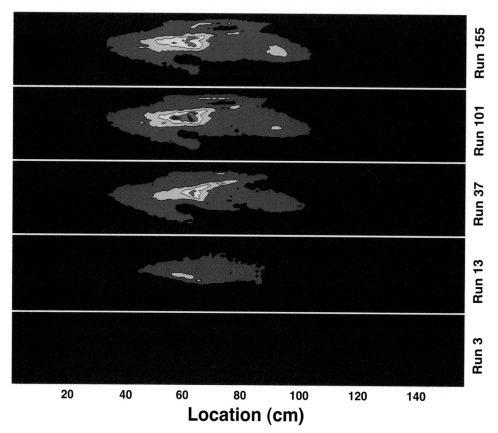

FIG. 8.—Plot showing five cutouts of 3D cubes from runs 3, 13, 37, 101, and 155. All cutouts are at sample depth 480. These data clearly show the consistency of the imaging as well as the complexity and subtle change of the oil flow. Scale is in centimeters. Size of each of the cutouts is 30 cm by 150 cm.

controlled DNAPL release by geophysical methods: Groundwater, v. 33, p. 977–987.

BURKHART, T.R., HOOVER, A.R., AND FLEMINGS, P.B., 2000, Time-lapse (4D) seismic monitoring of primary production of turbidite reservoirs at South Timbalier Block 295, offshore Louisiana, Gulf of Mexico: Geophysics, v. 65, p. 351–367.

COHEN, J.K., AND STOCKWELL, J., 2000, Seismic Unix Release 34: a free package for seismic research and processing: Center for Wave Phenomena, Colorado School of Mines.

CREAGER, K.C., 1997, Inner core rotation rate from small-scale heterogeneity and time-varying travel times: Science, v. 278, p. 1284–1288.

ELSON, L., ALLEN, M., GOLDSMITH, J., ORTON, M., AND WEIBEL, W., 2001, An example of a network based approach to data access, visualization, interactive analysis and distribution: American Meteorological Society, Bulletin, v. 81, p. 555–566.

FANCHI, J.R., PAGANO, T.A., AND DAVIS, T.L., 1999, State of the art of 4D seismic monitoring: the technique, the record, and the future: Oil and Gas Journal, v. 97, no. 22, p. 38–40.

LABRECQUE, D., AND YANG, X., 2000, Difference inversion of ERT data: a fast inversion method for 3-D in-situ monitoring (abstract): SAGEEP 2000, Environmental and Engineering Geophysics Society, Washington, D.C., p. 907–924.

LANE, J.W., HAENI, F.P., AND DAY-LEWIS, F.D., 1998, Use of time-lapse attenuation difference radar tomography methods to monitor saline tracer transport in fractured crystalline bedrock: GPR 98, 7th International Conference on Ground Penetrating Radar: Lawrence, Kansas, p. 533–538.

LANE, J.W., WRIGHT, D., AND HAENI, F.P., 1999, Borehole radar tomography using saline tracer injections to image fluid flow in fractured rocks: Technical meeting of the U.S. Geological Survey, Toxic Substances Hydrology Program, U.S. Geological Survey, Charleston, South Carolina, p. 747–756.

SAUCK, W.A., ATEKWANA, E.A., AND NASH, M.S., 1998, High conductivities associated with an LNAPL plume imaged by integrated geophysical techniques: Journal of Engineering and Environmental Geophysics, v. 2, p. 203–212.

SONG, X., AND RICHARDS, P., 1996, Seismological evidence for differential rotation of the Earth's inner core: Nature, v. 382, p. 221–224.

VERSTEEG, R., 2000, Understanding subsurface processes using ultrahigh timelapse geophysics and temporal difference inversion (abstract): American Geophysical Union, 2000 Fall Meeting, Proceedings, San Francisco.

VERSTEEG, R., AND BIRKEN, R., 2001a, An automated facility to study processes using 4D GPR (abstract): Symposium of the Application of Geophysics to Engineering and Environmental Problems (SAGEEP) 2001, Environmental and Engineering Geophysics Society, Denver, Colorado.

VERSTEEG, R., AND BIRKEN, R., 2001b, Imaging fluid flow and hydrologic conductivity using ground penetrating radar in a controlled setting (abstract): Symposium of the Application of Geophysics to Engineering and Environmental Problems (SAGEEP) 2001, Environmental and Engineering Geophysics Society, Denver, Colorado.

VERSTEEG, R., BIRKEN, R., SANDBERG, S., AND SLATER, L., 2000, Controlled imaging of fluid flow and a saline tracer using time lapse GPR and electrical resistivity tomography: Symposium of the Application of Geophysics to Engineering and Environmental Problems (SAGEEP) 2000, Environmental and Engineering Geophysics Society, Washington, D.C., p. 283–292.

WEST, M., AND MENKE, W., 2000, Fluid-induced changes in shear velocity from surface waves: Symposium of the Application of Geophysics to Engineering and Environmental Problems (SAGEEP) 2000, Environmental and Engineering Geophysics Society, Washington, D.C., p. 21–28.

THE USE OF GROUND-PENETRATING RADAR FOR CHARACTERIZING SEDIMENTS UNDER TRANSIENT FLOW CONDITIONS

MICHAEL B. KOWALSKY AND YORAM RUBIN
Department of Civil and Environmental Engineering, University of California, Berkeley, California 94702, U.S.A.
AND
PETER DIETRICH
Institute of Geology and Paleontology, University of Tübingen, Germany

ABSTRACT: Understanding how heterogeneous sedimentary deposits affect fluid flow and contaminant transport has been greatly improved through outcrop studies. Such studies have aided in hydrogeological site characterization by identifying sedimentary structures that greatly impact flow and transport. The use of geophysical methods for delineating structures relevant to flow and transport such as fast paths, which control the initial breakthrough of contaminants, or sand-rich regions, which retard reactive contaminants, is beginning to receive much attention. In particular, ground-penetrating radar (GPR) was recently evaluated for this purpose within the framework of an aquifer analog study. Using models derived from digitized outcrop images, GPR simulations showed that field data were largely affected by non-uniform water saturation in addition to sediment heterogeneity. In the present work, we begin to explore the possibility of using GPR during transient flow to further aid in hydrogeological site characterization. A case study is presented in which a digitized outcrop image is chosen for the simultaneous simulation of variably saturated flow and GPR (for crosshole and surface reflection configurations). The sensitivity of the fluid distribution and of the GPR response to model parameters is investigated for the outcrop model during steady state and induced transient flow (ponding infiltration). In some cases, synthetic time-lapsed measurements are shown to offer information pertinent to hydrogeological site characterization.

INTRODUCTION

Shallow subsurface characterization methods are in great demand, especially for predicting fluid flow and the transport of contaminants into groundwater supplies (e.g., Foussereau et al., 2001; Russo et al., 2001). Geophysical methods, such as ground-penetrating radar (GPR) in particular, have proven to be valuable in site characterization. GPR methods have been applied successfully in fields such as agriculture (Collins et al., 1986; Freeland et al., 1998), archaeology (Vaughn, 1986; Tohge et al., 1998), and civil engineering (Zeng and McMechan, 1997; Saarenketo and Scullion, 2000). Applications of GPR in sedimentological studies are also numerous (Knoll, et al., 1991; Gawthorpe, et al., 1993; Huggenberger, 1993; Siegenthaler and Huggenberger, 1993; Beres et al., 1995; Bridge et al., 1995; Asprion and Aigner, 1997; McMechan et al., 1997; Bridge et al., 1998; van Overmeeren, 1998; Asprion and Aigner, 1999; Beres et al., 1999; Vandenberghe and Overmeeren, 1999; Heinz, 2001; Lunt et al., this volume). In heterogeneous braided-river gravel deposits, for example, GPR surveys were found to be useful in "illuminating" the structure of gravel bodies (Heinz, 2001). Different depositional structures can in some cases be distinguished on the basis of their reflector patterns after "calibrating" GPR profiles with excavated outcrop images. The thickness of sedimentary structures may be less than the vertical resolution of the GPR antennae (depending on the antenna frequency), making some structures difficult to detect even though they may have significant impacts on fluid flow parameters (Lunt et al., this volume). Techniques for combining additional types of information, such as core data, with GPR data interpretations are also being developed (Regli et al., 2002). What makes the delineation of sedimentary structure through GPR possible is variation of electromagnetic (EM) properties within and between different sedimentary deposits. However, the factors that render some sedimentary structures visible with GPR, and others not, are not fully understood but are being actively researched (van Dam and Schlager, 2000).

The Maxwell equations govern the propagation of GPR waves and depend on parameters including the permittivity (or, as defined below, the dielectric constant), the electrical conductivity, and the magnetic permeability (e.g., Daniels, 1996). A brief introduction to GPR measurements is provided next, including how to relate measurable wave attributes such as the reflection coefficient, velocity, and attenuation to EM parameters, and how to relate these EM parameters to soil porosity and fluid saturation. In order to provide context and motivation for the present work, some applications of GPR to hydrogeological site characterization are then described. The procedures for simulating both variably saturated flow (i.e., the flow of water through a variably saturated porous medium) and GPR are outlined after that. Then, in a synthetic case study, GPR simulations are performed using an outcrop model under steady-state saturation conditions and during induced transient flow (ponding infiltration), allowing evaluation of the sensitivity of GPR to realistic fluid distributions in heterogeneous environments. Finally, some brief conclusions are made.

INTRODUCTION TO GPR MEASUREMENTS

The dielectric constant k is a fundamental material property of great importance in GPR methods. It is equivalent to the relative permittivity, defined as the permittivity e normalized by that of free space e_0 (~ 8.854 x 10^{-12} As/Vm, where the ampere (A) and volt (V) are the SI units for electric current and electric potential, respectively. The effective dielectric constant of a soil is determined by the soil particles and pore fluids, such as soil water (in bound and free states) and air (Sihvola, 1999). Table 1 lists ranges of values for the dielectric constant, measured at 100 MHz, for some common materials, wet and dry. The dielectric constant of water is 81, as compared to the value of 1 for air and the values ranging between 2 and 9 for most solid constituents of soils and man-made materials (Daniels, 1996). This explains why the dielectric constant in soil increases dramatically with the presence

Aquifer Characterization
SEPM Special Publication No. 80, Copyright © 2004
SEPM (Society for Sedimentary Geology), ISBN 1-56576-107-3, p. 107–127.

TABLE 1.—Electrical properties for common earth materials
(data from Daniels, 1996).

Material	Dielectric Constant	Conductivity (S/m)
Air	1	0
Asphalt (dry)	2–4	10^{-3}–10^{-2}
Asphalt (wet)	6–12	10^{-2}–10^{-1}
Clay (dry)	2–6	10^{-3}–10^{-1}
Clay (saturated)	15–40	10^{-1}–1
Coal (dry)	3.5	10^{-2}
Coal (wet)	8	10^{-1}
Concrete (dry)	4–10	10^{-3}–10^{-2}
Concrete (wet)	10–20	10^{-2}–10^{-1}
Freshwater	81	10^{-4}–10^{-2}
Freshwater ice	4	10^{-3}
Granite (dry)	5	10^{-8}–10^{-6}
Granite (wet)	7	10^{-3}–10^{-2}
Limestone (dry)	7	10^{-9}–10^{-6}
Limestone (wet)	8	10^{-2}–10^{-1}
Permafrost	4–8	10^{-5}–10^{-2}
Rock salt (dry)	4–7	10^{-4}
Sand (dry)	4–6	10^{-7}–10^{-3}
Sand (saturated)	10–30	10^{-4}–10^{-2}
Sandstone (dry)	2–3	10^{-9}–10^{-6}
Sandstone (wet)	5–10	10^{-5}–10^{-6}
Seawater	81	4
Seawater ice	4–8	10^{-2}–10^{-1}
Shale (saturated)	6–9	10^{-2}–10^{-1}
Snow (firm)	8–12	10^{-6}–10^{-5}
Soil (sandy dry)	4–6	10^{-4}–10^{-2}
Soil (sandy wet)	15–30	10^{-2}–10^{-1}
Soil (loamy dry)	4–6	10^{-4}–10^{-3}
Soil (loamy wet)	10–20	10^{-2}–10^{-1}
Soil (clayey dry)	4–6	10^{-4}–10^{-1}
Soil (clayey wet)	10–15	10^{-1}–1

The dielectric constant is dimensionless, and conductivity values
are given in units of Siemens (S) per meter (m).

of water. In fact, the amount and distribution of water in the subsurface largely influences GPR images (e.g., Greaves et al., 1996; van Overmeeren et al., 1997; Vandenberghe and Overmeeren, 1999; Kowalsky et al., 2001). van Dam and Schlager (2000) examined the causes of GPR reflections in sediments and found the presence of water to be a dominating factor. They inferred from laboratory and field measurements that iron oxide layers, for example, caused GPR reflections mainly because their values of dielectric constant varied from those of surrounding soils because of increased amounts of retained water rather than from differing electrical properties of the soil components. The increased water retention of the iron oxide layers was attributed to their pores being smaller and more slowly draining than those of the surrounding sandy material.

A typical application of GPR is the surface reflection survey, in which the transmitting and receiving antennae are pulled along the ground surface while emitting and recording electromagnetic pulses. Figure 1 shows two common configurations: the common offset profile, in which the separation between the

source and receiver remains constant, and the common-midpoint profile (CMP), in which the source and receiver separation is successively increased. In both cases, the receiving antenna records reflections originating from subsurface reflectors and from direct air and ground waves traveling between the antennae. The key parameter that determines the strength of reflected waves is the reflection coefficient, which depends on the contrast in dielectric constant between materials. At an interface between nonmetallic soil materials, the reflection coefficient can be defined for normal incidence as

$$R = \frac{\sqrt{\kappa_1} - \sqrt{\kappa_2}}{\sqrt{\kappa_1} + \sqrt{\kappa_2}} \qquad (1)$$

where k_i is the effective dielectric constant for material i.

Another measurable wave attribute largely governed by the dielectric constant, and therefore indicative of material type and water saturation, is the EM wave velocity, given by

$$v \approx \frac{1}{\sqrt{\mu\varepsilon}} = \frac{c}{\sqrt{\kappa}} \qquad (2)$$

for low-loss media (i.e., where electrical conductivity—defined later in this section—is relatively low), where μ is the magnetic permeability and c is the EM wave velocity in free space (~ 0.3 m/ns). Throughout the rest of this paper, EM wave velocity is referred to as wave velocity or just velocity. Although in some cases surface reflection methods allow for the estimation of velocity in the subsurface (described in the next section), velocity distributions between boreholes are obtained more easily through crosshole methods.

In crosshole GPR surveys, the transmitting and receiving antennae are lowered into separate boreholes, and EM pulses sent between boreholes are recorded. For multiple-offset gather (MOG) surveys, waveforms are recorded at multiple receiver positions for each transmitter position (Fig. 2A). Estimation of the velocity distribution between boreholes is then made possible through travel-time tomography methods (e.g., Peterson et al., 1985). Whereas two-dimensional velocity images are typically obtained for data collected between two boreholes, three-dimensional images can be obtained when additional boreholes are used (Eppstein and Dougherty, 1998). When the goal of a survey is to image quickly varying flow events, such as an infiltration front moving through regions of soil with high hydraulic conductivity, MOG surveys can be too time consuming. Zero-offset profile (ZOP) surveys are an alternative approach in which data are collected more quickly but yield only horizontally averaged information (e.g., Binley et al., 2001). For ZOP surveys (Fig. 2B), waveforms are collected only for the positions for which there is no offset between the antennae (i.e., for which both antennae are at equal depths and moved together for each measurement).

Because estimates of the dielectric constant can be obtained with GPR methods (e.g., with Equations 1 and 2), it is of great interest to have models relating the dielectric constant to soil type and water saturation. Site-specific models are commonly derived in the field or laboratory in order to model the effective value of the dielectric constant for a soil under different states of water saturation at a particular field site. However, the use of empirical and theoretical models for this purpose is also common. One popular empirical model was developed by Topp et al. (1980) by compiling data for many soils under varying moisture conditions:

$$\kappa = 3.03 + 9.3\theta + 146.0\theta^2 - 76.7\theta^3 \qquad (3)$$

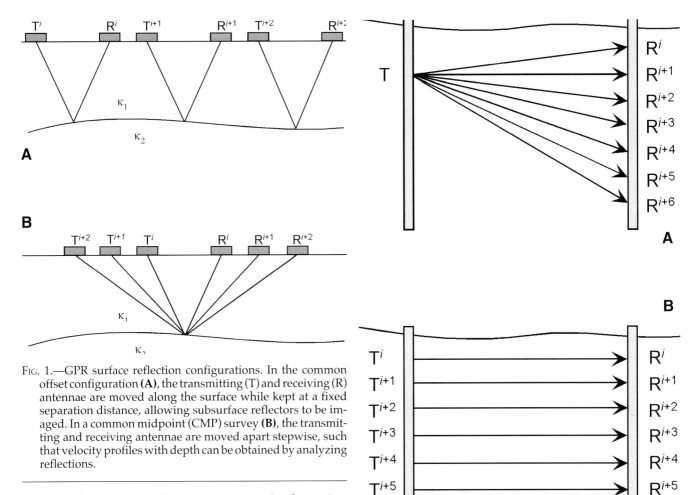

FIG. 1.—GPR surface reflection configurations. In the common offset configuration **(A)**, the transmitting (T) and receiving (R) antennae are moved along the surface while kept at a fixed separation distance, allowing subsurface reflectors to be imaged. In a common midpoint (CMP) survey **(B)**, the transmitting and receiving antennae are moved apart stepwise, such that velocity profiles with depth can be obtained by analyzing reflections.

where θ is the volumetric soil water content, equal to the product of the water saturation and the porosity. A polynomial expression for water content as a function of the dielectric constant was reported as well:

$$\theta = -5.3\text{x}10^{-2} + 2.92\text{x}10^{-2}\theta - 5.5\text{x}10^{-4}\kappa^2 + 4.3\text{x}10^{-6}\kappa^3 \qquad (4)$$

This relationship can be used to estimate the water saturation from GPR-inferred values of the dielectric constant given that the soil porosity is known.

Another common way to model the dielectric constant is through a mixing model, which equates the sum of the square roots of the component dielectric constants with the square root of the mixture dielectric constant (Birchak et al., 1974; Sihvola, 1999). This model is commonly referred to as the CRIM (component refractive index model). It has been used to estimate porosity with both borehole logging data in fully saturated rock (Wharton et al., 1980) and also with crosshole data in a fully saturated alluvial aquifer (Peterson et al., 1999). For the more general case of partially saturated soil, the CRIM model can be written as

$$\kappa = \left[(1-\varphi)\sqrt{\kappa_s} + S_w\varphi\sqrt{\kappa_w} + (1-S_w)\varphi\sqrt{\kappa_a}\right] \qquad (5)$$

where k_s, k_w, and k_a are the dielectric constants for the solid, water, and air components of the soil, respectively, φ is the soil porosity, and S_w is the water saturation (Roth et al., 1990). Sihvola (1999) thoroughly reviews methods for modeling the effective dielectric constant for different types of heterogeneous mixtures, including anisotropic ones.

FIG. 2.—Two GPR crosshole configurations. **A)** A multiple-offset gather (MOG) where the transmitter T (at position j) sends an electromagnetic pulse from a borehole across a measurement plane, where the signal is recorded in another borehole at multiple receiver positions R. **B)** For the zero-offset profile (ZOP), each measurement is made with the transmitter and receiver at the same depths.

GPR attenuation is another important wave attribute governed by both the dielectric constant and the electrical conductivity. For wave propagation in low-loss material, the attenuation coefficient is approximated by

$$\alpha \approx 0.5\sigma\sqrt{\mu/\varepsilon} = \sqrt{\mu/\kappa\varepsilon_0} \qquad (6)$$

where σ is the electrical conductivity (Table 1). In general, the presence of water, and other conductive materials such as clay, tends to increase attenuation and decrease GPR penetration depth (e.g., Davis and Annan, 1989; Turner and Siggins, 1994). Noon et al. (1998) discuss how to estimate the penetration depth given material properties and performance characteristics for of a GPR system.

One way to model the electrical conductivity of variably saturated soils was derived from Archie's Law (Archie, 1942) and is given by

$$\frac{\sigma}{\sigma_\omega} = \left[\frac{1}{S_w^n} \frac{a}{\varphi^m} \right]^{-1} \qquad (7)$$

where s_w is the electrical conductivity of the pore fluid, and a, m, and n are empirically determined parameters, typical values for which can be found in Schön (1996). Noting that the value of the exponent n is commonly near 2, Schön (1996) shows high sensitivity of the electrical conductivity, and thus attenuation, to water saturation.

APPLICATION OF GPR TO HYDROGEOLOGICAL SITE CHARACTERIZATION

The application of GPR to hydrogeological site characterization can be divided into several categories: (1) using estimates of EM wave velocity to map water distribution, (2) relating GPR reflection images to spatial distributions of hydraulic parameters, (3) converting GPR attributes to hydraulic parameters, and (4) using time-lapsed GPR to infer hydraulic parameters. Some examples from each of these categories follow.

Using Estimates of EM Wave Velocity to Map Water Distribution

GPR wave arrival times can be used in various ways to calculate wave velocities, which can then be converted first to dielectric constant and then to water content or water saturation with appropriate models (as discussed previously). For the surface reflection configuration (Fig. 1), both air and ground waves traveling between the antennae are recorded, as are reflections originating from the subsurface. Although the wave velocity in air is constant (~ 0.3 m/ns), that of the (slower moving) ground wave depends on the dielectric constant in the upper region of the soil. Not surprisingly, then, use of the groundwave for estimating water content in the uppermost soil regions is being developed and shows promise (Du and Rummel, 1994; Wollny, 1999; Huisman et al., 2001; Hubbard et al., 2002).

Another surface-reflection-based technique is the common-midpoint profile (CMP), which is used for obtaining depth-interval velocity estimates (e.g., Greaves et al., 1996; van Overmeeren, 1997). In a CMP survey, the transmitting and receiving antennae are moved apart stepwise such that the midpoint between them remains fixed at the same location (Fig. 1B). As opposed to the linear move-out of the direct air and ground waves, reflections generated at interfaces between materials of contrasting electrical parameters can be observed in the data set as hyperbolas, their curvatures depending on the average dielectric constant of the soil (van Overmeeren et al., 1997). Successful processing of a CMP data set yields the average velocity values between reflectors.

Greaves et al. (1996) collected CMP data sets consecutively along a horizontal line and obtained an image of GPR-derived water content that showed significant vertical and lateral variation. This image compared favorably with, and in fact improved, a borehole-derived hydrogeological description. The CMP method was further validated through comparison of the GPR-derived soil-water profile with that inferred from capacitance-probe measurements (van Overmeeren et al., 1997).

In some cases, reflectors at known depths allow a simplified conversion of arrival times to velocity and a more rapid determination of lateral variation in water content; because the transmitter and receiver offset are held constant, only one measurement at each location is necessary. Grote at al. (2002) performed reflection surveys in a sandpit at different antenna frequencies after burying reflectors at depths on the order of a meter. Accurate estimates of average water content were obtained using the fixed reflectors. The method was then employed to monitor water content in the drainage layer of a pavement section by measuring changes in wave velocity for that layer. Velocity distributions derived from crosshole GPR can also be used to infer moisture distributions. This application is addressed below.

Relating GPR Reflection Images to Spatial Distributions of Hydraulic Parameters

When the subsurface is laterally heterogeneous, borehole information alone is commonly insufficient for constructing hydrogeological models (Whittaker and Teutsch, 1999). GPR potentially provides high-resolution data between boreholes, but the challenge is in extracting meaningful information from GPR data that maps into flow and transport models. Sedimentary deposits can be identified with GPR in some cases, and this can be helpful in characterizing hydrogeological properties at a field site (e.g., Huggenberger, 1993; Rauber et al., 1998; Klingbeil et al., 1999; Lunt et al., this volume). Requisite for such an approach is a means of relating GPR-derived facies distributions to hydrogeological properties. Numerous studies have explored connections between hydrogeology and sedimentology by relating measurements of hydraulic parameters to lithofacies (e.g., Jussel et al., 1994; Bierkens, 1996; Klingbeil et al., 1999; Lunt et al., this volume; Heinz et al., 2003). Klingbeil et al. (1999) found that hydraulic parameters varied among different lithofacies (in Quaternary gravel deposits) though each lithofacies did not comprise a unique hydrofacies—facies with distinct flow properties. Each of 23 lithofacies fell into one of five hydrofacies categories. Methods aiming to transform GPR reflection images directly into hydrogeological models are in their infancy, and their success is likely to depend on the ability of GPR methods to detect and properly account for the (in many cases thin and continuous) structures that govern flow and transport.

Rea and Knight (1998) explored the possibility of generating spatial correlation models for permeability using GPR reflection-survey images. Their approach assumed equivalence of the semivariograms of the permeability and those calculated from the GPR reflection images. Because the subsurface region investigated in their study was above the water table and was composed of two GPR reflection-producing facies of highly contrasting permeability, GPR reflections were assumed related to interfaces between the two facies, and therefore related to the geometry of the permeability distribution. They found reasonable agreement between the GPR-derived semivariograms and those derived from a digitized outcrop image that was obtained from a site geologically similar to that where the GPR data were collected. Spatial correlation models derived in this way from GPR data would be especially useful for modeling variability in the horizontal direction, because such information is not easily obtained from limited borehole measurements. However, transient and non-uniform water saturation could complicate such an analysis by, for example, altering reflection amplitudes in regions that are wetter than others. In addition, a means for calculating the semivariogram of any one facies at a site that contains more than two reflection-causing facies is not evident.

Szerbiak et al. (2001) developed a framework for obtaining 3-D permeability models at an unsaturated reservoir-analog site. The main bounding surfaces were defined deterministically (with the help of borehole and outcrop information) and the internal features were defined statistically (with the help of GPR-derived correlation functions). They assumed that reflections were produced primarily by the contrast in electrical properties at sand–clay interfaces due to the comparatively large water retention of clay. A three-dimensional migration method was developed in order to convert reflections (recorded in time) into the depths at which they occurred. This resulted in the construction of 3-D velocity models. Because clay was thought to be the dominant cause of wave reflection, as in the work of Rea and Knight (1998), the mapped reflectors were assumed to define the geometry of the clay distribution, and therefore the geometry of the permeability distribution. Semivariogram analysis of the inferred permeability distribution yielded a model for its spatial variability. The contrast between fully saturated sand and clay is likely less than between the partially saturated sand and clay of the aquifer analog site. Before it is clear whether this approach can be applied to actual reservoir modeling (i.e., in a saturated aquifer), the effect of different saturation conditions on the GPR-derived correlation function needs to be addressed.

These last two examples demonstrate the potential for GPR to reveal spatial variability patterns of hydraulic parameters in idealized subsurface environments. Both studies were limited to the case where GPR reflections occurred only at the lithofacies that dominated fluid flow and transport (i.e., in both cases reflections occurred at clay facies whose permeability contrasted with that of the surrounding facies by orders of magnitude). This is, of course, commonly not the case in more complex sedimentary environments, where reflections are caused by many sedimentary structures that influence flow and transport differently.

Converting GPR Attributes to Hydraulic Parameters

Another approach to site characterization involves "directly" transforming GPR attributes such as velocity (Hubbard et al., 1999), attenuation (Chen et al., 2001), or reflection amplitudes (Schmalz et al., 2002) to hydraulic parameters through empirical relationships. Efforts have also been made to relate GPR attributes to physical parameters such as porosity, which can then be linked to hydrogeological properties through petrophysical models (e.g., Hubbard et al., 1997; Hubbard and Rubin, 2000). Considerable work has been done in developing petrophysical models that relate lithological indicators (e.g., porosity or grain-size distribution) to hydraulic properties such as hydraulic conductivity and permeability (Koltermann and Gorelick, 1995). In addition to empirically based techniques—ranging from site-specific correlations between porosity and permeability to statistical regressions between grain size and hydraulic conductivity—physically based models are available but require a considerable amount of information about pore geometry and grain size (Koltermann and Gorelick, 1995).

Knoll and Knight (1994) developed and tested in the laboratory a physically based petrophysical model linking the dielectric constant to permeability for variably saturated sand–clay mixtures (see also Knoll et al., 1995). This model made use of porosity values derived from measurements of dielectric constant (using the CRIM model), as well as some empirical parameters, as input into an equation for permeability—a form of the Kozeny–Carmen equation developed by Yin (1993) for sand and clay mixtures. One application of this model was presented by Hubbard et al. (1997; Hubbard and Rubin, 2000) in which a framework was developed for estimating the water saturation and permeability in a heterogeneous field from theoretical GPR crosshole data. Their synthetic model consisted of sand and clay facies, which gave non-unique velocity (or dielectric constant) values. Estimates of water saturation were not uniquely determined by the GPR-derived velocity values because the porosity (i.e., facies type) was unknown at any given location except for at the boreholes. The GPR-derived values for dielectric constant were related to possible values of water saturation and used together with borehole measurements in a maximum likelihood formalism to obtain the "most likely" distribution of water saturation or permeability. To apply their approach in the field, the use of site-specific petrophysical models would be preferred, because of the many assumptions of the Knoll and Knight (1994) model.

In a GPR reflection survey over an unconfined aquifer, Gloaguen et al. (2001) observed a reflection at the interface between the unsaturated and saturated sand (actually at the capillary fringe) and a reflection from an impermeable clay layer underlying the saturated sand at a depth of about 3.5 meters. Cokriging the two-way GPR travel times with actual depth measurements to the capillary fringe and to the clay layer allowed estimation of the reflector depths for the survey region. Velocity distributions in each layer could then be calculated (using the travel times and estimated reflector depths) and converted to 2-D parameter distributions of average values of water content in the upper layer and porosity in the lower layer (using both travel times and GPR attenuation). In addition, porosity values were converted to hydraulic conductivity using another variation of the Kozeny–Carmen equation (Mavko and Nur, 1997). However, this formulation also contains pore-shape parameters that could not be estimated from GPR. Unfortunately, these parameters had to be assumed constant in space, and average values from some presumably representative laboratory measurements were used. A method was also suggested for calculating porosity in the unsaturated zone through a curious combination of empirical relationships (Equations 4 and 5). This gave an unexpectedly low variation in porosity in the unsaturated zone.

Direct conversion of GPR attributes to hydraulic parameters at this time is limited to a few ideal cases (such as those mentioned above). However, it is expected that more information about the hydraulic parameters can be obtained indirectly, as by examining the movement of fluids or tracers in the subsurface—using time-lapsed GPR for this purpose shows promise.

Using Time-Lapsed GPR to Infer Hydraulic Parameters

It is the high sensitivity of GPR wave velocity to fluid distribution that makes using time-lapsed GPR during transient flow promising for improved characterization. Some studies have successfully demonstrated the potential of time-lapsed GPR surveys. For example, Tsoflias et al. (2001) used reflected wave amplitudes to infer changes in water saturation within a fracture plane during a pump test. Other studies aimed at using GPR for detecting liquid contaminants in the vadose zone (Brewster and Annan, 1994; Daniels et al., 1995). Brewster and Annan (1994) monitored contaminant movement using time-lapsed surface reflection surveys during the controlled release of a dense liquid contaminant (tetrachloroethylene) into a saturated sandy aquifer. This was made possible by the large contrast in reflection coefficient between the liquid contaminant, with a dielectric constant of 2.3, and the displaced water, with a dielectric constant of 81. Birken and Versteeg (2000) developed a method to further process such data sets. A qualitative hydrogeological model (i.e., of contaminant migration paths) was constructed on the basis of the inferred locations of contaminants with time. Although these results are encouraging, "questions on what we really observe and can extract in terms of subsurface fluid flow and hydrogeological properties need to be investigated" (Birken and Versteeg, 2000, p. 226).

Efforts have also been made to monitor fluid movement between boreholes with crosshole GPR methods (e.g., Eppstein and Dougherty, 1998; Alumbaugh et al., 2000; Binley et al., 2001). Eppstein and Dougherty (1998) obtained from crosshole measurements three-dimensional distributions of wave velocity before and after injection of a salt-water tracer into the vadose zone. They interpreted the differences in velocity before and after injection to be caused by changes in soil moisture, the distribution of which appeared to be highly influenced by soil heterogeneity. Unfortunately, independently measured data on soil type and moisture distribution were very limited.

If the changes in the spatial distribution of moisture can be detected and mapped with GPR methods, then such information might be used to infer the distribution of hydraulic parameters such as absolute permeability, or the parameters describing the relative permeability and capillary pressure functions (e.g., Binley et al., 2002; Kowalsky et al., 2004). Here, we begin to assess the feasibility of mapping moisture changes with GPR by simulating GPR for various data-collection configurations in a model undergoing steady-state and transient flow. Two ponding infiltration tests will be presented after a brief description of the procedures used for simulating variably saturated flow and GPR.

SIMULATION OF VARIABLY SATURATED FLOW

In order to simulate infiltration in the vadose zone, the variable-saturation flow simulator TOUGH2 (Pruess, 1991) was used with "EOS9", a module specially adapted for solving the Richards equation for incompressible flow of water in non-deformable porous media, which can be written as

$$\phi \frac{\partial S_w}{\partial t} \nabla \left[\frac{K(S_w)}{\rho_w g} \nabla P^c(S_w) - K(S_w) \hat{\mathbf{z}} \right] = 0 \qquad (8)$$

where K and P^c, both functions of water saturation S_w, are the effective hydraulic conductivity [m/s] and the capillary pressure [pascals (Pa)], respectively, ρ_w is the water density [kg/m³], g is the acceleration due to gravity [m/s²], ϕ is the porosity, and $\hat{\mathbf{z}}$ is the vertically oriented unit vector (e.g., Bear, 1988). The effective hydraulic conductivity is defined as

$$K = k \frac{k_{rel}(S_w) \rho_w g}{\eta_w} \qquad (9)$$

where k is the absolute (or intrinsic) permeability [m²], k_{rel} is the dimensionless relative permeability (the only component of K that is a function of water saturation), and η_w is the dynamic viscosity of water [pascal-seconds (Pa s)].

In addition to needing hydraulic parameters such as absolute permeability and porosity distributions, solving Equations 8–9 requires functions that cast the relative permeability and capillary pressure in terms of water saturation. Faybishenko (2000) reviewed the field and laboratory techniques used to measure these relationships as well as the numerous closed-form expressions used to model them, each containing soil-specific fitting parameters (e.g., Brooks and Corey, 1964; Mualem, 1976; van Genuchten, 1980). One formulation for the relative-permeability and capillary-pressure functions, respectively, is given by van Genuchten (1980):

$$k_{rel} = \sqrt{S} \left[1 - (1 - S^{1/\lambda})^\lambda \right]^2 \qquad (10)$$

$$P^c = -\frac{\rho_w g}{\alpha} (S^{-1/\lambda} - 1)^{1-\lambda} \qquad (11)$$

where λ and α [m⁻¹] are fitting parameters for a given soil, and S is the normalized water saturation, defined as

$$S = \frac{S_w - S_w^{res}}{S_w^{sat} - S_w^{res}} \qquad (12)$$

where S_w^{res} and S_w^{sat} are the residual and maximal water saturation values, respectively. Most of the desired relative-permeability and capillary-pressure functions, including those of van Genuchten (1980), are easily incorporated into TOUGH2 for flow modeling. See Pruess (1991, 1994) for further details.

SIMULATION OF GPR SURVEYS

Methods for simulating GPR wave propagation commonly involve the numerical solution of some form of the Maxwell equations. The Maxwell equations, which relate the time-varying electric and magnetic fields, govern the propagation of GPR waves and are given by

$$\nabla \times \mathbf{H} = \frac{\partial \mathbf{D}}{\partial t} + \mathbf{J} \qquad (13)$$

$$\nabla \times \mathbf{H} = \frac{\partial \mathbf{D}}{\partial t} + \mathbf{J} \qquad (14)$$

$$\nabla \cdot \mathbf{D} = \rho \qquad (15)$$

$$\nabla \cdot \mathbf{B} = 0 \qquad (16)$$

where $\mathbf{H}$ is the magnetic field vector [amperes per meter $(A \cdot m^{-1})$], $\mathbf{D}$ the dielectric flux density vector [ampere-seconds per square meter $(A \cdot s \cdot m^{-2})$], $\mathbf{J}$ the current density vector [amperes per square meter $(A \cdot m^{-2})$], $\mathbf{E}$ the electric field vector [volts per meter $(V \cdot m^{-1})$], $\mathbf{B}$ the magnetic flux density vector [volt-seconds per square meter $(V \cdot s \cdot m^{-2})$], and ρ is the charge density scalar [ampere-seconds per cubic meter $(A \cdot s \cdot m^{-3})$]. The constitutive relations between the electric and magnetic fields and their respective fluxes, and between the electric field and the current density, respectively, are as follows

$$\mathbf{D} = \varepsilon \mathbf{E} \qquad (17)$$

$$\mathbf{B} = \mu \mathbf{H} \qquad (18)$$

$$\mathbf{J} = \sigma \mathbf{E} \qquad (19)$$

where ε, σ, and μ are the permittivity [ampere-seconds per volt-meter $(A \cdot s \cdot (V \cdot m)^{-1})$], the electrical conductivity [amperes per volt-meter $(A \cdot (V \cdot m)^{-1})$, or Siemens per meter $(S \cdot m^{-1})$], and the magnetic permeability [$V \cdot s \cdot (A \cdot m)^{-1}$], respectively, where Siemens (S) is the SI unit for electrical conductance. The magnetic permeability is equal to that of free space $(4\pi \times 10^{-7} [V \cdot s \cdot (A \cdot m)^{-1}])$ for most earth materials that contain no metals (Turner and Siggins, 1994). As mentioned previously, the dielectric constant κ of a material is the real part of the effective permittivity normalized by that of free space. Recall that κ (and therefore, ε) and σ vary for soil type and water saturation. They can also vary with frequency (Guegeun and Palciauskas, 1994) but are commonly considered frequency independent for many materials for the range of frequencies used in GPR (Daniels, 1996).

Substitution of Equations 17–19 into Equations 13 and 14 gives the EM equations for media whose parameters ε, σ, and μ can be considered frequency independent:

$$\nabla \times \mathbf{E} = -\mu \frac{\partial \mathbf{H}}{\partial t} \qquad (20)$$

$$\nabla \times \mathbf{H} = \varepsilon \frac{\partial \mathbf{E}}{\partial t} + \sigma \mathbf{E} \qquad (21)$$

from which three scalar equations can be written

$$\varepsilon \frac{\partial E_y}{\partial t} = \frac{\partial H_x}{\partial_z} - \frac{\partial H_z}{\partial_x} - \sigma E_y \qquad (22)$$

$$\mu \frac{\partial H_x}{\partial t} = \frac{\partial E_y}{\partial_z} \qquad (23)$$

$$\mu \frac{\partial H_z}{\partial t} = \frac{\partial E_y}{\partial x} \qquad (24)$$

where the three unknown scalar quantities are the electric field in the y direction (E_y), and the magnetic fields for the x and z directions (H_x and H_z, respectively). These are the 2-D equations for the so-called transverse electric (TE) polarization. A set of orthogonal equations, uncoupled from Equations 22–24, can similarly be obtained to describe the coupled components H_y, E_x, and E_z. Those equations comprise the transverse magnetic (TM) polarization. Because typical GPR systems radiate power into the TE polarization, the equations for this polarization are commonly used for modeling (Stutzman and Thiele, 1981; Casper and Kung, 1996).

Numerous techniques for simulating GPR wave propagation have been developed, ranging from ray-based methods (Cai and McMechan, 1995) to pseudo-spectral methods (Casper and Kung, 1996), to time-domain finite-difference techniques (Kunz and Luebbers, 1993). Numerical techniques also account for such issues as modeling antennae radiation patterns (Carcione, 1998), as well as frequency dependence of the dielectric permittivity (e.g., Luebbers and Hunsberger, 1992; Xu and McMechan, 1997), and frequency dependence of both the dielectric permittivity and the conductivity (Carcione, 1996; Bergmann et al., 1998).

We followed the procedure of Bergmann et al. (1998), using a staggered-grid finite-difference scheme with fourth-order accurate approximations for the spatial derivatives, and second-order accurate approximations for the time derivatives. However, in this work we used frequency-independent parameters, as is fairly common in GPR modeling studies (e.g., Casper and Kung, 1996; Wang and McMechan, 2002). This makes the equations being solved equivalent to Equations 22–24, where attenuation and wave velocity vary in space because the electrical permittivity and conductivity are functions of water content and porosity (Equations 5 and 7).

Absorbing boundaries are implemented with a method similar to that of Casper and Kung (1996) to minimize artificial reflections from the boundaries of the model. The GPR transmitter pulse is modeled as a point source with a Ricker wavelet of desired central frequency. The air–ground interfaces (on the ground surface and in the boreholes) are not modeled, to simplify interpretation, because we are interested primarily in examining the effects of water saturation and soil heterogeneity on GPR data. The effects of coupling between the antennae and the boreholes and at the air–ground surface have been considered elsewhere (e.g., Kunz and Luebbers, 1993; Taflove, 1995; Holliger and Bergmann, 2000; Wang and McMechan, 2002).

CASE STUDY: MONITORING PONDING INFILTRATION TESTS WITH GPR

Previous work involved the use of an outcrop model to simulate GPR for different saturation conditions (Kowalsky et al., 2001). A model with non-uniform water saturation best reproduced main reflections seen in field data. However, to obtain a non-uniformly saturated model some simplistic assumptions were made regarding the distribution of water in the various sedimentary units. The open-framework (OF) gravel units were assumed to be more drained (i.e., at lower water saturation) than the surrounding ones, and water saturation was assumed to be constant and uniform throughout each sedimentary unit. Here, we extend this outcrop modeling study to include the simulation of variably saturated flow. This allows: (1) the simulation of GPR surveys under more realistic conditions in which water saturation is non-uniform within and between sedimentary units, and (2) examining the use of GPR during transient flow.

Description of Site

The field site modeled in this study is at a gravel quarry in Herten, a city in southwestern Germany. Detailed descriptions of this field site and available data were previously reported (Bayer, 2000; Kowalsky et al., 2001). Sedimentary deposits in this region were formed in a braided-river environment and consist mainly of layers of poorly sorted to well-sorted sand and gravel with little silt or clay (Bayer, 2000). During the summer of 1999, geophysical data (including GPR measurements) were collected at the quarry previous to its excavation. After completion of the GPR surveys, excavation of the quarry proceeded in such a way as to produce parallel outcrop faces (with spacing of 1–2 meters), each roughly corresponding to the vertical plane underneath a GPR reflection survey line. High-resolution photographs of the receding outcrop face were then analyzed and converted to sedimentary maps (Bayer, 2000). For each of the sedimentary units, some field and laboratory measurements of absolute permeability and porosity were made (Klingbeil, 1998). Inspection of the successive outcrop images showed the variation of sedimentary structure in the direction perpendicular to the outcrop planes to be significant but gradual enough to justify two-dimensional modeling of fluid flow and GPR for a single outcrop plane.

The distribution of porosity and absolute permeability for one of the outcrop images (discretized with 5 cm by 5 cm block size) from the Herten site are shown in Figures 3A and 3B, respectively. The OF gravel units, shown as black and dark gray in Figure 3B, have the highest permeability values. In a fully saturated aquifer, these units can act as fast paths for contaminants, whereas in the vadose zone they can act as capillary barriers causing water ponding above them (refer to Hillel, 1982, p. 109–110). The lowest–permeability unit (shown as white in Figure 3B) contains fine particles, and the remaining units are various mixtures of sand and gravel with varying porosities and permeabilities. Further descriptions of such sedimentary deposits are described elsewhere (Klingbeil, 1998; Heinz, 2001; Heinz et al., 2003).

Simulation of Steady-State Saturation and Ponding-Infiltration Tests

The van Genuchten relations (Equations 10–12) were chosen to model the relative-permeability and capillary-pressure functions using the measured values of absolute permeability for each sedimentary unit and typical values for coarse sands for the remaining parameters. To obtain hydraulic parameter α_i (used in Equation 11) for each sedimentary unit i, scaling was performed according to

$$\frac{\alpha_i}{\sqrt{k_{r,i}}} = \frac{\alpha_{ref}}{\sqrt{k_{r,ref}}} \qquad (25)$$

where $k_{r,i}$ is the relative permeability for unit i, and $k_{r,ref}$ is the reference relative permeability (e.g., Leverett, 1941; Warrick et al., 1977). Values $\alpha_{ref} = 50\,m^{-1}$ and $k_{r,ref} = 1 \times 10^{-9}\,m^2$ were used (Pruess, 1994). Although hysteresis can substantially affect the redistribution of water following infiltration (e.g., Philip, 1991), for simplicity this effect was not modeled in the present work. Table 2

TABLE 2.—Summary of flow modeling parameters.

Fluid-Flow Parameters	Values
Fluid properties	$\eta = 1.002 \times 10^{-3}$ Pa s, $\rho_w = 1000$ kg/m^3, $P_{atm} = 1.01 \times 10^5$ Pa
Relative permeability and capillary pressure functions (see Equations 10–11)	$l = 0.457$, α (m^{-1}) determined by scaling (see Equation 25), $S_w^{res} = 0.15$, and $S_w^{sat} = 1.0$
Scaling (see Equation 25)	$\alpha_{ref} = 50$ m^{-1}, $k_{r,ref} = 10^{-9}$ m^2

Water viscosity η is given in pascals (Pa) per second, ρ_w is the fluid density, and P_{atm} is the assigned value of atmospheric pressure. The parameters λ and α are used in Equations 10 and 11, where S_w^{res} and S_w^{sat} are the residual and maximal water-saturation values. α_{ref} and $k_{r,ref}$ are the reference values used for estimating a for each soil through Equation 25.

provides a summary of the flow-modeling parameters used in this study.

For all flow simulations, the vertical side boundaries were modeled as no flow boundaries, and, because the water table was below the bottom of the outcrop at the field site, water saturation was held constant at a value of 0.75 at the lower boundary of the model. Steady-state conditions were first obtained by assigning atmospheric conditions (constant saturation of 0.25) to the surface and simulating flow until gravity–capillary equilibrium. Figure 3C shows the modeled water-saturation profile for steady-

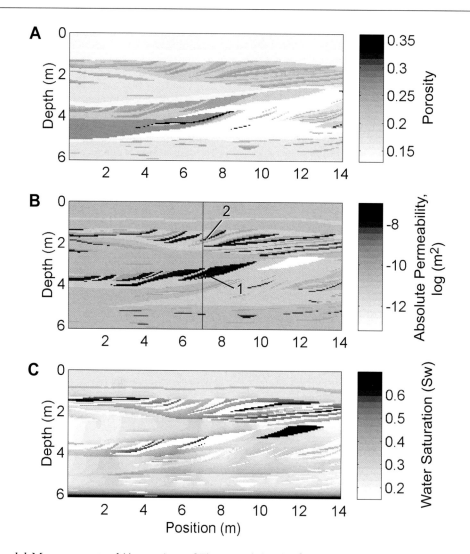

FIG. 3.—Outcrop model. Measurements of **A)** porosity and **B)** permeability for the sedimentary units allow the modeling of fluid flow and GPR. **C)** The simulated water-saturation profile for steady state (pre-infiltration) conditions. This water-saturation profile is used for initial conditions in simulating ponding-infiltration tests.

state conditions. As expected, non-uniform saturation is seen between and within sedimentary units.

The steady-state profile was then used to define the initial conditions for two ponding-infiltration tests in which a constant water head of 10 cm was imposed for 30 minutes over the entire model surface (i.e., a uniform water source) for the first case, and over a 2 meter region (i.e., representing a point source of water in the model plane, and a line source of water perpendicular to the model plane) for the second case. Following ponding, atmospheric conditions were returned to the surface for both cases, and the water-saturation profiles were recorded for increasing times as water redistribution occurred. A brief description of the GPR simulations is next given, followed by a summary of each simulated infiltration test.

Simulation of GPR Measurements

The previously outlined method was used to simulate GPR surveys in reflection and crosshole configurations for both before (at steady state) and during the infiltration tests. Following Bergmann et al. (1998), waveform amplitudes at each time were multiplied by the square root of time to allow for the waveforms generated by a 2-D line source to approximate those of a 3-D point source. The transmitter and receiver were separated by about 1 meter, and simulations were performed along the "surface" of the model (actually, the transmitter and receiver were placed in the upper layer because the air–ground interface was not modeled). For the crosshole surveys, the transmitting and receiving antennae were placed directly in the subsurface model (i.e., airfilled boreholes were not explicitly modeled). For all cases, the central frequency of the transmitter pulse was 100 MHz, set to match the central frequency seen in field data from the site (Bayer, 2000; Kowalsky et al., 2001).

The electrical parameters were modeled with Equations 5 and 7 along with the measured porosity values (Fig. 3A) and simulated water-saturation values (as in Figure 3C). The component dielectric constant values used for Equation 5 were 6.9 for the solid component (the value for quartz as measured in the laboratory by Knoll and Knight, 1994), 81 for water, and 1 for air. The parameters a and m in Equation 7 were assigned values of 0.88 and 1.37, respectively, average values for unconsolidated sand, and n was 2 (Schön, 1996). Site-specific measurements could improve the accuracy of these values. However, because the goal of the present work is to investigate the general response of GPR measurements to changing water saturation for a known, plausible model, highly accurate parameters are unnecessary. The electrical conductivity of the pore fluid is taken to be 0.4 mS/cm (milli-Siemens per centimeter), a value typical for the site investigated. Table 3 lists the various parameters used in the GPR simulations.

Infiltration Test #1: Uniform Ponding over Entire Surface

In the first experiment, ponding was applied uniformly across the entire surface of the model. As opposed to studies where GPR was used to delineate an advancing infiltration front (as in Kuroda et al., 2002), the main focus here is to see how the redistribution of water that occurs after the infiltration front has already passed through the model affects simulated GPR images. Therefore, we focus our attention mostly on two later times (6 hours and 7 days after the end of ponding), by which time the infiltration front had already reached the lower boundary of the model.

The vertical saturation profile for an arbitrary horizontal position (at $x = 7$ m in Figure 3) is shown in Figure 4.1 for several times, as is the change in saturation from 6 hours to 7 days after ponding in Figure 4.2. For reference, a vertical black line at $x = 7$ m in Figure 3B shows the location of the vertical section plotted in Figure 4. In addition, the absolute permeability for the vertical section is shown in Figure 4.3, and the location of the high-permeability OF gravel units are indicated by gray shading (Figs. 4.1–4.3). Water ponding is observed (labeled A in Figure 4.1) above regions of increased permeability serving as capillary barriers, such as the partially saturated open-framework gravel layers (labeled 1 and 2 in Figure 3b). Water saturation below the thick gravel layer between 3 and 4 meters depth drains more quickly with time (see region labeled B in Figure 4.2). This trend forms the basis for understanding the time-varying change in electrical properties. It may also allow delineation of zones containing OF gravel, or interfaces between units with contrasting permeability, with time-lapsed GPR measurements.

Two-dimensional flow phenomena are substantial in this model. For instance, the inclination of capillary barriers affects drainage and causes water to be directed laterally. For example, an apparent increase in drainage occurs in one location despite there being an underlying capillary barrier (the uppermost OF gravel layer seen in Figure 4.2). This is due to the fact that the underlying OF gravel layer is inclined (labeled 2 in Figure 3 and labeled C in Figure 4.2) and allows water to easily flow downward and toward the left side of the model. It should be noted that the water distribution in the near vicinity of the side boundaries is influenced by the no-flow boundary conditions (Rubin and

TABLE 3.—Summary of parameters for simulating GPR.

Electrical Parameters	Values
Dielectric constant (see Equation 5)	$\kappa_s = 6.9$, $\kappa_w = 81$, $\kappa_a = 1$, $\varepsilon_o = 8.854 \times 10^{-12}$ As/Vm
Electrical conductivity (see Equation 7)	$a = 0.88$, $n = 2$, $m = 1.37$, $\sigma_w = 0.4$ mS/cm
Magnetic permeability	$\mu = 4\pi \times 10^{-7}$ Vs/Am
2-D Finite-difference parameters	$\Delta x = \Delta y = 50$ cm, $\Delta t = 0.13$ ns

The dielectric constants for the solid, water, and air components of the soil (κ_s, κ_w, and κ_a, respectively) are used in Equation 5 along with model porosity values (see Figure 3A) for calculating the effective dielectric constant of partially saturated soil. The electrical permittivity ε_o is given in units of ampere-seconds per volt-meter (As/Vm). The empirical constants a, n, and m are used, along with a value of the electrical conductivity of pore water (σ_w), given in milli-Siemens (mS) per centimeter, to calculate the effective electrical conductivity through Equation 7. The magnetic permeability μ is equal to that of free space and given in units of volt-seconds per ampere-meter (Vs/Am). In order to simulate wave propagation, the model is discretized in Δx increments in the horizontal direction and Δy in the vertical direction, and the time step Δt is given in nanoseconds (ns).

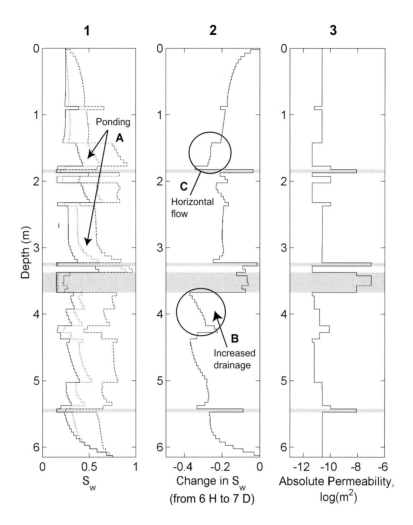

FIG. 4.—Vertical slice of simulated water saturation. **1)** The simulated water-saturation profiles at *x* = 7 m (see Fig. 3) for steady state (pre-infiltration) conditions (solid line), for 6 hours after ponding (dashed line) and 7 days after ponding (dotted line); **2)** change in water saturation from 6 hours to 7 days after ponding; and **3)** corresponding absolute permeability for vertical slice. The OF gravel units are shaded gray. Ponded (or perched) water is observed above the OF gravel (labeled A). In addition, increased drainage is seen to occur below the OF gravel (labeled B). 2-D flow effects are seen as well (an inclined OF gravel layer allowed lateral movement of water (i.e., increased drainage in region labeled C).

Dagan, 1989). This causes: (1) accumulation of water above capillary barriers that slope upward away from the side boundary, and (2) a lack of recharge for regions underneath such barriers that slope downward from the boundary. The regions chosen for simulated crosshole surveys (described in the next section) are in the middle of the model so that effects from the no-flow boundaries are minimal.

Surface Reflection Surveys.—

GPR surface reflection measurements were simulated in increments of 15 cm requiring a total of 96 simulations for each survey. 2-D diffraction migrations (with a lateral summation width of 3.5 meters) were performed on the simulated waveforms using Reflex-Win (Sandmeier, 1999) to minimize the occurrence of diffracted waves in the GPR images while accounting for lateral and vertical variations of velocity in the outcrop models. The 2-D velocity distributions used for the migration were constructed in Reflex-Win by importing 1-D profiles of velocity versus depth (from the actual velocity models) in horizontal increments of 1 meter. The time axes were then converted to depth using the 2-D velocity distributions for each model.

The GPR image obtained for steady-state conditions is shown in Figure 5.1. There is a good correspondence between the observed reflections and the sedimentary units of the outcrop model (Fig. 3). Some dipping reflections occur in the region of the OF gravel layers (labeled A). An example of a clearly visible reflector is that which occurs at a depth of 5 m (labeled B). Note that the reflection at 6 meters is the reflection from the bottom of the model, where the water saturation increases to 0.75.

Figure 5.2 shows a survey simulated 20 minutes after the termination of ponding. At this time, the infiltration front has not reached the bottom of the model, and different reflection patterns arise (labeled C). Figure 5.3 shows the GPR image 6 hours after ponding, by which time the infiltration front has already reached the bottom of the model so that the modeled subsurface is undergoing drainage (water redistribution). Comparison of Figures 5.1 and 5.3 shows overall similarities but also significant

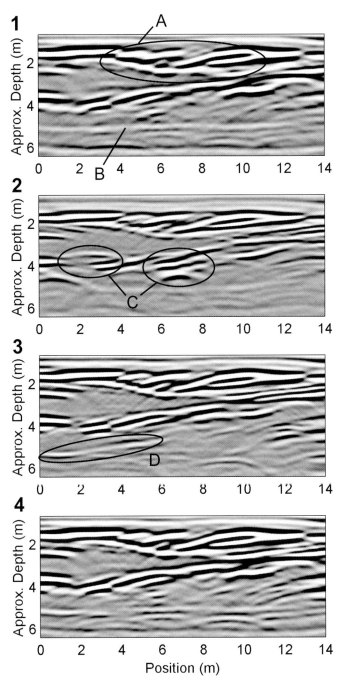

differences. Reflections off the bounding surfaces of the sedimentary zones in the upper half of the model are similar. The OF gravel units produce reflections in both cases. This similarity is expected, though, because reflections occur at boundaries where the contrast in water saturation is large. After 6 hours, water has drained more quickly from the OF gravel than from the other units. Therefore, these contrasts exist during both steady-state conditions and during infiltration. However, the deeper reflector at a depth of about 5 meters is no longer clearly visible. On the contrary, a new reflector appears (labeled D). The simulation for 7 days (Fig. 5.4) shows that, as moisture conditions return toward steady state, the GPR image begins to resemble that seen at steady state.

The effects of infiltrating water are seen to be visible and significant in the GPR reflection images. Altered saturation conditions caused new sedimentary structure to be seen (Fig. 5.3) in some cases, but it also caused the loss of coherent reflectors in other cases (Fig. 5.2). This suggests that it may be important to take previous and current weather conditions at a site into account when planning GPR surveys. How long GPR data will be affected by, for example, a strong rainfall event is difficult to know in advance. Repeating surveys under varied surface conditions may be worthwhile.

Crosshole (MOG) Surveys. —

Crosshole GPR measurements were simulated for a region in the middle of the outcrop model. The velocity distributions for this region are shown in Figures 6A and B for steady-state conditions and for 6 hours after the end of ponding, respectively. Three boreholes were placed at $x = 4, 7,$ and 10 m (as indicated in the figures), defining two planes for crosshole tomography. Accordingly, the transmitter and receiver were moved in the boreholes surrounding each plane in increments approximately equal to a quarter-wavelength of the GPR wave (~ 25 cm). The straight-ray-path algebraic reconstruction technique (ART) inversion algorithm given by Peterson et al. (1985) was used to calculate the distributions of wave velocity (i.e., velocity tomograms) from the recorded arrival times of the simulated MOG survey for each plane.

The resulting tomograms for steady-state conditions and 6 hours after ponding, respectively, are shown in Figures 6C and D. The tomograms are quite smooth compared to the actual velocity models. A fairly continuous region of low velocity is observed at a depth of about two meters. Although this region consists of layers of OF gravel that have low water saturation (high GPR velocity), the units alternating with the OF gravel contain enough trapped water to give an overall low velocity.

Although the variation of GPR velocity is not large for steady-state conditions, variation in velocity within the tomograms increases during the infiltration experiment (compare Figure 6C and Figure 6D). The manner in which the tomograms change with time after the infiltration event offers additional information. The frequency distributions for the tomogram velocity values are shown for increasing times in Figures 7A–C. During steady-state conditions, the mean velocity is highest (~ 0.108 m/ns) because the model is driest at that time (Fig. 7A). The mean velocity is lowest (~ 0.091 m/ns) 6 hours after infiltration (Fig. 7B), when the average water saturation is higher than for the other two times shown. The relative frequency plots also show an increase in the spread of velocity values from steady-state conditions to 6 hours after infiltration (i.e., the standard deviation changes from 0.011 to 0.021), indicating the potential for improved detection of structure after ponding infiltration.

Figures 7D–F depict the tomograms in terms of deviation from their mean velocities (i.e., how many percent above or

FIG. 5.—GPR reflection surveys **1)** simulated during steady-state (pre-infiltration), and **2)** at 20 minutes, **3)** 6 hours, and **4)** 7 days after end of ponding. Some dipping reflections occur in the region of the OF gravel layers (A). An example of a clearly visible reflector is that which occurs at a depth of 5 m during steady-state conditions (B). Note that the reflection at 6 meters is the reflection from the bottom of the model, where the water saturation increases to 0.75. At 20 minutes after ponding, the infiltration front has not reached the bottom of the model, and different reflection patterns arise (C). A new reflector (D) appears after 6 hours. After 7 days, the GPR image begins to resemble that seen at steady state (compare 5.1 and 5.4). The wave amplitude is represented by color, where black is minimum and white is maximum.

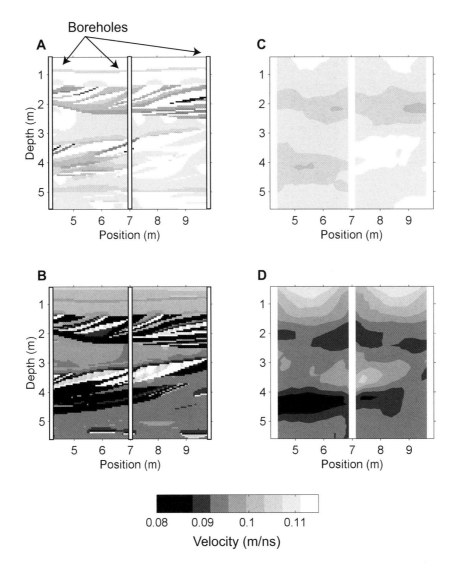

FIG. 6.—Crosshole GPR simulations before and after ponding infiltration. The velocity distributions for the region being modeled are shown for **A)** steady-state conditions and **B)** for 6 hours after the end of ponding. Three boreholes were placed at $x = 4, 7$, and 10 m, defining two planes for crosshole measurements. Inversion of simulated travel times gives velocity tomograms for **C)** steady-state conditions and **D)** for 6 hours after ponding.

below the mean velocity each pixel in the tomogram is). During steady-state conditions, the total difference in velocity between regions A and B is on the order of 5%, a contrast that might be considered low and difficult to observe in the field, especially when appreciable noise is present in the data. However, 6 hours after ponding, the contrast in velocity between the same regions more than doubles to over 10%, a contrast more likely to be observed in field data. At another location, where there was no apparent contrast during steady state, there exists a contrast between two regions (regions shown by arrows labeled with C in Fig. 7B) at 6 hours after ponding. Thus, lithofacies or boundaries between lithofacies become visible as saturation conditions are altered.

In addition to comparing time-lapsed tomograms with each other, there is potential information about sedimentary structure to be gained by mapping the relative change in velocity with time. Figure 8 shows the percent increase in velocity from 6 hours to 7 days after infiltration. During that time, the model is mostly

drying, and the velocity is increasing, but not uniformly. A laterally continuous region (as noted in the Figure 8B) is evident where velocity has increased by about 20%, significantly more than directly above this region. This is because the region lies below some layers of OF gravel, which impede drainage from above but which allow drainage of water below.

New sedimentary structures became visible with synthetic crosshole measurements during transient water flow. Compared to crosshole measurements simulated during steady-state conditions, simulated time-lapsed measurements were seen to offer an improved understanding of the hydrogeological behavior of the model.

Crosshole (ZOP) Surveys.—

Simulated ZOP surveys were also performed and examined for the tomogram plane between boreholes at $x = 4$ and 7 meters at steady state and during the infiltration experiment. The simu-

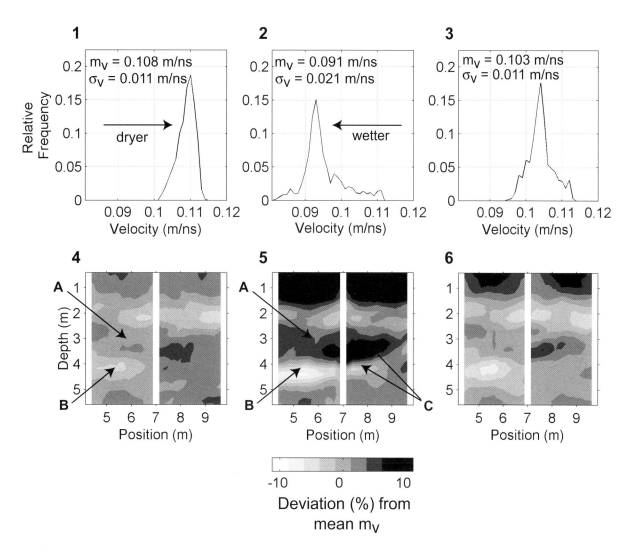

Fig. 7.—Variation of GPR tomogram velocity during ponding infiltration. Relative frequency distributions are shown from velocity tomograms for **A)** steady state, **B)** 6 hours, and **C)** 7 days after ponding. The mean velocity value (m_V) and standard deviation (σ_V) of each distribution are shown as well. The distribution with the highest mean velocity corresponds to the survey performed under "driest" conditions (pre-infiltration), and the distribution with the lowest mean velocity corresponds to the survey done under "wettest" conditions (6 hours after ponding).

lated travel times were used to calculate the horizontally averaged wave velocities. With real field data, corrections would also need to be made for the GPR system delay and travel time through the boreholes. The ZOP velocity profiles are shown in Figure 9A for increasing times, each relatively smooth and with a decrease at near 2 meters depth. The change in the velocity profile from 6 hours to 7 days after ponding is shown in Figure 9B to show how the draining process appears with ZOP measurements.

Velocity images can be converted to water content without knowing porosity (as mentioned earlier). In the case of homogeneous or layered material, velocity profiles can also be converted to water saturation because the porosity of the material can be estimated (e.g., from borehole measurements). However, in cases where lateral heterogeneity in porosity exists, conversion from velocity to water saturation is uncertain, and an average porosity may or may not suffice. By use of the average porosity of the model, the ZOP velocity profiles were converted to water satura-

tion, as shown in Figure 10A. In addition, the simulated water-saturation profile was horizontally averaged and smoothed in the vertical direction with a moving window of 0.5 meters—half the GPR wavelength (also shown in Figure 10A). Though the overall match is good, not all the peaks and troughs in water saturation are captured with the ZOP estimated profile. A depth-varying porosity function (obtained from taking the average of the two porosity profiles at the boreholes) was also used to convert the ZOP velocity to water saturation (also shown in Figure 10A). These GPR-derived estimates match the known profile somewhat better, illustrating the benefit of including variable porosity data.

Estimating the change in water saturation with time, inferred from time-lapsed ZOP measurements, appears to be somewhat less sensitive to the actual porosity value (as shown in Figure 10B), indicating that reasonably accurate estimates of changes in water saturation can be obtained from ZOP measurements using an average value of porosity.

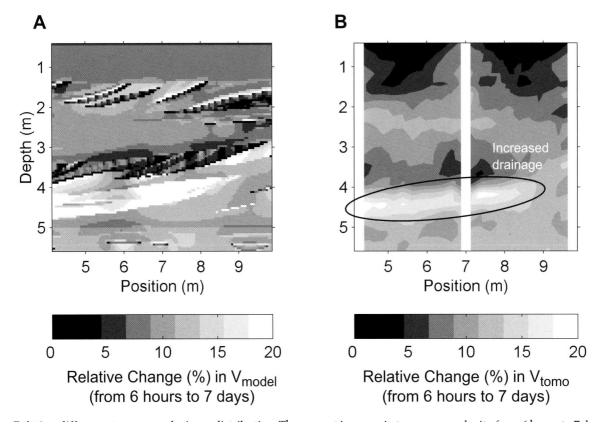

FIG. 8.—Relative-difference tomogram during redistribution. The percent increase in tomogram velocity from 6 hours to 7 days after the infiltration event **A)** for the actual velocity model and **B)** for the simulated tomogram. A region showing increased drainage is indicated.

Infiltration Test #2: Ponding Over 2 Meter Region

In the second infiltration test, ponding was applied over a 2 meter region toward the center of the model surface. Because 2-D flow is modeled, this represents a point source of water in the model plane and a line source of water perpendicular to the model plane. The main focus of this test was to examine how an infiltration plume affects GPR measurements and whether the infiltration front and plume shape can be tracked using GPR ZOP measurements (as was examined by Binley et al., 2001, and Kuroda et al., 2002, with field experiments). We focus our attention on the simulated water distribution at several early times (at 1 hour, 6 hours, and 24 hours after termination of ponding), before which the infiltration front had yet to reach the lower boundary of the model at a depth of 6 meters (see Fig. 11, 1a–4a). The uniform infiltration front in the previous test already reached a depth of 6 meters by 6 hours after ponding. However, the present configuration allows increased lateral water movement, ultimately resulting in a more slowly moving front.

Surface Reflection Surveys.—

GPR surface reflection measurements were simulated in increments of 10 cm from $x = 4$ to 10 m (see Figure 3), making a total of 61 simulations for each survey. In Figure 11 (1b–4b) the unprocessed GPR images are shown for pre-infiltration and at increasing times after ponding. For display purposes the arrival times were converted to approximate depth using a constant

velocity. However, the lateral and vertical variations in velocity are severe in the post-ponding models because of sharp contrasts in water saturation within and outside the infiltrating water plume. 2-D diffraction migrations (with a lateral summation width of 3.5 meters) were again performed on the simulated waveforms using Reflex-Win (Sandmeier, 1999) to minimize the occurrence of diffracted waves in the GPR images and especially to account for lateral and vertical variations of velocity in the models. The 2-D velocity distributions used for the migration were constructed in Reflex-Win by importing 1-D depth velocity profiles (from the actual velocity models) in horizontal increments of 50 cm. The time axes were then converted to depth using the 2-D velocity distributions for each model giving the processed GPR images shown in Figure 11 (1c–4c).

Strong diffractions that likely originate at the edges of the plume are seen in the unprocessed image at one hour after ponding in Figure 11 (2b). Processing the waveforms removes some of the diffracted waves, as shown in Figure 11 (2c), but the resulting image is not easy to interpret. In the image shown in Figure 11 (3b) for 6 hours after ponding, a reflection in the center of the model from OF gravel (labeled A) is seen to be lower in depth and higher in amplitude than for the pre-infiltration case. This reflection is delayed in time because of the (lower-velocity) wet soil above it. The increased amplitude can be attributed to an increase in ponded water above the gravel, which increases the contrast in water saturation between the gravel layer and the soil above it and, accordingly, increases the reflection coefficient. The processed image obtained with the detailed 2-D velocity model gives an image (Fig. 11 (3c)) similar to that for the

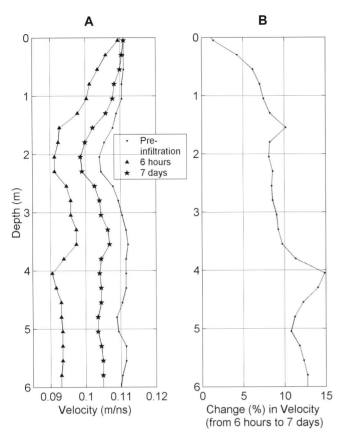

FIG. 9.—Simulated zero-offset (ZOP) velocity profiles. **A)** Estimated velocity profiles, calculated assuming horizontal travel paths; the dotted line, triangles, and stars correspond to simulations performed under steady state (pre-infiltration) conditions, 6 hours, and 7 days after ponding, respectively. **B)** The percent change in velocity from 6 hours to 7 days.

pre-infiltration survey (Fig. 11 (1c)). Although we have assumed it to be known, the 2-D velocity model is often the goal of a survey and obtained using CMP measurements when possible. However, examining the unprocessed image already gives worthwhile information—the movement a reflector indicates increased water saturation (i.e., water movement) above that reflector. By 24 hours after ponding, the GPR images shown in Figure 11 (4b-4c) have become similar to those seen in the pre-infiltration case (Fig. 11 (1b-1c)). However, the reflection seen before infiltration at 5 meters depth is still not visible at this time. As compared to the simulated crosshole measurements (shown next), the infiltration front was not clearly detectable using GPR reflection surveys, although some reflectors were seen to move, indicating changing water saturation.

Crosshole (ZOP) Surveys.—

Simulated ZOP surveys were also performed between two boreholes located at $x = 4$ and 10 meters (see Figure 3) at times before and during the infiltration test. The simulated travel times were again used to calculate the horizontally averaged wave velocities for each survey (Fig. 12A). The pre-infiltration velocity profile has a minimum value at near 2 m depth, similar to that seen in the ZOP surveys in the first ponding test, and a region of increased velocity between 3 and 3.5 meters depth due

to the occurrence of OF gravel. The changes from the pre-infiltration velocity profile to those for the above times are shown in Figure 12B. For the survey taken 1 hour after ponding, the velocity values above ~ 4 meters are reduced, which indicates that water saturation increased and that the infiltration front had reached 4 meters. The maximum reduction occurs at 2 meters depth (within the zone of inclined OF gravel layers). It can be accurately inferred from the ZOP velocity profiles that the depth of the infiltration front was at 4.5–5 meters and 5.5–6 meters after 6 and 24 hours, respectively. As opposed to the larger relative changes (~ 10–15%) in velocity observed in the measurements from the first test, changes in velocity from the steady-state profile are smaller (between 5% and 8%) and potentially difficult to measure in real field data, depending on signal quality. Thus, the amount and distribution of water introduced into the subsurface influence how much the GPR signal is affected. From this it is concluded that GPR is promising for monitoring infiltration tests but that careful planning of such a test is important to achieve adequate sensitivity of the GPR measurements to changes in water saturation.

CONCLUSIONS

In this study, realistic conditions of water saturation were obtained for an outcrop model of a braided-river sedimentary environment. These were used for the simulation of GPR surveys. Non-uniform distributions of water (and therefore of electrical parameters) were observed within sedimentary units and resulted from such phenomena as water ponding above capillary barriers. In addition to simulating steady-state conditions, ponding-infiltration tests were simulated to allow the investigation of GPR during transient flow.

With both GPR surface surveys and crosshole surveys, zones containing sedimentary units of importance to fluid flow could be identified, though individual features were not necessarily resolved. During infiltration, the range of tomogram velocity values obtained from crosshole surveys increased, implying better detection of different units. Increased contrasts in velocity between some sedimentary units were observed and were caused by differential draining above and below potential capillary barriers (e.g., OF gravel). Transient flow caused GPR reflection survey images to change significantly, as by causing the loss of reflectors in some cases and the addition of new reflectors in other cases. Such changes could conceivably affect the interpretation of a real GPR reflection survey. While surface reflection surveys are not expected to be the most useful for tracking movement of an infiltration front, ZOP surveys were found to be useful for this purpose, though how sensitive GPR will be to changes in water saturation depends on the experimental design (e.g., distance between boreholes, amount and duration of water introduced into the ground).

The GPR response for different units varied depending on saturation conditions. In very dry conditions, zones containing OF gravel could be high-velocity zones, as observed by Tronicke (2001), because they have relatively high porosity and contain a fair amount of air. In more saturated conditions, as in the present study (recall that the surface was assumed to be at a saturation of 0.25 for steady state conditions), where OF gravel layers can increase water retention, these zones are predicted to be low-velocity zones. Accordingly, one recommendation in interpreting GPR results is to take weather conditions at a site into account before and during data collection. In some cases, it may be worth repeating surveys for different conditions. Furthermore, it may be valuable to impose changes in saturation conditions in the subsurface during a measurement campaign.

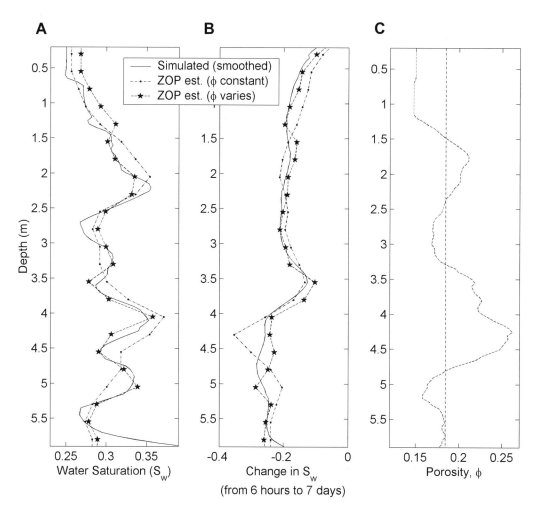

FIG. 10.—Estimates of water saturation and changes in water saturation from zero-offset profiles. **A)** Water-saturation profiles were calculated from the ZOP-derived velocity profile for steady-state conditions using an average porosity value (dash-dotted line), and depth-varying porosity. For comparison, the simulated water-saturation profile was horizontally averaged and smoothed in the vertical direction with a moving window of 0.5 meters (solid line). **B)** Time-lapsed ZOP-derived estimates of change in water saturation from 6 hours to 7 days after infiltration. **C)** The porosity models (constant and depth-varying) used in the conversion to obtain A and B.

GPR measurements cannot measure hydraulic conductivity directly. However, because GPR images can be related to changes in water saturation, future work in relating GPR-derived images to hydraulic parameters, such as permeability (or hydraulic conductivity), is promising. For this the development of inverse methods that combine transient hydrological and GPR measurements is required. Practical considerations concerning time-lapsed measurements must also be considered but were not addressed in this work. Such considerations include difficulty in repeating measurements at the same locations, and difficulty in accounting for changes in coupling between the antennae and the ground surface, the electrical properties of which can vary with changes in foliage or moisture conditions.

ACKNOWLEDGMENTS

This research is supported by National Science Foundation Grant EAR 9628306 and United States Department of Agriculture Grant 2001-35102-09866. The authors would like to thank Stefan Finsterle for assistance with the TOUGH2 flow modeling and John Peterson for use of the ART inversion code. We also appreciate the thoughtful comments from John Bridge, Roelof Versteeg, and an anonymous reviewer.

REFERENCES

ALUMBAUGH, D., PAPROCKI, L., BRAINARD, J., AND RAUTMAN, C., 2000, Monitoring infiltration within the vadose zone using cross-borehole ground penetrating radar, *in* Proceedings of the Symposium on Applications of Geophysics to Engineering and Environmental Problems (SAGEEP 2000) Environmental and Engineering Geophysical Society, p. 273–281.

ARCHIE, G.E., 1942, The electrical resistivity log as an aid in determining some reservoir characteristics: American Institute of Mining, Metallurgical, and Petroleum Engineers, Transactions, v. 146, p. 54–62.

ASPRION, U., AND AIGNER, T., 1997, Aquifer architecture analysis using ground-penetrating radar: Triassic and Quaternary examples (S. Germany): Environmental Geology, v. 31, p. 66–75.

ASPRION, U., AND AIGNER, T., 1999, Towards realistic aquifer models: a three-dimensional georadar case study of Quaternary gravel deposits

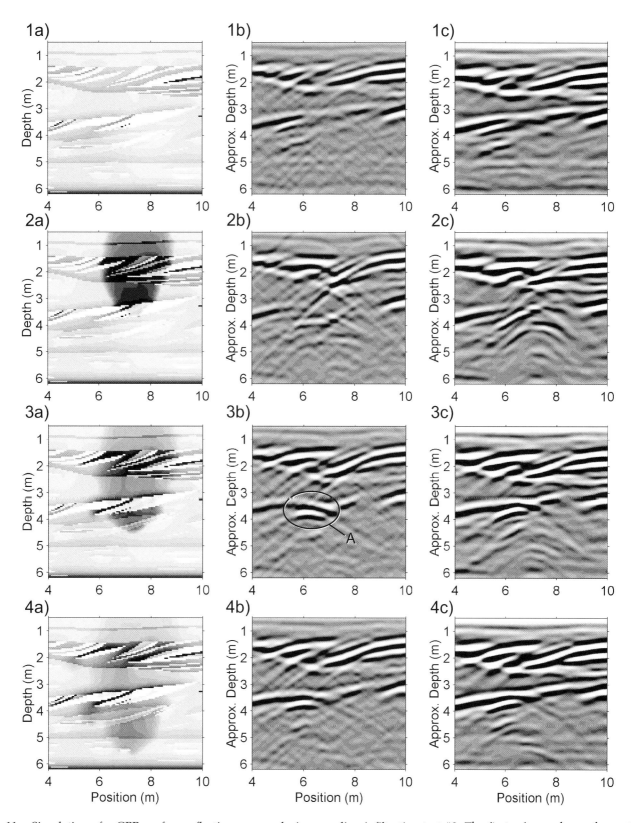

Fig. 11.—Simulation of a GPR surface reflection survey during ponding infiltration test #2. The first column shows the water distributions during steady state (1a), 1 hour (2a), 6 hours (3a), and 24 hours (4a) after infiltration, respectively. For each time, the simulated GPR surface surveys are shown in the second column (1b–4b), where no processing was performed (for display purposes, conversion to depth was done with a constant velocity). The processed simulated GPR measurements are shown in 1c–4c and were obtained by migration and time-depth conversion using the actual 2-D velocity models.

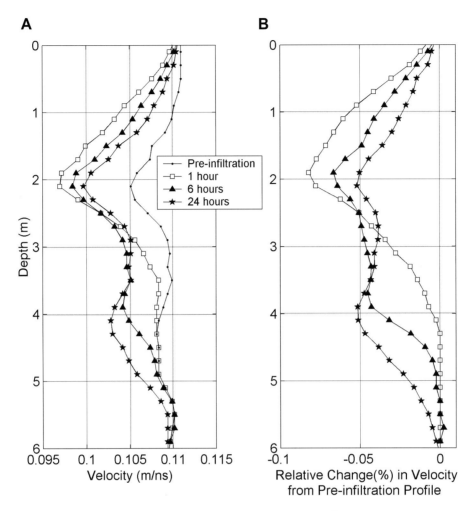

Fig. 12.—Simulated crosshole (ZOP) surveys for ponding infiltration test #2. Boreholes were placed at $x = 4$ and 10 m, giving a measurement plane 6 m wide and about 6 m deep. **A)** Simulated zero-offset profiles show changes in (horizontally averaged) velocity with movement of the infiltration front. Dots, squares, triangles, and stars denote the velocity profiles for steady-state (pre-infiltration) conditions, and 1 hour, 6 hours, and 1 day after ponding, respectively. **B)** The relative changes (%) from pre-infiltration to 1 hour (squares), 6 hours (triangles), and 1 day (stars).

(Singen Basin, SW Germany): Sedimentary Geology, v. 129, p. 281–297.

BAYER, P., 2000, Aquifer-Anolog-Studie in grobklastischen 'braided river' Ablagerungen: Sedimentäre / hydrogeologische Wandkartierung und Kalibrierung von Georadarmessungen. Diplomkartierung, University of Tübingen, Germany, 85 p.

BEAR, J., 1988, Dynamics of Fluids in Porous Media: New York, Dover Publications, Inc., p. 485–486.

BERES, M., GREEN, A.G., HORSTMEYER, H., AND HUGGENBERGER, P., 1995, Mapping the architecture of glaciofluvial sediments with three-dimensional georadar: Geology, v. 23, p. 1087–1090.

BERES, M., HUGGENBERGER, P., GREEN, A., AND HORSTMEYER, H., 1999, Using two- and three-dimensional georadar methods to characterize glaciofluvial architecture: Sedimentary Geology, v. 129, p. 1–24.

BERGMANN, T., ROBERTSSON, J.O.A., AND HOLLIGER, K., 1998, Finite-difference modeling of electromagnetic wave propagation in dispersive and attenuating media: Geophysics, v. 63, p. 856–867.

BIERKENS, M.F.P., 1996, Modeling hydraulic conductivity of a complex confining layer at various scales: Water Resources Research, v. 32, p. 2369–2382.

BINLEY, A., WINSIP, P., AND MIDDLETON, R., 2001, High-resolution characterization of vadose zone dynamics using cross-borehole radar: Water Resources Research, v. 37, p. 2639–2652.

BINLEY, A., CASSIANI, G., MIDDLETON, R., AND WINSHIP, P., 2002, Vadose zone flow model parameterization using cross-borehole radar and resistivity imaging: Journal of Hydrology, v. 267, p. 147–159.

BIRCHAK, J.R., GARDNER, L.G. HIPP, J.W., AND VICTOR, J.M., 1974, High dielectric constant microwave probes for sensing soil moisture: IEEE Proceedings, v. 62, p. 93–98.

BIRKEN, R., AND VERSTEEG, R., 2000, Use of four-dimensional ground penetrating radar and advanced visualization methods to determine subsurface fluid migration: Journal of Applied Geophysics, v. 43, p. 215–226.

BREWSTER, M.L., AND ANNAN, A.P., 1994, Ground-penetrating radar monitoring of a controlled DNAPL release: 200 MHz radar: Geophysics, v. 59, p. 1211–1221.

BRIDGE, J.S., ALEXANDER, J., COLLIER, R.E.LL, GAWTHORPE, R.L., AND JARVIS, J., 1995, Ground-penetrating radar and coring used to study the large-scale structure of point-bar deposits in three dimensions: Sedimentology, v. 42, p. 839–852.

BRIDGE, J.S., COLLIER, R.E.LL., AND ALEXANDER, J., 1998, Large-scale structure of Calamus River deposits (Nebraska, USA) revealed using ground penetrating radar: Sedimentology, v. 45, p. 977–986.

BROOKS, R.H., AND COREY, A.T., 1964, Hydraulic properties of porous media, in Hydrology Papers, No. 3, Colorado State University, Fort Collins, Colorado.

CAI, J., AND MCMECHAN, G.A., 1995, Ray-based synthesis of bistatic ground-penetrating radar profiles: Geophysics, v. 60, p. 87–96.

CARCIONE, J.M., 1996, Ground penetrating radar: wave theory and numerical simulation in lossy anisotropic media: Geophysics, v. 61, p. 1664–1677.

CARCIONE, J.M., 1998, Radiation patterns for 2-D GPR forward modeling: Geophysics, v. 63, p. 424–430.

CASPER, D.A., AND KUNG, K.-J. S., 1996, Simulation of ground-penetrating radar waves in a 2-D soil model: Geophysics, v. 61, p. 1034–1049.

CHEN, J., HUBBARD, S., AND RUBIN, Y., 2001, Estimating the hydraulic conductivity at the South Oyster Site from geophysical tomographic data using Bayesian techniques based on the normal linear regression model: Water Resources Research, v. 37, p. 1603–1613.

COLLINS, M.E., SCHELLENTRAGER, G.W., DOOLITTLE, J.A., AND SHIH, S.F., 1986, Using ground-penetrating radar to study changes in soil map unit composition in selected Histosols: Soil Science Society of America, Journal, v. 50, p. 408–412.

DANIELS, D.J., 1996, Surface Penetrating Radar: London, Institute of Electrical Engineers, 320 p.

DANIELS, J.J., ROBERTS, R., AND VENDL, M., 1995, Ground penetrating radar for the detection of liquid contaminants: Journal of Applied Geophysics, v. 33, p. 195–207.

DAVIS, J.L., AND ANNAN, A.P., 1989, Ground-penetrating radar for high-resolution mapping of soil and rock stratigraphy: Geophysical Prospecting, v. 37, p. 531–551.

DU, S., AND RUMMEL, P., 1994, Reconnaissance studies of moisture in the subsurface with GPR, in 5th International Conference on Ground Penetrating Radar, Proceedings, p. 1241–1248.

EPPSTEIN, M.J., AND DOUGHERTY, D.E., 1998, Efficient three-dimensional data inversion: Soil characterization and moisture monitoring from cross-well ground-penetrating radar at a Vermont test site: Water Resources Research, v. 34, p. 1889–1900.

FAYBISHENKO, B., 2000, Vadose zone characterization and monitoring: current technologies, applications, and future developments, in Looney, B.B., and Falta, R.W., eds., Vadose Zone: Science and Technology Solutions: Columbus, Ohio, Battelle Press, p. 133–509.

FOUSSEREAU, X., GRAHAM, W.D., AKPOJI, G.A., DESTOUNI, G., AND RAO, P.S.C., 2001, Solute transport through a heterogeneous coupled vadose–saturated zone system with temporally random rainfall: Water Resources Research, v. 37, p. 1577–1588.

FREELAND, R.S., YODER, R.E., AND AMMONS, J.T., 1998, Mapping shallow underground features that influence site-specific agricultural production: Journal of Applied Geophysics, v. 40, p. 19–27.

GAWTHORPE, R.L., COLLIER, R.E., ALEXANDER, J., BRIDGE, J.S., AND LEEDER, M.R., 1993, Ground-penetrating radar—Application to sandbody geometry and heterogeneity studies, in North, C.P., and Prosser, D.J., eds., Characterization of Fluvial and Aeolian Reservoirs: Geological Society of London, Special Publication 73, p. 421–432.

GLOAGUEN, E., CHOUTEAU, M., MARCOTTE, D., AND CHAPUIS, R., 2001, Estimation of hydraulic conductivity of an unconfined aquifer using cokriging of GPR and hydrostratigraphic data: Journal of Applied Geophysics, v. 47, p. 135–152.

GUEGUEN, Y., AND PALCIAUSKAS, V., 1994, Introduction to the Physics of Rocks: Princeton, New Jersey, Princeton University Press, 329 p.

GREAVES, R.J., LESMES, D.P., LEE, J.M., AND TOKSÖZ, M.N., 1996, Velocity variations and water content estimated from multi-offset, ground-penetrating radar: Geophysics, v. 61, p. 683–695.

GROTE, K., HUBBARD, S., AND RUBIN, Y., 2002, Monitoring spatial and temporal variations in soil water content for transportation applications using GPR reflection data: The Leading Edge of Exploration, Society of Exploration Geophysics, v. 21, p. 482–485.

HEINZ, J., 2001, Sedimentary Geology of Glacial and Periglacial Gravel Bodies (SW-Germany): Dynamic Stratigraphy and Aquifer Sedimentology: Ph.D. Thesis, Tübinger Geowissenschaftliche Arbeiten, 59, 102 p.

HEINZ, J., KLEINEIDAM, S., TEUTSCH, G., AND AIGNER, T., 2003, Heterogeneity patterns of Quaternary glaciofluvial gravel bodies (SW-Germany): application to hydrogeology: Sedimentary Geology, v. 158, p. 1–23.

HILLEL, D., 1982, Introduction to Soil Physics: Orlando, Florida, Academic Press, 365 p.

HOLLIGER, K., AND BERGMANN, T., 2000, Finite difference modelling of borehole georadar data, in Noon, D., Stickley, G., and Longstaff, D., eds., 8th International Conference on Ground Penetrating Radar, 23–26 May 2000, Gold Coast, Australia, Proceedings, no page numbers.

HUBBARD, S.S., RUBIN, Y., AND MAJER, E., 1997, Ground-penetrating-radar-assisted saturation and permeability estimation in bimodal systems: Water Resources Research, v. 33, p. 971–990.

HUBBARD, S.S., RUBIN, Y., AND MAJER, E., 1999, Spatial correlation structure estimation using geophysical and hydrogeological data: Water Resources Research, v. 35, p. 1809–1825.

HUBBARD, S.S., AND RUBIN, Y., 2000, Hydrological parameter estimation using geophysical data: a review of selected techniques: Journal of Contaminant Hydrology, v. 45, p. 3–34.

HUBBARD, S. GROTE, K., AND RUBIN, Y., 2002, Estimation of near-subsurface water content using high frequency GPR ground wave: Leading Edge of Exploration, Society of Exploration Geophysics, v. 21, p. 552–559.

HUGGENBERGER, P., 1993, Radar facies: Recognition of facies patterns and heterogeneities within Pleistocene Rhine gravels, NE Switzerland, in Best, J.L., and Bristow, C.S., eds., Braided Rivers: Geological Society of London, Special Publication 75, p. 163–176.

HUISMAN, J.A., SPERL, C., BOUTEN, W., AND VERSTRATEN, J.M., 2001, Soil water content measurements at different scales: accuracy of time domain reflectometry and ground-penetrating radar: Journal of Hydrology, v. 245, p. 1–13.

JUSSEL, P., STAUFFER, F., AND DRACOS, T., 1994, Transport modeling in heterogeneous aquifers: 1. Statistical description and numerical generation of gravel deposits: Water Resources Research, v. 30, p. 1803–1817.

KLINGBEIL, R., 1998, Outcrop Analog Studies: Implications for groundwater flow and Contaminant Transport in Heterogeneous Glaciofluvial Quaternary Deposits: Ph.D. Dissertation, University of Tübingen, Germany, 111 p.

KLINGBEIL, R., KLEINEIDAM, S., ASPRION, U., AIGNER, T., AND TEUTSCH, G., 1999, Relating lithofacies to hydrofacies: outcrop-based hydrogeological characterisation of Quaternary gravel deposits: Sedimentary Geology, v. 129, p. 299–310.

KNOLL, M.P., HAENI, F.P., AND KNIGHT, R., 1991, Characterization of a sand and gravel aquifer using ground-penetrating radar, Cape Cod, Massachusetts, in Mallard, G.E., and Aronson, D.A., eds., U.S. Geological Survey Toxic Substances Hydrology Program—Proceedings of the Technical Meeting, Monterey, California, March 11–15, 1991: U.S. Geological Survey, Water Resources Investigations, Report 91-4034, p. 29–35.

KNOLL, M.P., AND KNIGHT, R., 1994, Relationships between dielectric constant and hydrogeological properties of sand-clay mixtures: Fifth International Conference on Ground Penetrating Radar, Environmental and Engineering Geophysical Society, Proceedings, p. 45–61.

KNOLL, M.P., KNIGHT, R., AND BROWN, E., 1995, Can accurate estimates of permeability be obtained from measurements of dielectric properties?: SAGEEP, Environmental and Engineering Geophysical Society, Annual Meeting, Extended Abstracts.

KOLTERMANN, C.E., AND GORELICK, S.M., 1995, Fractional packing model of hydraulic conductivity derived from sediment mixtures: Water Resources Research, v. 31, p. 3283–3297.

KOWALSKY, M.B., DIETRICH, P., TEUTSCH, G., RUBIN, Y., 2001, Forward modeling of ground-penetrating radar data using digitized outcrop images and multiple scenarios of water saturation: Water Resources Research, v. 37, p. 1615–1625.

KOWALSKY, M.B., FINSTERLE, S., AND RUBIN, Y., 2004, Estimating flow parameter distributions using ground-penetrating radar and hydrological measurements during transient flow in the vadose zone: Advances in Water Resources, v. 27, p. 583–599.

KUNZ, K.S., AND LUEBBERS, R.J., 1993, The finite difference time domain method for electromagnetics: Boca Raton, Florida, CRC Press, 496 p.

KURODA, S., NAKAZATO, H., HIHIRA, S., HATAKEYAMA, M., AND TAKEUCHI, M., 2002, Cross-hole georadar monitoring for moisture distribution and migration in soil beneath an infiltration pit: a case study of an artificial groundwater recharge test in Niigate, Japan, *in* Koppenjan, S.K., and Lee, H., eds., Ninth International Conference on Ground Penetrating Radar, Santa Barbara, California, USA, April 29–May 2, 6 p., (on CD).

LEVERETT, M.C., 1941, Capillary behavior in porous solids: AIME, Society of Petroleum Engineering, Transactions, v. 142, p. 152–169.

LUEBBERS, R., AND HUNSBERGER, F., 1992, FDTD for Nth Order Dispersive Media: IEEE Transactions on Antennas and Propagation, v. 40, p. 1297–1301.

MAVKO, G., AND NUR, A., 1997, The effect of a percolation threshold in the Kozeny–Carmen relation: Geophysics, v. 62, p. 1480–1482.

McMECHAN, G.A., GAYNOR, G.C., AND SZERBIAK, R.B., 1997, Use of ground-penetrating radar data for 3-D sedimentological characterization of clastic reservoir analogs: Geophysics, v. 62, p. 786–796.

MUALEM, Y., 1976, A new model for predicting the hydraulic conductivity of unsaturated porous media: Water Resources Research, v. 12, p. 513–522.

NOON, D.A., STICKLEY, G.F., AND LONGSTAFF, D., 1998, A frequency-independent characterisation of GPR penetration and resolution performance: Journal of Applied Geophysics, v. 40, p. 127–137.

PETERSON, J.E., MAJER, E.L., AND KNOLL, M.D., 1999, Hydrogeological property estimation using tomographic data at the Boise hydrogeophysical research site, *in* Symposium on Applications of Geophysics to Engineering and Environmental Problems (SAGEEP99), Environmental and Engineering Geophysical Society, Proceedings, p. 629–638.

PETERSON, J.E., PAULSSON, B.N., AND McEVILLY, T.V., 1985, Applications of algebraic reconstruction techniques to crosshole seismic data: Geophysics, v. 50, p. 1566–1580.

PHILIP, J.R., 1991, Horizontal redistribution with capillary hysteresis: Water Resources Research, v. 27, p. 1459–1469.

PRUESS, K., 1991, TOUGH2—A general purpose numerical simulator for multiphase fluid and heat flow: Lawrence Berkeley National Laboratory, Berkeley, California, Report no. LBL-29400, 103 p.

PRUESS, K., 1994, On the validity of a Fickian diffusion model for the spreading of liquid infiltration plumes in partially saturated heterogeneous media: Computation Methods in Water Resources X, Vol. 1: Dordrecht, The Netherlands, Kluwer Academic Publishers, p. 527–544.

RAUBER, M., STAUFFER, F., HUGGENBERGER, P., AND DRACOS, T., 1998, A numerical three-dimensional conditioned/unconditioned stochastic facies type model applied to a remediation well system: Water Resources Research, v. 34, p. 2225–2233.

REA, J., AND KNIGHT, R., 1998, Geostatistical analysis of ground-penetrating radar data: a means of describing spatial variation in the subsurface: Water Resources Research, v. 34, p. 329–339.

REGLI, C., HUGGENBERGER, P., AND RAUBER, M., 2002, Interpretation of drill core and georadar data of coarse gravel deposits: Journal of Hydrology, v. 255, p. 234–252.

ROTH, K.R., SCHULIN, R., FLUHLER, H., AND ATTINGER, W., 1990, Calibration of time domain reflectometry for water content measurement using a composite dielectric approach: Water Resources Research, v. 26, p. 2267–2273.

RUBIN, Y., AND DAGAN, G., 1989, Stochastic analysis of the effects of boundaries on spatial variability in groundwater aquifers: 2. Impervious boundary: Water Resources Research, v. 25, p. 707–712.

RUSSO, D., ZAIDEL, J., AND LAUFER, A., 2001, Numerical analysis of flow and transport in a combined heterogeneous vadose zone–groundwater system: Advances in Water Resources, v. 24, p. 49–62.

SAARENKETO, T., AND SCULLION, T., 2000, Road evaluation with ground-penetrating radar: Journal of Applied Geophysics, v. 43, p. 119–138.

SANDMEIER, K.J., 1999, Reflex-Win (Version 1.03): Program for processing and interpreting reflection and transmission data: Karlsruhe, Germany, Sandmeier Software.

SCHÖN, J.H., 1996, Physical Properties of Rocks; Fundamentals and Principles of Petrophysics: Tarrytown, New York, Pergamon Press, Seismic Exploration Series, no. 18, 583 p.

SCHMALZ, B., LENNARTZ, B., WACHSMUTH, D., 2002, Analyses of soil water content variations and GPR attribute distributions: Journal of Hydrology, v. 267, p. 217–226.

SIHVOLA, A., 1999, Electromagnetic mixing formulas and applications: IEEE Electromagnetic Waves Series 47, The Institute of Electrical Engineers, London, U.K., 284 p.

SIEGENTHALER, C., AND HUGGENBERGER, P., 1993, Pleistocene Rhine gravel: deposits of a braided river system with dominant pool preservation, *in* Best, J.L. and C.S. Bristow, eds., Braided Rivers: Geological Society of London, Special Publication 75, p. 147–162.

STUTZMAN, W.L., AND THIELE, G.A., 1981, Antenna Theory and Design: New York, John Wiley & Sons, Inc., 598 p.

SZERBIAK, R.B., McMECHAN, G.A., CORBEANU, R., FORSTER, C., AND SNELGROVE, S.H., 2001, 3-D characterization of a clastic reservoir analog: From 3-D GPR data to a 3-D fluid permeability model: Geophysics, v. 66, p. 1026–1037.

TAFLOVE, A., 1995, Computational Electrodynamics; The Finite-Difference Time-Domain Method: Norwood, Massachusetts, Artech House, 852 p.

TOPP, G.C., DAVIS, J.L., AND ANNAN, A.P., 1980, Electromagnetic determination of soil water content: Measurements in coaxial transmission lines: Water Resources Research, v. 16, p. 574–582.

TOHGE, M., KARUBE, F., KOBAYASHI, M., TANAKA, A., AND ISHII, K., 1998, The use of ground penetrating radar to map an ancient village buried by volcanic eruptions: Journal of Applied Geophysics, v. 40, p. 49–58.

TRONICKE, J., 2001, Improving and evaluating GPR techniques for subsurface characterization: case strategies and advanced analysis strategies: Ph.D. Thesis, University of Tübingen, Germany, 79 p.

TSOFLIAS, G.P., HALIHAN, T., AND SHARP, J.M., JR., 2001, Monitoring pumping test response in a fractured aquifer using ground-penetrating radar: Water Resources Research, v. 37, p. 1221–1229.

TURNER, G., AND SIGGINS, A.F., 1994, Constant Q attenuation of subsurface radar pulses: Geophysics, v. 59, p. 1192–1200.

VAN DAM, R.L., AND SCHLAGER, W., 2000, Identifying causes of ground-penetrating radar reflections using time-domain reflectometry and sedimentological analyses: Sedimentology, v. 47, p. 435–449.

VANDENBERGHE, J., AND VAN OVERMEEREN, R.A., 1999, Ground penetrating radar images of selected fluvial deposits in the Netherlands: Sedimentary Geology, v. 128, p. 245–270.

VAN GENUCHTEN, M.TH., 1980, A closed-form equation for predicting the hydraulic conductivity of unsaturated soils: Soil Science Society of America, Journal, v. 44, p. 892–898.

VAN OVERMEEREN, R.A., SARIOWAN, S.V., AND GEHRELS, J.C., 1997, Ground-penetrating radar for determining volumetric soil water content: results of comparative measurements at two test sites: Journal of Hydrology, v. 197, p. 316–338.

VAN OVERMEEREN, R.A., 1998, Radar facies of unconsolidated sediments in the Netherlands: a radar stratigraphy interpretation method for hydrogeology: Journal of Applied Geophysics, v. 40, p. 1–18.

VAUGHN, C.J., 1986, Ground-penetrating radar surveys used in archaeological investigation: Geophysics, v. 51, p. 595–604.

WANG, D., AND MCMECHAN, G.A., 2002, Finite-difference modeling of borehole ground penetrating radar data: Journal of Applied Geophysics, v. 49, p. 111–127.

WARRICK, A.W., MULLEN, G.J., AND NIELSEN, D.R., 1977, Scaling field-measured soil hydraulic properties using a similar media concept: Water Resources Research, v. 13, p. 355–362.

WHARTON, R.P., HAZEN, G.A., RAU, R.N., AND BEST, D.L., 1980, Electromagnetic propagation logging: Advances in technique and interpretation: Society of Petroleum Engineers, Paper 9267, 12 p.

WHITTAKER, J., AND TEUTSCH, G., 1999, The simulation of subsurface characterization methods applied to a natural aquifer analogue: Advances in Water Resources Research, v. 22, p. 819–829.

WOLLNY, K.G., 1999, Die Natur der Bodenwelle des Georadar und ihr Einsatz zur Feuchtebestimmung: Ph.D. dissertation, Ludwig-Maximilians-Universität, Munich, 180 p.

Yin, H., 1993, Acoustic velocity and attenuation of rocks: Ph.D. dissertation, Stanford University, Stanford, California,

ZENG, X., AND MCMECHAN, G.A., 1997, GPR characterization of buried tanks and pipes: Geophysics, v. 62, p. 797–806.

XU, T., AND MCMECHAN, G.A., 1997, GPR and its numerical simulation in 2.5 dimensions: Geophysics, v. 62, p. 403–414.

CHARACTERIZATION OF HETEROGENEITY IN UNSATURATED SANDSTONE USING BOREHOLE LOGS AND CROSS-BOREHOLE TOMOGRAPHY

ANDREW BINLEY
Department of Environmental Science, Lancaster University, Lancaster LA1 4YQ, U.K.
GIORGIO CASSIANI
Dipartimento di Scienze Geologiche e Geotecnologie,
Università di Milano-Bicocca, Piazza della Scienza 4, 20125 Milano, Italy
AND
PETER WINSHIP
Department of Environmental Science, Lancaster University, Lancaster LA1 4YQ, U.K.

ABSTRACT: Characterization of the spatial variability of hydraulic properties of an aquifer is essential for reliable modeling of the fate of contaminants in the subsurface. Many geophysical methods offer the potential to derive such information, because of the high spatial density of sampling and the, albeit indirect, relationship between many geophysical and hydraulic parameters. In particular, borehole-to-borehole imaging may provide high-resolution sampling at scales which will permit detailed site characterization. Here, we examine the high-resolution spatial variability of electric and electromagnetic properties in the vadose zone at a specific field site in the Triassic Sherwood Sandstone aquifer in the UK, using cross-borehole radar. Assessment of spatial variability in the vadose zone is achieved through computation of experimental semivariograms of geophysical properties obtained from inter-well tomograms. The variability is compared with that deduced from conventional geophysical well-logging tools. The stratified nature of the site is clearly identified by gamma-log measurements. Single-hole and cross-hole geophysical measurements involving electrical properties are affected by both the stratification and the hydrological forcing conditions at the surface, and all show a similar spatial correlation structure. These data suggest that a representation of one-dimensional recharge processes is appropriate at the site. Data on moisture content from cross-hole radar are quantitatively compared against the results of stochastic unsaturated-flow simulations, accounting for the lithological spatial variability as described by gamma logs. The results demonstrate how improved conceptualization of the hydrological model of the site is achieved through incorporation of such geophysical data. Such a methodology permits improved assessment of mechanisms of recharge and transport at the site.

INTRODUCTION

Characterization of the spatial variability of hydraulic properties of an aquifer is essential for reliable modeling of the fate of contaminants in the subsurface. Assessment using conventional field hydraulic measurements is limited, because of the spatially averaged nature of the system response, in the case of a pumping test, for example, or the very small spatial scale of the measurement support volume, as in the case of pore-water sampling. Many geophysical methods offer additional information which may provide characteristics of the spatial structure of the subsurface environment. While the geophysical parameters are not directly related to single hydraulic properties of interest, indirect relationships do exist in many cases; see, for example, Mazac et al. (1985). Such a fact is well recognized in many studies by utilizing, for example, well logs to delineate hydrogeological units.

Geophysical well logs are rarely used to quantify the spatial variability of subsurface properties, because well spacing is often too large. Surface-deployed geophysical surveys offer a means of providing variability over a wide range of scales. Investigations of vadose-zone processes typically comprise such surveys, for example using direct-current (DC) resistivity (Kean et al., 1987; Frohlich and Parke, 1989; Benderitter and Schott, 1999), or GPR profiling (Greaves et al., 1996; van Overmeeran et al., 1997; Huisman et al., 2001). These two methods, although widely used for shallow investigations, have limited usefulness for characterization at depth in many sites. In the case of GPR, significant attenuation from highly electrically conductive near-surface sediments restricts depth penetration of signals. In the case of DC-resistivity surface surveys, sensitivity at depth is limited by restricted resolution.

Well-to-well, or cross-borehole, methods, however, offer a means of determining the inter-well variability and characterization, at depth, of small-scale structures which may have significant effect on transporting or retarding subsurface contaminants. Recently, a number of hydrogeological studies have benefited from the additional information brought from the use of cross-borehole geoelectrical tomographic imaging, in particular electrical resistivity tomography (ERT) and transmission radar (GPR) tomography. In comparison with conventional surface-deployed surveys, these methods have been shown to provide high-resolution images of hydrogeological structures and, in some cases, detailed assessment of dynamic processes in the subsurface environment.

The aims here are to examine the spatial variability of geophysical properties in the vadose zone at a specific field site on the Triassic Sherwood Sandstone aquifer in the UK using both cross-borehole radar and conventional geophysical well-logging tools. Variability of geophysical properties is rarely assessed quantitatively, but there have been a number of recent attempts to use geostatistical methods for such a purpose. Rea and Knight (1998), for example, used variogram analysis in order to characterize the spatial variability of shallow sediments by use of surface GPR signals. More recently, Hubbard et al. (1999) show the potential value, albeit from synthetic case studies, of geostatistical analysis of geophysical images in cases where a direct relationship between hydraulic and geophysical parameters exists. We adopt an approach here similar to that of Rea and Knight (1998), by computation of experimental semivariograms, in our case using well-log and borehole-to-borehole geophysical surveys.

Demonstrations of how the spatial variability of geophysical properties can be used to improve hydrological models are even less common. Our ultimate objective is to understand the lithological control of recharge and vadose-zone contaminant transport at the site. Given this objective, we show how the spatial variability of hydrological properties deduced from geophysical data can be quantitatively incorporated in a hydrological model to provide improved conceptualization of the hydrological processes.

CROSS-BOREHOLE RADAR

Cross-borehole radar tomography consists of applying a sequence of signals through multiple transmitter positions in one borehole and then measuring signals at multiple receiver positions in an adjacent borehole. Inversion of the data is necessary in order to estimate an image of the electrical properties. The sequence of transmitter–receiver signals is modeled to estimate the appropriate distribution of electrical properties between the two boreholes. By discretizing the domain of interest into parameter cells, the objective of the inversion procedure is to compute the "best" set of parameter values which satisfies both the measured dataset and any *a priori* constraints.

In order to determine dielectric properties at the field scale, borehole-to-borehole radar surveys can be conducted in two transmission modes. Measurement of the travel time of the received wave permits determination of the first arrival and hence the velocity of the electromagnetic wave (v). In tomographic mode, using a multiple-offset gather (MOG), the receiver is moved to different locations in one borehole whilst the transmitter remains fixed. The transmitter is then moved and the process repeated. Following collection of all data in this mode and determination of the travel time for each wave pathline, it is possible to derive a tomogram of velocity in the plane of the borehole pair. Most applications of cross-borehole radar tomography adopt an iterative procedure to determine an image of electromagnetic wave velocity, using measured wave signals in the receiver borehole to determine the first arrival. By assuming that the transmitted signals follow straight rays for cases of low contrast in velocity, the complexities of solving, at least approximately, the physics of the electromagnetic wave propagation problem are removed and the problem is greatly simplified. Algebraic reconstruction techniques and simultaneous inversion reconstruction techniques are normally used to formulate the iterative process (see, for example, Peterson et al., 1985).

In contrast, a zero-offset profile (ZOP) can be determined by keeping transmitter and receiver at equal depth. By systematically lowering or raising the pair of antennae in the two boreholes it is possible to build up a one-dimensional profile of travel time over the entire borehole length. In both tomographic (MOG) and profile (ZOP) cases, in low-loss materials and at high frequency, the relative permittivity, or bulk dielectric constant, is derived from

$$\sqrt{\kappa_r} = \frac{c}{v} \qquad (1)$$

where c is the radar wave velocity in air (= 0.3 m/ns).

Early applications of cross-borehole-mode GPR arose from pioneering work by Lager and Lytle (1977). Daily and Lytle (1983)

document some initial field studies applying the technique to geological site characterization. The increasing availability of commercial borehole radar systems and growing acceptance of radar in the hydrological community has led to a number of recent hydrogeological applications of the technique in unsaturated systems (for example, Hubbard et al., 1997; Eppstein and Dougherty, 1998; Alumbaugh et al., 2000; Binley et al., 2001, Day-Lewis et al., 2002).

SITE DESCRIPTION

The field site is located near Eggborough, North Yorkshire, UK, adjacent to a small sand quarry (National Grid Reference SE 570 232). The field site is one of two selected for detailed study of the vadose-zone dynamics in the Sherwood Sandstone using borehole geophysics. Recent papers (Binley et al., 2001; Binley et al., 2002) show how borehole radar and resistivity measurements at the site have been used to reveal changes in moisture content of the sandstone, caused by natural and artificial (tracer) loading.

Eleven boreholes were drilled at the Eggborough site during June 1999. The boreholes were drilled using 127 mm diameter tip rotary air-flush to a depth below the water table (approximately 17 m). Six of the boreholes (labeled R1, R2, R3, R3, A, B) were drilled for deployment of borehole radar. The other boreholes (E1, E2, E3, E4, C) were installed for DC resistivity measurements in both cross-hole and single-hole mode. In March 2000, a further borehole (labeled D) was drilled and cored by colleagues at Leeds University. Figure 1 shows the layout of the boreholes.

Hydraulic and geophysical analysis of core samples have been the focus of West et al. (2001) and Pokar et al. (2001). From analysis of the core (L.J. West, personal communication), the sandstone sequence at the site consists of fluvially derived fining-upward sequences 1 to 3 m thick, grading from medium-grained to fine-grained sandstone. Drift cover (mainly gravels and cobbles) at the site is typically 1–2 m thick.

In each of the radar boreholes, a 76 mm diameter PVC casing was installed, surrounded by a sand–cement backfill. In boreholes E1, E2, E3, E4, a sand–cement backfill was also used to grout the borehole electrode arrays. All boreholes (except E1 because of weakness of the borehole wall and thus possible collapse) were geophysically logged using natural gamma and electromagnetic induction (EM) conductivity sondes prior to final completion.

ANALYSIS OF GEOPHYSICAL LOGS

The natural-gamma logs illustrate the sequence of contrast in clay content in the sandstone, which relates to the sedimentary cyclicity. Figure 2 shows examples of these logs from E3, R3, R4, and E4, from which considerable correlation is apparent. In contrast, the EM conductivity logs (also shown in Figure 2 for E3, R3, R4, and E4) reveal the effects of these lithological contrasts on volumetric moisture content, which mainly controls the bulk electrical conductivity, assuming minimal effects of clay conductivity. Figure 2 shows marked horizontal zoning of high conductivity at depths of 2.5, 5.5, and 12 m. The correlation between gamma and conductivity logs in the four boreholes shown is clearly visible.

The high spatial density of borehole drill sites within the plot permit analysis of spatial characteristics of the logged parameters, thus giving insight into the horizontal and vertical extent of lithological and hydrological features. In order to perform such analysis the semivariogram in the horizontal and vertical direction was computed, using logs from all eleven boreholes. The experimental semivariogram is defined as (Deutsch and Journel, 1998)

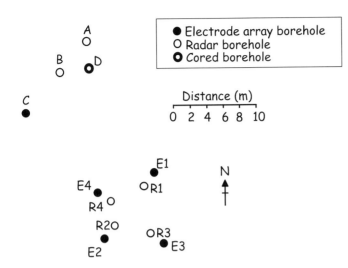

FIG. 1.—Layout of borehole arrays at the Eggborough site.

$$\gamma(l) = \frac{1}{2N} \sum_{i=1}^{N} \left[x_i - y_i\right]^2 \qquad (2)$$

where **x** and **y** are vectors of N measurements separated by distance, or lag, l. Figures 3 and 4 show the experimental semivariograms using the natural-gamma and induction logs.

The gamma-log semivariograms show a stationary (spatially homogeneous) behavior, with a well defined sill particularly evident in the vertical semivariograms at least for lags up to 10 meters (Fig. 3). The horizontal semivariogram is based on a considerably smaller dataset (11 boreholes), and it is unclear whether a large-scale sill is reached within the observed range of lags (Fig. 3) because of the maximum semivariogram value in the horizontal direction is smaller than the sill observed in the vertical direction. Assuming that the sill in the horizontal direction is the same as the one observed in the vertical semivariograms, an anisotropy ratio greater or equal to 8 is derived. Cyclic behavior in the vertical semivariogram ("hole effect") appears consistent with observations of a number of fining-upward sequences in the sandstone.

The geostatistical analysis of induction logs shows slightly different characteristics. A stationary (constant experimental semivariogram) behavior is observed in the horizontal direction (Fig. 4), but the magnitude of the sill in the horizontal direction is much smaller than the maximum semivariogram values in the vertical direction. This fact indicates that there is good horizontal continuity, but it also demonstrates that another factor, related to lithology, controls the vertical variability. This is to be expected, inasmuch as electrical conductivity depends, indirectly, on moisture content, whereas gamma logs are not sensitive to water content. Because moisture content at this site is found to be generally higher in the first 5 meters (above an impeding layer at about 5.5 m, corresponding to a peak in the gamma logs; see Fig. 2), the overall variability in the vertical direction is higher than in the horizontal direction (see for example, Fig. 2). A similar behav-

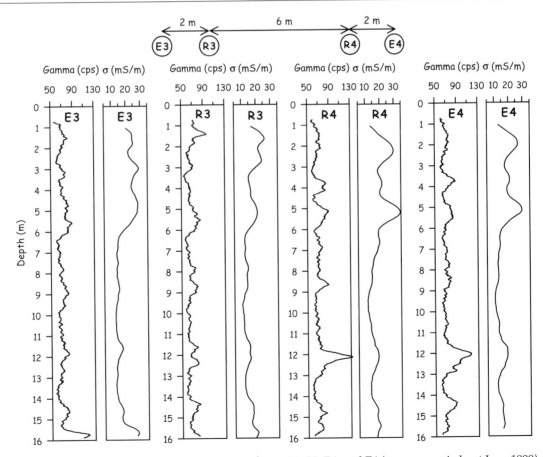

FIG. 2.—Natural-gamma and EM conductivity logs from boreholes E3, R3, R4, and E4 (surveys carried out June 1999).

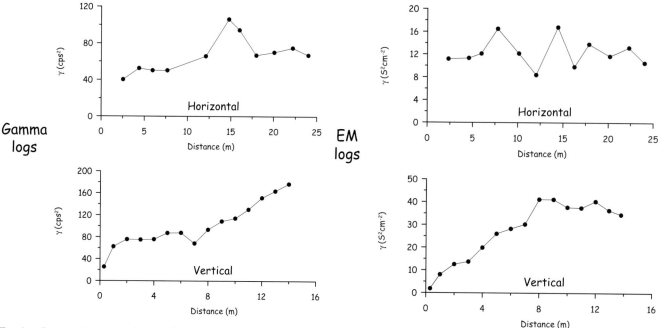

FIG. 3.—Semivariograms of natural-gamma logs.

FIG. 4.—Semivariograms of EM induction logs.

ior is therefore expected in the cross-borehole radar data because of the effect of moisture content on the relative permittivity.

Transitions at lags of 3 m and 7 m in the vertical semivariogram for the induction logs are noticeable and, as in the case of the gamma logs, are likely to be caused by the repeated fining-upward sequences in the sandstone.

ANALYSIS OF CROSS-BOREHOLE RADAR DATA

Borehole-to-borehole radar measurements in ZOP mode were made at the site shortly after completion of the boreholes. For all surveys the PulseEKKO borehole radar system was used with 50 MHz borehole antennae. Attempts were made to use 100 MHz antennae, but signals were noticeably weak over high-conductivity units at 5 m (see EM conductivity logs in Fig. 2). Figure 5 illustrates the observed variation in measured first arrivals from four ZOP surveys, using 0.25 m intervals between antennae positions. The profiles reveal distinct similarity between each other, as expected from the horizontal spatial correlation of gamma log reported above. When compared with the EM conductivity logs in Figure 2, the variation in velocity appears strongly linked to conductivity changes—a result of changes in saturation due to the sequence of layers of contrasting hydraulic conductivity. The location of hydraulically impeding (relatively low hydraulic conductivity) layers is indicated by peaks in the natural-gamma counts, as shown in Figure 2.

Tomographic (MOG) radar surveys were conducted using 0.25 m intervals between 50 MHz antennae positions over the range 1 to 16 m below ground level. Tomographic analysis of the MOG data was carried out using the straight ray inversion procedure of Jackson and Tweeton (1994) using a discretization of 0.55 m in the horizontal and 0.55 m in the vertical. To minimize effects of instrument drift, calibration of a zero-time value was done at transmitter positions of 1 m, 4 m, 7 m, 10 m, 13 m, and 16 m. Receiver positions were selected so that the maximum absolute vertical angle between the horizontal and the assumed straight ray path did not exceed 45°. Figure 6 shows an image of relative permittivity determined between borehole

pair R3–R4 on 16 September 1999. The image reveals a sequence of contrasting velocity, and provides evidence of the lateral continuity of some of the bedding features. The discontinuity of the low-velocity feature at approximately 5 m might be attributed to poor measured signals from long ray paths near this zone. For comparison the image of relative permittivity for borehole pair A–B (approximately 20 m from R3–R4; see Figure 1) is shown in Figure 7.

Semivariograms of the ZOP surveys based on values of relative permittivity computed using Equation 2 are presented in Figure 8. There is limited data coverage over a significant portion of the horizontal direction, because the radar boreholes are grouped into two distant clusters. However, both vertical and horizontal semivariograms in Figure 8 show characteristics totally analogous to the corresponding semivariograms for induction logs (Fig. 4). In particular, the sill in the horizontal direction is reached at small lags, but the sill value is much smaller than the maximum variability observed in the vertical direction. More precisely, as in the case of induction logs, the horizontal semivariogram sill (here around 1) is reached in the vertical variogram at about 2 m and the semivariogram values remain constant until vertical lags reach 4 m, and then increase beyond that.

Using the relative-permittivity tomograms, it is possible to compute semivariograms to assess smaller-scale variability. For illustration, Figure 9 shows the semivariograms for the R3–R4 image in Figure 6. The semivariograms computed on relative permittivity from MOG radar tomograms are very similar to those computed on ZOP relative permittivity (compare Figs. 8, 9). MOG data show larger vertical variability than ZOP data, but this is hardly surprising given the horizontal averaging induced by the ZOP acquisition geometry. In addition, MOG data allow a better characterization of small-scale features in the horizontal direction, especially at lags smaller than 3–4 m, a scale over which ZOP radar averages out spatial variability. It is recognized that data inversion, necessary for tomographic image reconstruction, will affect the resulting semivariograms, and thus quantitative

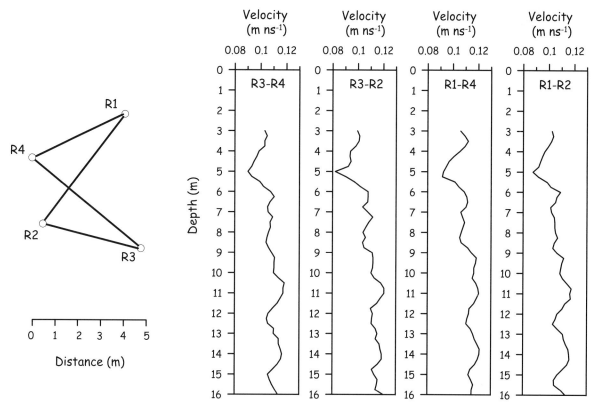

FIG. 5.—Selected first-arrival 50 MHz radar (ZOP) profiles measured July 1999.

estimates of geostatistical properties from such images must be used with caution.

The similarities between EM induction log semivariograms and radar semivariograms, both in ZOP and MOG acquisition mode, is very significant. In fact, the physical principles underlying induction and radar transmission logs are very different, as are the physical quantities these techniques measure (electrical conductivity and dielectric properties). Although these two quantities are affected by lithological properties (in particular, clay content and porosity), moisture content has a dominating effect, and the moisture content distribution is determined by (1) the lithology, as described by the gamma log analysis, and (2) the forcing conditions (net precipitation) at the ground surface.

USING GEOPHYSICAL DATA TO CONSTRAIN MODELS OF VADOSE-ZONE FLOW

One of the principal aims of developing the site at Eggborough was to monitor changes in moisture content in the unsaturated zone and ultimately develop improved models of vadose-zone flow dynamics. Cross-borehole radar measurements can be used to compute profiles of moisture content, as demonstrated by Binley et al. (2002). Such estimates offer an enhanced measurement support volume, in comparison to conventional techniques, such as neutron probes and time-domain reflectometry.

In order to describe the relationship between bulk dielectric constant (κ) and volumetric moisture content (θ), the complex refractive index method (CRIM) was used. The CRIM model can stated as

$$\sqrt{\kappa} = (1 - \phi)\sqrt{\kappa_s} + \theta\sqrt{\kappa_w} + (\phi - \theta)\sqrt{\kappa_a} \qquad (3)$$

where κ_σ is the dielectric constant of the sediment grains, κ_ω is the dielectric constant of water (assumed to be 81), κ_α is the dielectric constant of air (assumed to be 1), and ϕ is porosity. West et al. (2001) measured dielectric properties at different levels of water saturation in cores samples extracted from the site. On the basis of these measurements we assume here that $\kappa_\sigma = 5$ and $\phi = 0.32$.

At the Eggborough site, cross-borehole zero-offset radar profiles were measured on borehole pairs (R1, R2), (R3, R4) and (A, B) between 3 August 1999 and 20 February 2001 on 15 occasions at roughly regular intervals. Binley et al. (2002) show that the range of variation in moisture content over this period was approximately 0.05 between 3 m and 5 m depth and less than 0.02 at depths beyond 5 m. Given such a low degree of variation, a model of steady-state vadose-zone flow was adopted. In addition, the geostatistical analysis of radar data shown earlier suggests that a one-dimensional representation is an appropriate starting point for modeling flow due to rainfall inputs.

Under steady-state conditions the flow in unsaturated porous media is assumed to follow

$$\frac{\partial}{\partial z}\left[K(h)\frac{\partial(h+z)}{\partial z}\right] = 0 \qquad (4)$$

where z is elevation, h is pressure head, and $K(h)$ is the unsaturated hydraulic conductivity.

The relationships $\theta(h)$ and $K(h)$ are commonly represented by the equations proposed by van Genuchten (1980):

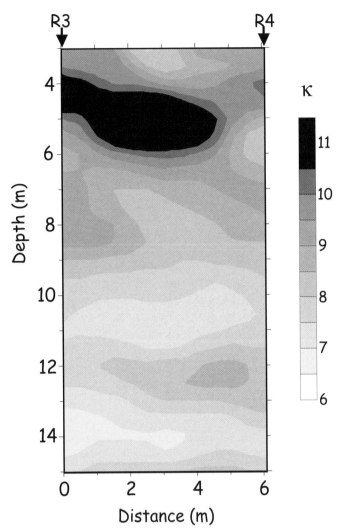

FIG. 6.—Image of relative permittivity between R3–R4 determined from measurements made on 16. September 1999.

$$\theta(h) = \theta_r + \frac{\theta_s - \theta_r}{\left[1 + |\alpha h|^n\right]^m} \qquad (5)$$

and

$$K(h) = K_s S_e^{0.5} \left[1 - \left(1 - S_e^{1/m}\right)^m\right]^2 \qquad (6)$$

where θ_r is the residual moisture content, θ_s is the saturated moisture content, K_s is the saturated hydraulic conductivity, S_e is effective saturation $(= (\theta - \theta_r)/(\theta_s - \theta_r))$, α and n are parameters, and it is often assumed that $m = 1 - 1/n$. Using such a formulation, solution of Equation 4 thus requires estimates of five parameters $(\theta_r, \theta_s, K_s, \alpha, n)$ for each soil type.

The vertical layering observed at the Eggborough site requires that parameters for different materials be hypothesized and that the spatial distribution of layers be inferred. Potentially both factors could be crucial when trying to match observed moisture-content profiles. On the basis of observations of a core extracted from the site, the 17 m unsaturated profile was parameterized into two geometrical units: a top layer, 2 m thick, representing surface soil and drift cover, and a sandstone unit 15 m

thick. The geophysical observations at the site show clearly that a uniform-sandstone model unit is inappropriate at the site: there is distinct layering of finer, more clay-rich sandstone within a predominantly medium-grained sandstone unit. In order to incorporate layering in the model, an approach was developed as follows:

i. The experimental semivariograms of gamma counts were matched with a model semivariogram built with two nested structures: (1) a small-scale exponential semivariogram with vertical correlation length equal to 35 cm and sill equal to 55 cps^2; (2) a large-scale Gaussian semivariogram with vertical correlation length equal to 1.5 m and sill equal to 22 cps^2. An anisotropy (ratio of horizontal to vertical correlation length) equal to 8 was used to match both vertical and horizontal semivariograms with the same nested model. Adopting the sequential Gaussian geostatistical simulator (SGSIM from GSLIB; Deutsch and Journel, 1998) a number of equally probable realizations of gamma counts in a soil column corresponding to the R3–R4 inter-well location were generated.

ii. On the basis of a designated threshold (in this case 75 counts per second) the 15 m unsaturated sandstone was parameterized into layers of fine sandstone and medium sandstone. Such a threshold can be designated using physical characteristics of core samples; see, for example, Pokar et al. (2001). The 17 m unsaturated zone was thus discretized into three material types, one with fixed geometry representing the near-surface cover, and the other two representing layered medium and fine sandstone.

iii. For a given realization of "geology" a series of Monte Carlo realizations of the five parameters in Equations 5 and 6 were created (i.e., 15 parameters in total, for the drift, fine-grained sandstone, and medium-grained sandstone). The parameters were selected randomly from a wide range of values consistent with observations in soils (Carsel and Parrish, 1988) and UK Triassic sandstone (Bloomfield et al., 2001). The ranges used for the three material types were identical and are given in Table 1. For each "hydrological" realization the steady-state Equation 4 was solved using an upper-boundary-condition infiltration rate equal to 1.741 x 10^{-3} m/d (based on rainfall and actual evapotranspiration estimates over the period of monitoring at the site) and a lower boundary condition representing a water-table depth of 17 m. Equation 4 was solved using a finite-difference discretization of 0.05 m. The output from this model was then compared with the average moisture-content profile observed between R3 and R4 using radar data over the 19 month period. In order to compare simulated and actual profiles of moisture content, the model output was averaged over 1 m intervals. This was done to achieve consistency between model and measurement support volumes—radar measurements have a double vertical averaging effect caused by (a) the antenna size itself and (b) the Fresnel zone (see Cerveny and Soares, 1992). The goodness of fit was quantified using the efficiency measure, $1 - \sigma_{error}^2/\sigma_{data}^2$ where σ_{error}^2 is the error of fit variance and σ_{data}^2 is the overall data variance.

The nested Monte Carlo search was conducted with 400 hydrological parameter realizations for each of 100 geological realizations. Figure 10 illustrates a sample of five geological realizations generated using the procedure above.

We recognize that even with 40,000 realizations our search in the parameter space is somewhat limited. Furthermore, each set

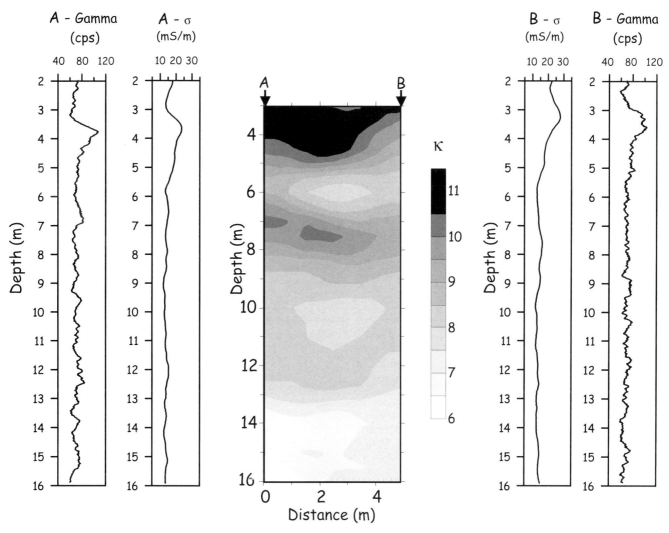

FIG. 7.—Images of relative permittivity between A–B determined from measurements made on 3 August 1999. Natural-gamma logs for the two boreholes are also shown.

of hydraulic parameters for each of the three material types was generated from uncorrelated uniform distributions. It is likely that correlation between parameters is significant, but no *a priori* information is available on samples from this site. We also recognize that the concept of a single optimum parameter set is simplistic given the large number of parameters in the model. However, we wish to simply use the procedure here as a means of demonstrating how the geophysical data can be incorporated with the hydrological modeling program. Figure 11A shows a comparison of the results of the model with best fit and the observed average moisture profile inferred from radar data between wells R3 and R4. The model follows reasonably well the observed profile: the efficiency measure for this model is 0.58.

In order to demonstrate the value of incorporating a layered structure in the sandstone unit, the model search was repeated using the same number of realizations as before, but in each case the sandstone was represented by one material type. In Figure 11B the profile from the "best" model in this case is shown. The misfit between model and observations is quantified by a poor efficiency measure of 0.06, illustrating that the model error variability is close to the observed variability, i.e., the model is only

able to reproduce the mean of the moisture content profile. The assumption of uniformity of the sandstone is clearly inappropriate at this site.

CONCLUSIONS

A range of borehole geophysical measurements has been used as part of a site characterization program in an attempt to assess the hydrogeological structure of the vadose zone in a regionally important sandstone aquifer. Analysis of geophysical logs from multiple boreholes in the site together with the cross-borehole radar velocity profiles and tomograms have permitted an assessment of horizontal and vertical spatial variability of hydraulically contrasting units in the sandstone. The analysis indicates that, from a lithological viewpoint, the system is anisotropic and stationary. This is supported by observations of fining-upward sequences 1 to 3 m thick in a core extracted from the site. Contrasts in hydraulic conductivity resulting from this sequence lead to relatively large changes in moisture content in a vertical profile, with values of larger moisture content in the first 5 m below ground. Semivariograms

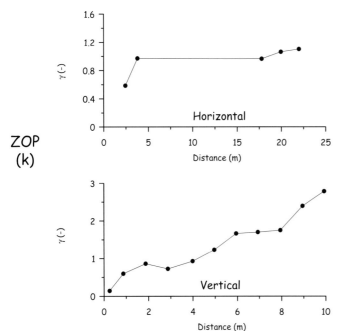

ZOP
(k)

FIG. 8.—Semivariograms of ZOP profiles, based on computed relative permittivity.

TABLE 1.—Parameter ranges selected for the three material types.

Parameter	Minimum	Maximum
$K_s\ (m\ d^{-1})$	0.1	2.0
$n\ (-)$	1.5	2.5
$\alpha\ (m^{-1})$	0.1	2.0
$\theta_s(-)$	0.25	0.35
$\theta_r(-)$	0.03	0.1

Whereas the geophysical well logs offer some insight into variability at the larger scale, borehole-to-borehole imaging methods can provide smaller-scale characteristics. Variogram analysis of cross-borehole radar tomograms suggests that most variability of relative permittivity occurs at scales of less than 3 m in the horizontal. Semivariograms of vertical variability based on these images show behavior similar to the well logs, with significant nonstationarity in the vertical, especially beyond lags of 4 m.

The variogram analysis here has been used to propose a range of hydrogeological representations of the site. The variograms of all geophysical data suggest that a one-dimensional model of natural recharge processes is a suitable starting point in a model search. Given this, the spatial correlation structure of gamma logs has been used to generate equally probable lithological scenarios to be used as input into stochastic unsaturated-flow simulations. Moisture-content data from cross-hole radar between one bore-

from electromagnetic-induction logs reveal fairly stationary behavior of electrical conductivity in horizontal direction but high anisotropy due to the influence of hydraulically impeding layers. Vertical semivariograms of induction logs manifest nonstationary features due mainly to trends in moisture content. Cross-borehole zero-offset radar profiles show characteristics similar to these induction logs.

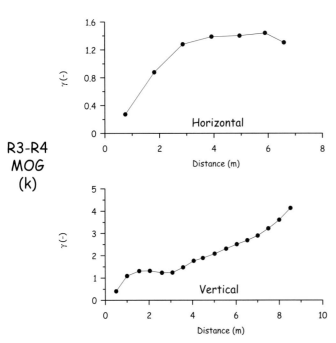

R3-R4
MOG
(k)

FIG. 9.—Semivariograms of computed relative permittivity in R3–R4 MOG image in Figure 6.

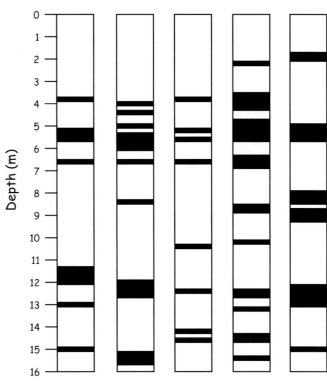

FIG. 10.—A sample of five realizations of geological structure generated for the region between boreholes R3 and R4. The black zones represent gamma counts above the designated threshold and are used to zone the fine sandstone layers within the medium sandstone unit.

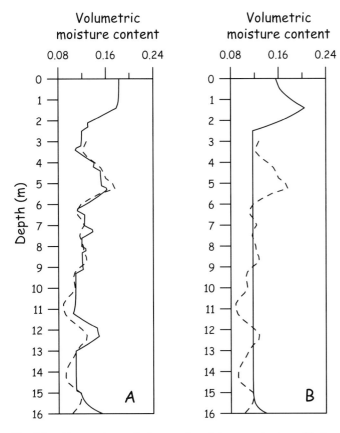

FIG. 11.—Comparison of observed moisture-content profile between R3 and R4 (dashed line) and "best" steady-state flow simulation result (solid line) using **A)** geological structure conditioned on gamma logs and **B)** assumption of one single uniform sandstone unit.

hole pair have been quantitatively compared against the results of unsaturated-flow-equation simulations. The results show clearly the improvement in simulated moisture profiles gained when these geophysical data are integrated into the modeling program.

We recognize that the application of this approach here has restricted the model and parameter search somewhat, but the procedure and results serve as an adequate demonstration of a flexible methodology for truly integrated hydrogeophysics. This approach is now being applied to study artificial water tracer tests at the same site, using three-dimensional geological representations, conditioned on borehole geophysical data, coupled with a three-dimensional stochastic-flow simulator.

ACKNOWLEDGMENTS

Some of the modeling ideas presented here originated from early discussion with Abe Ramirez and colleagues at Lawrence Livermore National Laboratory, USA. The field data used here were collected as part of NERC grant GR3/1150 funded by the UK Natural Environment Research Council. The fieldwork would not have been possible without agreement of site access by Hanson Aggregates Ltd, UK, and the support and expertise from John Aldrick, Ted Mould, and Albert Walmsley (Environment Agency, UK). Comments on an earlier version of this manuscript from Doug LaBrecque and an anonymous reviewer, together with editorial input from David Hyndman, have improved this manuscript.

REFERENCES

ALUMBAUGH, D., PAPROCKI, L., BRAINARD, J., AND RAUTMAN, C., 2000, Monitoring infiltration within the vadose zone using cross-borehole ground penetrating radar, *in* Symposium on Applications of Geophysics to Engineering and Environmental Problems (SAGEEP2000), 2000, Environmental and Engineering Geophysical Society, p. 273–281.

BENDERITTER, Y., AND SCHOTT, J.J., 1999, Short time variation of the resistivity in an unsaturated soil: The relationship with rainfall, European Journal of Environmental Engineering and Geophysics, v. 4, p. 37–49.

BINLEY, A., WINSHIP, P., MIDDLETON, R., POKAR, M., AND WEST, J., 2001, High resolution characterization of vadose zone dynamics using cross-borehole radar: Water Resources Research, v. 37, p. 2639–2652.

BINLEY, A., WINSHIP, P., WEST, L.J., POKAR, M., AND MIDDLETON, R., 2002, Seasonal variation of moisture content in unsaturated sandstone inferred from borehole radar and resistivity profiles: Journal of Hydrology, v. 67, p. 160–172.

BLOOMFIELD, J.P., GOODY, D.C., AND BRIGHT, M.I., 2001, Pore-throat size distributions in Permo-Triassic sandstones from the United Kingdom and some implications for contaminant hydrogeology: Hydrogeology Journal, v. 9, p. 219–230.

CARSEL, R.F., AND PARRISH, R.S., 1988, Developing joint probability distributions of soil-water retention characteristics: Water Resources Research, v. 24, p. 755–769.

CERVENY, V., AND SOARES, J.E.P., 1992, Fresnel volume ray tracing: Geophysics, v. 57, p. 902–915.

DAILY, W., AND LYTLE, J., 1983, Geophysical tomography: Journal of Geomagnetism and Geoelectricity, v. 35, p. 423–442.

DAY-LEWIS, F.D., HARRIS, J.M., AND GORELICK, S.M., 2002, Time-lapse inversion of crosswell radar data: Geophysics, v. 67, p. 1740–1752.

DEUTSCH, C.V., AND JOURNEL, A.G., 1998, GSLIB Geostatistical Software Library and User's Guide, II Edition: New York, Oxford University Press, 380 p.

EPPSTEIN, M.J., AND DOUGHERTY, D.E., 1998, Efficient three-dimensional data inversion: Soil characterization and moisture monitoring from cross-well ground-penetrating radar at the Vermont test site: Water Resources Research, v. 34, p. 1889–1900.

FROHLICH, R.K., AND PARKE, C.D., 1989, The electrical resistivity of the vadose zone—field survey: Ground Water, v. 27, p. 524–530.

GREAVES, R.J., LESMES, D.P., LEE, J.M., AND TOKSÖZ, M.N., 1996, Velocity variations and water content estimated from multi-offset, ground penetrating radar: Geophysics, v. 61, p. 683–695.

HUBBARD, S.S., PETERSON, J.E., MAJER, E.L., ZAWISLANSKI, P.T., WILLIAMS, K.H., ROBERTS, J., AND WOBBER, F., 1997, Estimation of permeable pathways and water content using tomographic radar data: Leading Edge, p. 1623–1628.

HUBBARD, S.S., RUBIN, Y., AND MAJER, E., 1999, Spatial correlation structure estimation using geophysical and hydrogeological data: Water Resources Research, v. 35, p. 1809–1825.

HUISMAN, J.A., SPERL, C., BOUTEN, W., AND VERSTRATEN, J.M., 2001, Soil water content measurements at different scales: accuracy of time domain reflectometry and ground penetrating radar: Journal of Hydrology, v. 245, p. 48–59.

JACKSON, M.J., AND TWEETON, D.R., 1994, MIGRATOM—Geophysical tomography using wavefront migration and fuzzy constraints: U.S. Bureau of Mines, Report RI9497, 35 p.

KEAN, W.F., WALLER, M.J., AND LAYSON, H.R., 1987, Monitoring moisture migration in the vadose zone with resistivity: Ground Water, v. 27, p. 562–561.

LAGER, D.L., AND LYTLE, R.J., 1977, Determining a subsurface electromagnetic profile from high frequency measurements by applying reconstruction-technique algorithms: Radio Science, v. 12, p. 249–260.

MAZAC, O., KELLY, W.E., AND LANDA, I., 1985, A hydrogeophysical model
for relation between electrical and hydraulic properties of aquifer:
Journal of Hydrology, v. 79, p. 1–19.

PETERSON, J.E., PAULSSON, B.N.P., AND MCEVILLY, T.V., 1985, Application of
algebraic reconstruction techniques to crosshole seismic data: Geophysics, v. 50, p. 1566–1580.

POKAR, M., WEST, L.J., WINSHIP, P., AND BINLEY, A.M., 2001, Estimating
petrophysical data from borehole geophysics, in Symposium on
Applications of Geophysics to Engineering and Environmental Problems (SAGEEP2001): Environmental and Engineering Geophysical
Society, Denver, Colorado, Proceedings,

REA, J., AND KNIGHT, R., 1998, Geostatistical analysis of ground penetrating
radar data: A means of describing spatial variations in the subsurface:
Water Resources Research, v. 34, p. 329–341.

VAN GENUCHTEN, M.TH., 1980, A closed-form equation for predicting the
hydraulic conductivity of unsaturated soils: Soil Science Society of
America, Journal, v. 44, p. 892–898.

WEST, L.J., HUANG, Y., AND HANDLEY, K., 2001, Dependence of sandstone
dielectric behaviour on moisture content and lithology, in Symposium on Applications of Geophysics to Engineering and Environmental Problems (SAGEEP2001): Environmental and Engineering
Geophysical Society, Denver, Colorado, Proceedings,

VAN OVERMEERAN, R.A., GEHRELS, J.C., AND SARIOWA, S.V., 1997, Ground
penetrating radar for determining volumetric soil water content:
Results of comparative measurements at two test sites: Journal of
Hydrology, v. 197, p. 316–338.

DEVELOPMENT OF A 3-D DEPOSITIONAL MODEL OF BRAIDED-RIVER GRAVELS AND SANDS TO IMPROVE AQUIFER CHARACTERIZATION

IAN A. LUNT

Department of Geological Sciences, Binghamton University, Binghamton, New York 13902-6000, U.S.A.
e-mail: ilunt@binghamton.edu

JOHN S. BRIDGE

Department of Geological Sciences, Binghamton University, Binghamton, New York 13902-6000, U.S.A.
e-mail: jbridge@binghamton.edu

AND

ROBERT S. TYE

Petrotel, Inc., 5240 Tennyson Parkway, Plano, Texas 75086, U.S.A.
e-mail: rtye@petrotel.com

ABSTRACT: Braided-river gravels and sands form important aquifers in the Quaternary fluvioglacial outwash deposits of many parts of the world. A detailed understanding of these deposits is vital for modeling groundwater flow and contaminant transport. A quantitative, 3-D depositional model that can aid characterization of gravelly fluvial aquifers is developed based on existing published information and extensive new data from the Sagavanirktok River in northern Alaska. Sagavanirktok River deposits were studied using trenches, cores, wireline logs, porosity and permeability measurements, and ground-penetrating radar profiles. The mode of origin of the deposits was interpreted using knowledge of: (1) channel geometry and mode of erosion and deposition derived from annual aerial photos, and (2) bed texture and bed topography during erosion–deposition events (floods).

Recognition of different scales of bedform and associated stratification is essential to the accurate modeling of fluvial deposits. Within a *channel belt*, the deposits of *compound braid bars*, *point bars*, and *major channel fills* are represented by compound sets of large-scale inclined strata. These compound sets fine upward, fine upward then coarsen upward, or show little vertical variation in grain size, and commonly have open-framework gravel near their bases. *Unit bars* and *minor channel fills* (associated with cross-bar channels) are represented by simple sets of large-scale inclined strata. These simple sets generally fine upward, and open-framework gravel commonly occurs at the bases and downstream ends of these sets. Superimposed simple sets form compound sets. *Dunes* and *bed-load sheets* that migrate over bars and in channels are represented by sets of medium-scale trough cross strata and gravelly planar strata, respectively. Cross strata in a medium-scale set can alternate between open-framework and closed-framework gravel. *Ripples* and *upper-stage plane beds* are represented by sets of small-scale trough cross-stratified sand and planar-laminated sand, respectively. At the top of the channel belt, these sands contain drifted plant remains, roots, and burrows.

The 3-D depositional model represents the geometry and spatial distribution of the different scales of strata that occur in all river deposits. Furthermore, the length : thickness ratios of different scales of strata are similar to the length : height ratios of the formative bed forms (e.g., bars, dunes) and scale with the channel geometry, suggesting that the model can be applied to different scales of river deposits.

Distributions of porosity and permeability are related to sediment textures and can be included in the model by predicting the spatial distribution of sediment textures within different scales of strata. Of particular importance is the distribution of high-permeability open-framework gravel strata that may be continuous for tens to hundreds of meters. Permeabilities of open-framework gravels can be two or three orders of magnitude greater than permeabilities of surrounding sediments, and significantly influence fluid flow and contaminant transport within the aquifer. Stochastic predictions of the spatial distribution of different scales of strata and their associated porosities and permeabilities in an aquifer will benefit from site-specific data (e.g., geophysical profiles, borehole logs, wireline logs, and pumping tests) combined with this three-dimensional model of gravelly fluvial deposits.

INTRODUCTION

The purpose of this paper is to develop a generalized, quantitative, 3-D model of gravelly braided-channel-belt deposits, and to show how such a model can aid aquifer characterization, given sparse subsurface data. The model is based on extensive new data from the Sagavanirktok River in northern Alaska (summarized here but described in more detail in Lunt et al., in press; Lunt and Bridge in press) and existing literature on gravelly braided rivers.

Gravelly aquifers in Pleistocene braided-river outwash deposits throughout the world are an important source of drinking water, and have strong hydraulic connections with freshwater aquatic habitats. Many of these aquifers have been contaminated and need to be cleaned up. Aquifer remediation commonly requires determining the 3-D geometry and spatial distribution of sediment types, and their associated porosity and permeability

(i.e., aquifer characterization). The most common approach to aquifer characterization involves the following steps: (1) analysis of borehole logs, cores, and hydraulic testing data in order to determine the sedimentological nature and origin of the strata, and their hydraulic properties; (2) stratigraphic correlation of borehole logs and cores in order to assess the lateral continuity of distinctive sediment types (facies) between boreholes; (3) use of geophysical profiles (seismic, GPR) to assess the orientation and structural continuity of sequences of strata, and to recognize distinctive geophysical patterns that can be related to distinctive sedimentary facies; (4) modeling of the geometry and distribution of sedimentary facies in the volume between boreholes, and (5) distribution of properties such as porosity and permeability as a function of sedimentary facies or using stochastic models. Successful completion of these steps involves a great deal of geological knowledge and the use of a range of stratigraphic models.

Aquifer Characterization
SEPM Special Publication No. 80, Copyright © 2004
SEPM (Society for Sedimentary Geology), ISBN 1-56576-107-3, p. 139–169.

Many hydrogeological models are unable to account realistically for the influence of different types, scales, and spatial distributions of sedimentary strata on fluid flow and contaminant transport in aquifers (e.g., Webb, 1994; Bierkens and Weerts, 1994; Jussel et al., 1994; Bierkens, 1996; Anderson et al., 1999). Other geometric simulation techniques (e.g., Scheibe and Freyberg, 1995) are geologically realistic at small scales (< tens of meters) but are not widely applicable to other deposits. Geostatistical modeling techniques (e.g., Carle et al., 1998; Fogg et al., 1998; Rauber et al., 1998; Weissmann and Fogg, 1999; Ritzi et al., 2000) used in combination with a detailed depositional model, may in future improve predictions of fluid flow and contaminant transport in the subsurface. Most existing depositional models of gravelly braided rivers (Miall, 1977, 1992, 1996; Rust, 1978; Bluck, 1979; Ramos et al., 1986; Bridge, 1993, 2003; Collinson, 1996) are qualitative, lack detail, and do not contain information on permeability and porosity, thereby limiting their use in aquifer characterization. This is because of difficulties in describing deposits in 3-D below the water table, and in studying depositional processes during the all-important high-flow stages and over large time and space scales (see review by Bridge, 1993). Some of these problems are starting to be overcome using ground-penetrating radar (GPR) profiles tied to cores and trenches in order to document the spatial distribution of the different types and scales of strata within channel belts (e.g., Huggenberger, 1993; Siegenthaler and Huggenberger, 1993; Bridge et al., 1995; Bridge et al., 1998; Beres et al., 1999; Regli et al., 2002; Best et al., 2003; Skelly et al., 2003). Porosity and permeability measured from core samples, wireline logs, or pumping tests can then be correlated with sediment textures. Despite this progress, a sufficiently detailed, 3-D depositional model for gravelly, braided channel belts is still not available. The model developed here relies heavily on extensive new data from the Sagavanirktok River in northern Alaska, but it also incorporates information from other studies of gravelly braided rivers and their deposits.

The deposits of the gravelly, braided Sagavanirktok River in northern Alaska (Fig. 1) were studied using trenches, cores, and wireline logs tied to ground-penetrating radar profiles in order to understand the three-dimensional nature of the deposits and the spatial variation of different scales of stratification. Porosity and permeability were measured from samples taken from undisturbed cores and related to their associated sedimentary structures and textures. The origin of these deposits was interpreted using knowledge of the mode of channel cutting, migration, and filling determined from aerial photographs, and inferences about the geometry, sediment textures, and bed forms of the channel bed during flood events, when most erosion and deposition occurs. In the study area (Fig. 1), the channel-belt width is 2.4 km, the mean valley slope is 1.35×10^{-3}, the bankfull discharge is 600 m^3/s, and the bed is composed of sand and gravel with mean grain size of 4.6 mm (Ecological Research Associates, 1983). The river is frozen between November and May, and melts over a period of a few days in late May to early June. Riverbanks are composed of gravelly alluvium capped by vegetated tundra soils composed of sandy silt. The modern channel belt is bordered by an alluvial plain, which contains ancient braided-river channels (Fig. 1). The study site is frozen during the winter, allowing easy access to the entire channel belt and collection of undisturbed gravel cores. Channel-belt dimensions, grain size, and climatic conditions are analogous to those of many fluvioglacial aquifers. These are the main reasons for choosing this study site. However, it will be shown that the depositional model developed using Sagavanirktok River data applies to a much broader range of gravelly rivers.

METHODS

Morphological features of the Sagavanirktok River were identified from aerial photographs and field observations of bed and water surfaces at ice breakup, and when the river was flowing in the summer. The morphology, dimensions, and orientation of various scales of bedforms were linked to their internal structures seen in trenches. The geometries of different scales of stratification were described from trenches up to 100 m long and 1.5 m deep that were dug in nonvegetated parts of the channel belt (Fig. 2). Most deposits are related to bedforms formed at flood stage. However, bedforms and associated deposits observed on exposed bed surfaces had been modified during falling-stage flow. The effects of falling-stage flow are relatively minor but can be recognized both on the bed surface and in deposits.

Seventeen cores up to 10 m long were obtained (using a hollow stem auger with a 3.5" (8.9 cm) diameter core barrel) in frozen channel-belt sands and gravels, and the boreholes were logged with gamma-ray, resistivity, and neutron-density wireline tools (Fig. 2). CAT scans and observations of the cores indicated minimal sediment disturbance around the perimeter of the core. Core samples were taken for optically stimulated luminescence (OSL) dating and for analysis of porosity and permeability. OSL dating determines the age that sands were last exposed to sunlight, hence the time since burial (Stokes, 1999). Exposure of quartz sand grains to sunlight resets (bleaches) the luminescence signal of the grains. Upon burial, the luminescence signal accumulates over time. If the grains are not completely bleached during exposure to sunlight, then the age dates are inaccurate. Sands from the Sagavanirktok River showed incomplete bleaching, probably due to high suspended-sediment concentrations in the flow during sediment transport events. However, the ages of deposits from different channel belts could be discerned. OSL dates were determined at the Department of Geosciences, University of Nebraska, Lincoln. Porosity and vertical and horizontal permeabilities of whole-core samples were measured by Corelab Inc. using a constant-head air permeameter. Epoxy resin peels were made from the cores in order to construct sedimentary logs.

Ground-penetrating radar (GPR) profiles were collected in rectangular grids across the channel belt and along the tops of trenches. 53 km of 110 MHz GPR profiles were obtained over the entire width of the channel belt and part of an adjacent, partially abandoned channel belt (Fig. 2). Profile spacing in the grid is 100 m over the active channel belt and 200 m over the partially abandoned channel belt. Signal penetration depths ranged between 6 m and 10 m. 29 km of 450 MHz GPR profiles at 50 m grid spacing were taken parallel and perpendicular to flow across the frozen main channel and were used to reconstruct the channel geometry (Fig. 2). Common-midpoint (CMP) radar profiles taken on the partially abandoned channel belt and at 11 of the borehole locations were used to determine the vertical variation in radar velocity of the frozen sediment. In addition, 450 MHz and 900 MHz GPR profiles were taken along the tops of the trenches to calibrate the GPR response to observed sediment types and scales of stratification. GPR data were processed (using the DOS-based software GRADIX) by: application of a high-pass filter to remove the "wow" signal noise; bandpass filtering using a Parzen taper; removal of background ringing by subtraction of a mean trace (averaged over 1000 adjacent traces); setting time zero; and static elevation correction.

The frequency of GPR antennae, the radar velocity, and the reflection coefficients of strata determine the resolution of GPR profiles and the scale of strata that can be observed (Fig. 3). Medium-scale cross sets and large-scale strata thicker than 0.1 m can be seen on 450 MHz profiles, whereas only large-scale strata

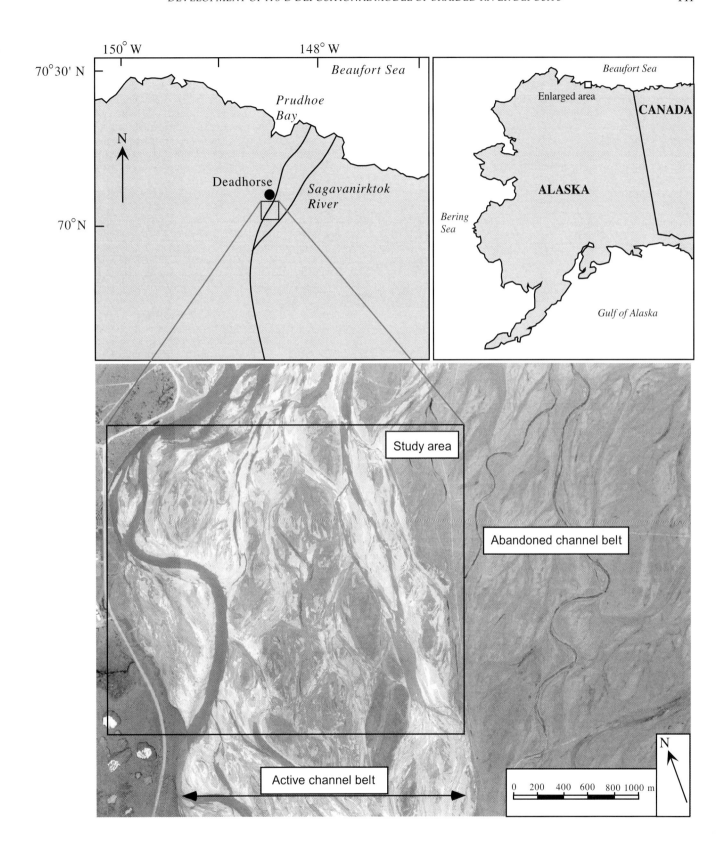

FIG. 1.—Aerial photograph showing location of study area on the Sagavanirktok River. The upper maps show the location of the study area on the North Slope of Alaska.

thicker than 0.3 m can be observed on 110 MHz GPR profiles. However, 110 MHz profiles are three or four times deeper than 450 MHz profiles. It is necessary to emphasize the frequency of GPR antennae and depth scale of the radar profile when interpreting subsurface sedimentary deposits. This is especially important given the similarity in morphology and internal structures between different scales of deposits, especially alongstream views through deposits of dunes and unit bars.

Aerial photographs taken between 1949 and 2001 (yearly after 1979) were used to reveal the temporal and spatial evolution of channels and bars, and rates of channel and bar migration. Photographs were generally taken during low-flow stages. However, variation in river stage when photos were taken complicates the interpretation of channel and bar migration. The riverbed and bars were surveyed using a differential GPS and TOTAL station. Topographic surveys were used to correct the surface elevation of the GPR profiles and also to make topographic maps of the bar surfaces. Surface sediment samples were collected from bars and within the river channels. Samples were collected on a 100 m x 50 m grid with sample sizes large

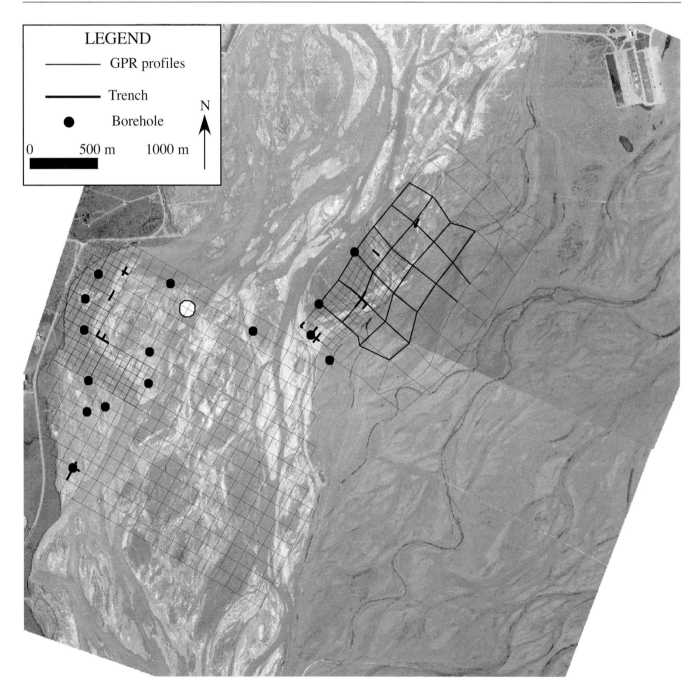

FIG. 2.—Locations of GPR profiles, boreholes, and trenches. Data were collected in March and August 1998 and 2000. Large white dot indicates borehole location in Figure 12.

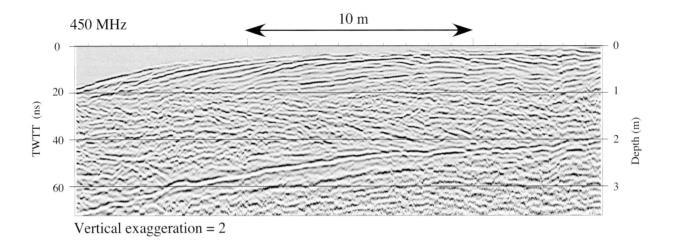

450 MHz

10 m

Vertical exaggeration = 2

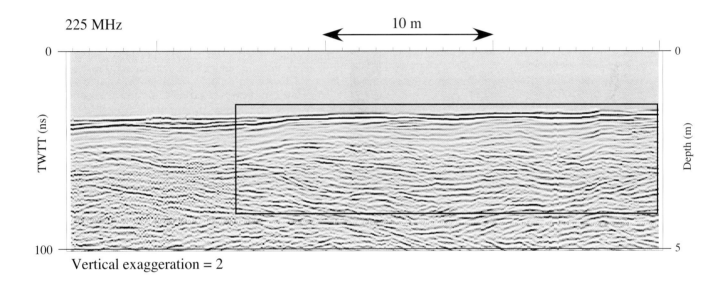

225 MHz

10 m

Vertical exaggeration = 2

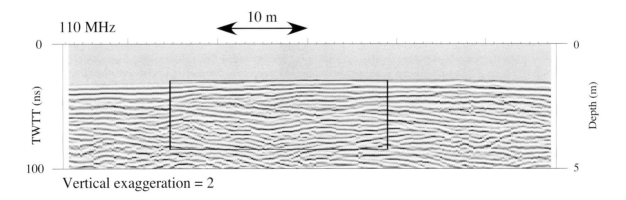

110 MHz

10 m

Vertical exaggeration = 2

FIG. 3.—Radar profiles obtained using 110, 225, and 450 MHz antennae. Boxes on 225 and 110 MHz profiles correspond to the area of the 450 MHz profile. Resolution increases and penetration depth decreases at higher antenna frequencies. TWTT is the two-way travel time of the radar wave in nanoseconds (ns). Depths were calculated using a constant velocity of 0.1 m/ns.

enough that the largest grain is no heavier than 5% of the sample weight (Church et al., 1987).

SURFACE FEATURES AND THEIR DEPOSITS

Knowledge of the geometry, orientation, and migration of bedforms is critical to understanding how their internal structures are formed and preserved. Reviews of the different types of bedforms and associated sedimentary structures formed under unidirectional flows are given by Allen (1982), Yalin (1992), Best (1996), and Bridge (2003), and the details are not repeated here. In the following sections, bedform or channel geometry and migration are described first, followed by a description of their deposits as observed in cores, trenches, and ground-penetrating radar profiles. Examples of most bedform types are shown in Figure 4A. Table 1 contains a summary of the dimensions of different scales of bedforms and channels and their corresponding strata. In order to develop a general model, the relationship between the geometries of the sedimentary strata and their formative bedforms and channels is emphasized. Obviously, the strata observed in trenches and GPR profiles are not necessarily formed under the same conditions as the bedforms observed on exposed bar surfaces. Nevertheless, the evidence suggests that most morphological features observed were formed at high flow stage and were not substantially modified during falling flow stage. Confirmation of this would require a much more detailed study.

Ripples

Ripples in the Sagavanirktok River are 0.1 to 0.2 m long and 20 to 30 mm high, and have sinuous crestlines (Fig. 4B). Ripples occur in sands with mean grain sizes less than 0.7 mm. Ripple lengths (l) are related to the mean grain size (D) of the bed sediment, such that $\lambda \approx 1000\,D$ (Allen, 1982). Ripples form during low-flow stage, or during floods in areas of slow-moving water. They are commonly found in dune troughs, swales of unit bars, channel fills, compound bar tails, and overbank deposits.

Sinuous-crested ripples form sets of small-scale trough cross strata (Fig. 5A). Small-scale cross sets occur either in sandy lenses at the bases of medium-scale cross sets and simple sets of large-scale strata, or in the upper parts of decimeter-thick sand strata. Small-scale cross sets are up to 30 mm thick and up to 0.3 m long, and cosets are up to 0.7 m thick and 30 m long. Cross-set length/thickness is between 5 and 20, whereas coset length/thickness can be between 5 (as a low-flow drape in a dune trough) to 600 (as low-flow drapes over unit bar deposits in a channel fill). Cross-set thickness is comparable to ripple height, and cross-set length is comparable to ripple length (Table 1).

Pebble Clusters

Pebble clusters (Fig. 4C) are closely packed accumulations of relatively large imbricated grains leaning against the upstream side of a dominant clast (obstacle clast; Brayshaw 1984). Most dominant clasts are larger than D_{98} in diameter (Church et al., 1998; Manaeus and Hassan, 2002). Tails immediately downstream of the large clast are made of sands and gravels less than D_{50} in size. Pebble clusters form and are destroyed intermittently on lower-stage plane beds and bedload sheets when only partial bedload transport occurs. In the Sagavanirktok River, length of pebble clusters is between 0.05 and 0.2 m depending on the grain size of the bed material. Cluster width is equivalent to cluster height and is approximately half cluster length.

Bedload Sheets

Bedload sheets are asymmetrical bedforms in alongstream profile, with a steep leading edge (Fig. 4D). Bedload sheets form on lower-stage plane beds on bar surfaces and in channels at flow velocities just above the threshold of gravel motion. Bedload sheets sampled on the Sagavanirktok River bed are lobate (linguoid) in plan view, between 5 and 20 m long, and 3 to 5 m wide. In general, bedload sheets are a few grain diameters high (up to 0.2 m), with wavelength: height ratios between 50 and 300 (Livesey et al., 1998). There can be significant variation in the height and length of bedload sheets, because they are a transitional bedform that can develop into gravel dunes. Bedload sheets may have either fine-grained crests (Kuhnle and Southard, 1988; Bennett and Bridge, 1995; Livesey et al., 1998), or coarse-grained crests (Whiting et al., 1988; Dietrich et al., 1989; Dinehart, 1992; Wilcock, 1992). Fine-grained crests are more commonly observed in flume experiments. Imbricated grains and pebble clusters occur in the troughs and lower stoss sides of the bedload sheets where the bedload is relatively immobile (Brayshaw, 1984; Bennett and Bridge, 1995), whereas smaller and more mobile gravel grains are moved on the bedform crests.

Planar strata composed of open-framework or sandy gravel are formed by the migration of bedload sheets (Fig. 5B). Some planar strata have an erosional base, fine upward from 3–7 mm grains at the base to 1–2 mm grains near the top of the set, and are commonly overlain by sand. Planar strata may also show no vertical grain-size trend or coarsen upward. Coarsening-upward planar strata may be associated with bedload sheets (or low dunes) migrating under higher flow velocities when all bed grains are in motion. Platy gravel grains are imbricated, and pebble clusters (Brayshaw, 1984; Bennett and Bridge, 1995) occur at the base of the set. Gravelly planar strata are 20 to 80 mm thick and extend laterally for 2 to 30 meters. Length/thickness of these planar strata ranges from 150 to 750. Thickness of planar strata is less than the height of bedload sheets, but the length of planar strata may be much greater than the length of bedload sheets (Table 1). Sandy planar strata are rare, and can be formed by migration of low-relief ripples or low-relief bedwaves on upper-stage plane beds.

Dunes

Dunes occur in sands and gravels on the surfaces of most bars, and in channels, during high flow stage (Figs. 4A, E). On exposed bars, gravelly, sinuous-crested dunes have wavelengths of 10 to 15 m and are 0.3 to 0.7 m high and 10 to 20 m wide. Dune lengths of 10 to 15 m suggest maximum local flow depths of 2 to 3 m, because mean dune lengths are commonly 5 to 7 times the formative flow depth (Allen, 1982; Yalin, 1992). These flow depths would occur at flood stage. Dunes in gravel-bed rivers have dimensions similar to their sand-bed counterparts, with maximum height : length ratios of 0.06 (Allen, 1982; Carling, 1999). As flow velocity and depth decrease during falling stage, dune lengths and heights may decrease given sufficient time. However, dunes observed on aerial photographs and on exposed bars formed at high flow stages, although they were modified by falling-stage flows (Fig. 4E). Sandy drapes in dune troughs also form during falling-stage flows.

Sets of medium-scale trough cross strata formed by sinuous-crested dunes (Fig. 5C) are by far the most common internal structure of bars and channel fills. These sets can be composed of sands and/or gravels. Gravelly, medium-scale cross sets have concentrations of coarse grains at the base associated with pebble

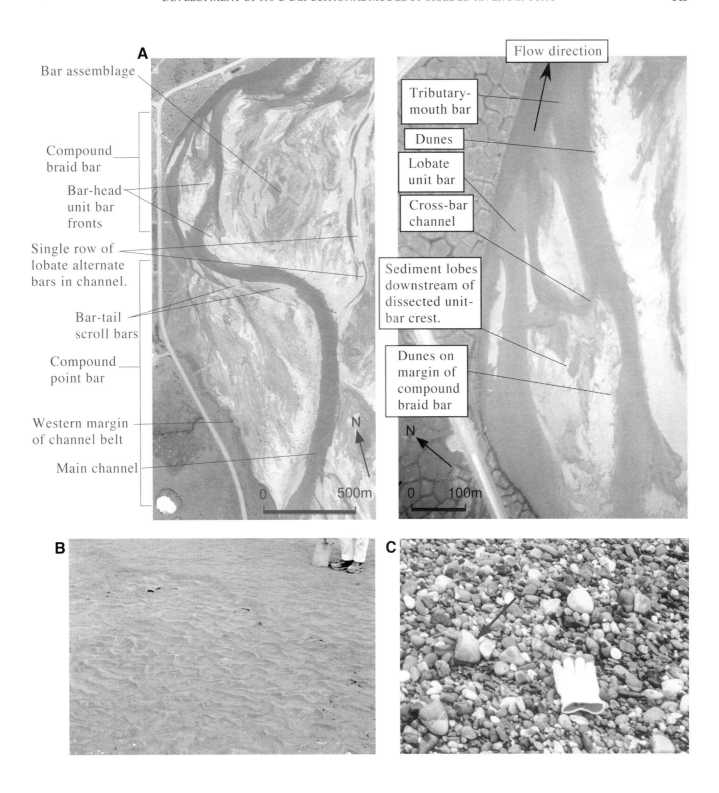

Fɪɢ. 4—**A)** Definition of bedforms from aerial photographs showing most scales of bedform, including a bar assemblage, compound braid bars and point bars, and lobate unit bars in active channels. Lobate fronts of unit bars typically occur at the head of unit bars. Scroll bars are sides of unit bars preserved in tail areas of compound bars. Tributary-mouth bars are unit bars at channel confluences. Dunes are ubiquitous on the bed surface during floods. Only low-flow-stage dune remnants are seen on this photograph. Some sediment lobes and cross-bar channels form during falling flow stages. Western margin of channel belt is also indicated. **B)** Sinuous-crested current ripples. **C)** Pebble clusters (arrowed) occur commonly on bar surfaces. Flow is from right to left.

FIG. 4 (continued)—**D)** Bedload sheets (arrowed) migrating over the top of a unit bar. Crests are coarse-grained and sand in troughs is a low-flow drape. **E)** Dunes (arrowed) on a compound bar surface. Note the steep avalanche face and sand drapes (light areas) in the trough. A falling-stage gravel lobe has formed downstream of the lower dune. **F)** Crescent-shaped scour formed during breakup flood around an ice block at the upstream end of a gravelly point bar. **G)** Edge of a unit bar and adjacent swale, looking upstream. Frontal lobes of upstream unit bars (1), cross-bar channels (2), and gravelly lobes (3) formed during waning flow are indicated. **H)** Aerial photograph showing unit bars and scroll bars within channel fill. Bankfull channel width is 120 m. Flow is towards the top of the picture.

TABLE 1.—Dimensions of bedforms and channels and their corresponding scales of cross stratification.

Bedform	Bedform dimensions (m)			Corresponding type of stratification	Set thickness (m)	Set length (m)	Set length to thickness ratio
	length	width	height				
Ripple	0.1–0.2	0.05–0.5	up to 0.03	Small-scale cross strata	up to 0.03	up to 0.3	5–20
Bedload sheet	5–20	3–5	0.05–0.2	Planar strata	0.02–0.08	2–15	75–375
Crescent-shaped scour	2–20	2–20	0.3–1	Isolated scour fill	0.3–1	2–20	17–40
Dune	10–15	10–20	0.3–0.7	Medium-scale cross strata	0.1–0.4	2–7	7–53
Unit bar*	50–400	10–80	0.5–2	Simple large-scale sets	0.3–1.7	36–151	20–150
Compound bar*	500–1500	200–600	1–4	Compound large-scale sets	1–3.8	200–1100	80–500

* Cross-set lengths cannot be distinguished from cross-set widths on GPR profiles.

Channel type	Bankfull dimensions (m)		Corresponding type of stratification	Maximum thickness (m)	width to max. thickness ratio
	width	max. depth			
Cross bar channel	5–40	0.2–1	Small channel fill	0.1–1	25–80
Large channel	100–200	1–3.9	Compound channel fill	1–3.5	30–100

clusters (Brayshaw, 1984; Bennett and Bridge, 1995). Wedges of sand and sandy trough fills occur in the bases of some gravelly medium-scale cross sets. Such sands probably accumulate during falling flow stages. Sets of medium-scale trough cross strata are 0.1 to 0.4 m thick, and extend laterally for 1 to 5 m in flow-normal sections and 2 to 7 m in flow-parallel sections (Fig. 5C). Cross-set length/ thickness in both across-stream and along-stream trench sections is 7 to 53 (Fig. 6A). Mean set thickness in a medium-scale coset is related to the mean height of the formative dunes (Bridge, 1997; Leclair et al., 1997; Leclair and Bridge, 2001). Cross sets that are 0.1 to 0.4 m thick would typically be formed by dunes with mean heights between 0.3 and 1.2 m. Dunes between 0.3 and 0.7 m high have been observed on bar surfaces in the Sagavanirktok River, and higher dunes occur in deeper parts of the channel. Cross-set lengths are less than dune lengths (Table 1), as found by Leclair (2002).

Individual medium-scale cross strata are 5 to 50 mm thick and are distinguished by grain-size variations and pseudo-imbrication (orientation of platy gravel particles parallel to cross strata). Cross strata are composed of sandy gravel, open-framework gravel, or alternations between open-framework gravel and sandy gravel (Fig. 5C), similar to cross strata described by Smith (1974), Steel and Thompson (1983), and Dawson (1989). Some cross strata fine upwards from 5–10 mm, well-sorted, open-framework gravel at the base to 2–3 mm gravel near the top of the stratum. Cross strata composed of alternating open-framework gravel and sandy gravel may form as a result of temporal variations in flow strength, or by smaller bedforms (e.g., bedload sheets) migrating over dune crests. Open-framework gravel layers are interpreted as being formed by transport to the dune lee side of the sediment constituting mobile armor layers. These armor layers form on lower-stage plane beds containing bedload sheets. Sand is selectively removed from the gravelly armor layers because of differential mobility. Sandy gravels are associated with higher flow stages when gravel is more mobile, and when sand in suspension is deposited with gravel on the lee side of dunes. It is also possible that the bedforms migrating over dunes have differences in grain size along their lengths (e.g., from crest to trough).

Crescent-Shaped Scours

Crescent-shaped scours (Fig. 4F) observed on bar tops are decimeters deep and 2–20 m long and wide, and may resemble the avalanche faces and troughs of dunes in form and dimension. They are formed by scour around ice blocks or vegetated mudclasts

that are eroded from cut banks and transported during flood events. Vegetated mudclasts on bar surfaces have horseshoe-shaped scours on their upstream sides and sand ridges on their downstream sides. These mudclasts form by slump failure of vegetated cut banks during floods and either remain at the base of the cut bank, protecting it from erosion, or are carried downstream and deposited in channel bases or on bar surfaces. The locations of crescent-shaped scours depend on the positions of grounded ice or large mudclasts. They are not likely to migrate and probably do not persist for more than one flood.

Crescent-shaped scours are filled by migrating dunes and bedload sheets after the obstacle block is either melted or broken down. The steep upstream face of the scour is filled with steeply dipping large-scale cross strata that become shallower and concave upward at the downstream end of the scour fill. Small-scale cross-stratified sands may drape the upper parts of scour fills.

Bars

Bars are defined as within-channel depositional features with lengths proportional to channel width and heights comparable to formative channel depth. The main (or first-order) channels and bars are the largest in the channel belt. Smaller (second-order) channels cut across the first-order bars. These cross-bar channels may have their own associated (second-order) bars (Bridge, 1993). Channel bars are either unit bars, which have had a relatively simple depositional history (Smith, 1974, 1978; Ashmore, 1982), or compound bars, which comprise more than one unit bar and have a complex depositional and erosional history. Bar assemblages are areas of floodplain comprising abandoned compound bars and channels (Fig. 4A).

Unit Bars. —

A unit bar is located immediately downstream of an erosional pool, is elongated in the flow direction, and has a lobate front (Figs. 4A, G). Unit bars are asymmetrical in alongstream section, with the steepest side facing downstream. This steep face is inclined at the angle of repose or less. Unit bars are referred to as alternate bars if they occur in trains on alternate sides of a channel (Fig. 4A). The frontal, lobate parts of unit bars deposited on the upstream parts of compound bars are called bar-head lobes (Figs. 4A, G), whereas the lateral parts on the downstream areas of compound bars make up what are referred to as scroll bars and tributary-mouth bars (Fig. 4A). Scroll bars form on the inner banks of curved channels downstream of the

Fig. 5.—**A)** Small-scale trough cross sets in core. Sets are less than 0.03 m thick, and cross strata generally dip to the left. **B)** Planar strata formed by migration of a bedload sheet or low-relief dune. Basal gravels are imbricated, and underlie 0.08 m of open-framework gravel that fine upward. **C)** Medium-scale cross set formed by migration of a dune from left to right. Set is 0.3 m thick and is composed of downstream-steepening sandy gravel and open-framework gravel. Proportion of open-framework gravel increases downstream. **D)** Two sets of large-scale strata (arrowed) formed by migration of unit bars from left to right. Lower set is made up of shallow large-scale strata. Upper set contains more steeply dipping strata and sandy trough fills. Open-framework gravel forms at base of large-scale strata. **E)** Formation of open-framework gravels associated with steepening large-scale strata and thickening stratasets, which occurs periodically with a spacing of tens of meters. Two large-scale sets shown (arrowed). Strata steepen from subhorizontal to between 15 degrees and the angle of repose and show alternations of thick open-framework gravel strata and thin sandy gravels and sands. Stakes in Parts D and E are 1.5 m apart.

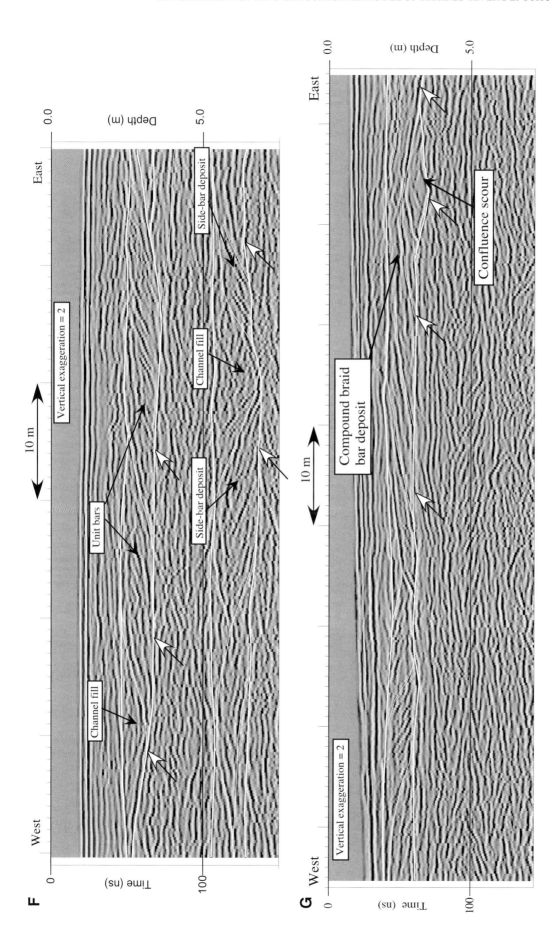

Fig. 5. (continued)—**F)** Upper compound set of large-scale inclined strata formed by lateral accretion of two unit bar deposits. Channel fill occurs west of the compound-bar deposit. Compound set is 1 m thick. Lower set of compound large-scale strata formed by lateral accretion of side bars in opposite directions into confluence, which has subsequently filled. Compound set is 2 m thick. In both compound sets, basal erosion surface (marked by white arrows) deepens towards the channel fill. **G)** Deposit formed by downstream migration of a compound braid bar over a confluence scour. Basal erosion surface of compound bar (white arrows) is deeper over the confluence scour. Compound-bar deposit is 2 m thick. Thick white lines denote bounding surfaces of compound-bar deposits in Parts F and G.

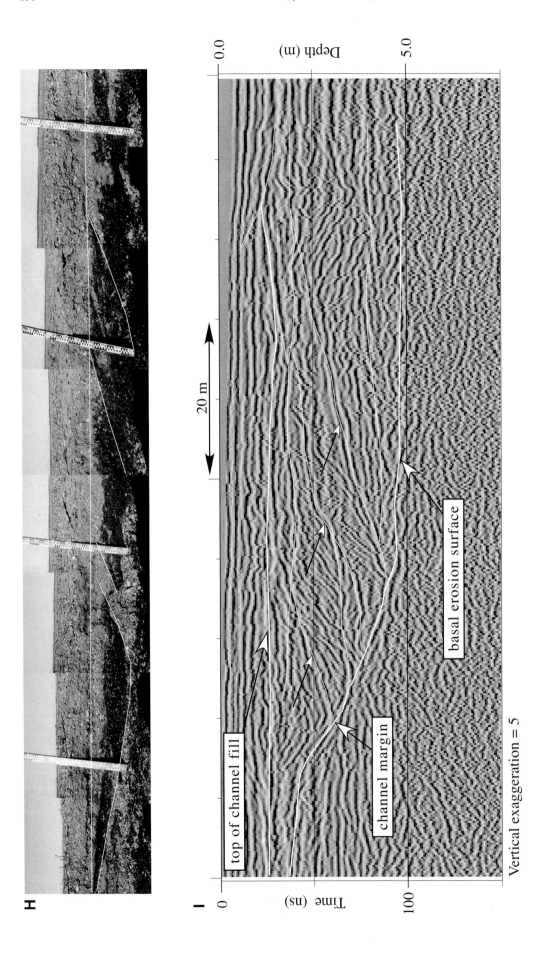

Vertical exaggeration = 5

Fɪɢ. 5. (continued)—**H**) Small channel fill at the top of a compound point bar. West-dipping large-scale strata decrease in dip and form a concave-upward set of large-scale sandy gravel and sand strata at the left of the photo. Stakes are spaced 1.5 m apart. **I**) Channel filling with unit-bar deposits (bases arrowed) that accreted onto the western margin of a compound bar. The final concave-upward channel fill contains medium-scale sets of sand and sandy gravel. Large-scale set boundaries are represented by white lines. Large channel fill is 4 m thick.

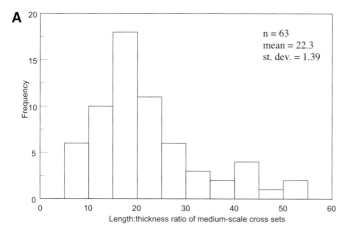

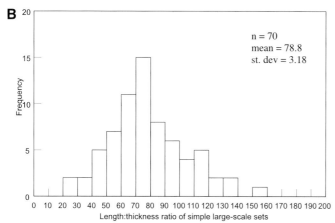

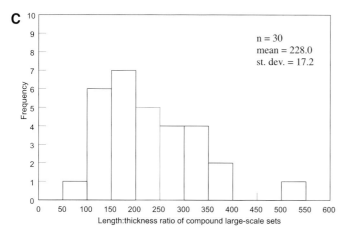

FIG. 6.—Frequency distributions of ratio of set length to thickness for **A)** medium-scale cross strata, **B)** simple sets of large-scale strata, and **C)** compound sets of large-scale strata. Based on 110 MHz GPR profiles and trenches.

bend apex and are elongated subparallel to the channel margin (Fig. 4A). Unit bars may migrate downstream at up to 100 m/yr. Unit bars at the upstream ends of compound bars generally migrate farther than unit bars in bar-tail regions. Theoretical, experimental, and field studies show that unit-bar heights are comparable to channel depth, and that unit-bar length/channel width falls between 3 and 12 (e.g., Lewin, 1976; Whiting and Dietrich, 1993; Tubino et al., 1999; Lanzoni, 2000a, 2000b; review

in Bridge, 2003). In the Sagavanirktok River, unit bars have lengths between 50 and 400 m, widths ranging from 10 to 80 m, and maximum heights of 0.5 to 2 m, depending on the dimensions of the channel in which they form. Unit-bar length/channel width is commonly 2.5 to 4. Falling-stage features on unit bars include a number of parallel channels, 1 to 10 m long, cut through the crest and steep downstream face of the unit bar. Each channel terminates in a delta-like gravel lobe (Figs. 4A, G). Lobes are 0.05 to 0.25 m high, 0.2 to 1 m wide, and 0.5 to 5 m long. Unit bars also show distinctive trends in surface grain size, with the coarsest grains occurring on the bar crest and finest grains on the back of the bar. Their surfaces display pebble clusters and bedload sheets at low-flow stages and are covered with migrating dunes during flood flow.

A simple set of large-scale inclined strata is formed by migration of a unit bar (Fig. 5D). Simple large-scale sets have a sharp, coarse-grained base, are composed mainly of sandy gravel, and fine upwards. Open-framework gravels commonly occur at set bases, whereas sands occur preferentially towards the tops (Fig. 7). Other large-scale sets have no vertical grain-size trends. Set thickness in cores is between 0.3 and 1.7 m, with a mean of 0.68 m (Fig. 9A). Simple large-scale sets observed in trenches and GPR profiles extend laterally for meters to tens of meters in the across-stream direction and tens to hundreds of meters in the along-stream direction, though identifying along-stream and across-stream orientations of large-scale sets in GPR profiles is not always possible (Fig. 6B). Ratios of set length to thickness from trenches (i.e., untruncated surface sets) in the across-stream and along-stream orientation are 35 to 80 and 50 to 190, respectively. The set length-to-thickness ratios from 110 MHz GPR profiles (truncated subsurface sets) are 20 to 150. Simple sets of large-scale strata have length and thickness comparable to but less than the length and height of the formative unit bars.

Between four and eight large-scale inclined strata occur within the vertical thickness of one set. Simple large-scale inclined strata are recognized by contrasts in grain size, and are most commonly cosets, 0.1 to 0.6 m thick, of medium-scale trough cross strata that extend across-stream and along-stream for meters to tens of meters (Fig. 5D). Most large-scale strata have inclinations less than 10 degrees. However, they may increase in inclination in the dip direction and may attain the angle of repose (Fig. 5E). Trenches and GPR profiles show that steeply dipping, open-framework gravels occur at intervals of 20 to 50 m (10 to 25% of the unit-bar length) along the length of a single set of large-scale strata. Steeply dipping open-framework gravel strata are tens of centimeters thick and are interbedded with sand and sandy gravel strata (Fig. 5E). These zones of steeply dipping strata extend over along-stream distances up to 30 m (13% of the unit-bar length) and over across-stream distances of up to 20 m. Figure 8 shows that open-framework gravels can also occur randomly anywhere along the length of a unit-bar deposit. Sandy strata (small-scale and medium-scale cross sets) occur randomly throughout unit-bar deposits, but especially toward their tops and downstream ends. They occur interbedded with steeply dipping, open-framework gravel strata (see above), as drapes and fills of unit-bar troughs, and in associated small channel fills (Fig. 5D).

Steepening of large-scale inclined strata along the length of set, and associated increase in the proportion of open-framework gravel, is interpreted to be due to periodic migration and change in geometry of the formative unit bar. Stratal steepening is due to increase in the asymmetry (in alongstream profile) of a unit bar as it grows in height during rising and peak flood stage. During this period, sandy gravel is transported as dunes over the unit bar surface. As flow stage decreases, a mobile

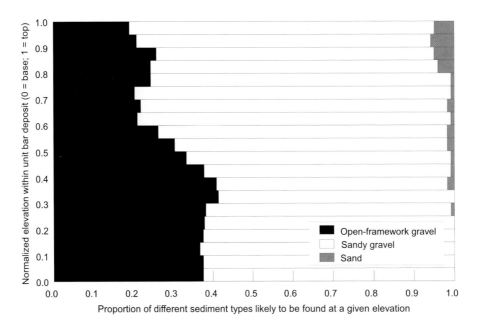

FIG. 7.—Distribution of sediment types within normalized thickness of simple large-scale sets. Data averaged from interpretations of truncated unit bar deposits and sediment types in core logs. 0 is the base of the unit-bar deposit; 1 is the top of the unit-bar deposit. Simple large-scale sets show upward decrease in open-framework gravel and increase in sand content within the top 20% of set thickness.

armor layer develops on the back of the unit bar, sand is preferentially entrained and removed from the armor layer, and bedload sheets transport open-framework gravel to the steep leeside of the unit bar. The sand may be deposited in the trough region of the unit bar. At the lowest flow stages, wedges of sand form on the lee side of the unit bar and in the trough region immediately downstream. The alongstream spacing of these variations in stratal dip, on the order of tens of meters, is coincident with the distance of migration of unit bars during

floods. However, laterally extensive large-scale strata composed of open-framework gravel may be formed over a series of floods, during which the flow was capable of moving only the gravel as a mobile armor layer.

Medium-scale and large-scale cross sets have overlapping thickness within the 0.3 to 0.6 m range, and downstream-dipping inclined surfaces. This leads to difficulty in the correct interpretation of these deposits. The best method of resolving this problem is either by looking at the lateral dimensions of the deposit or

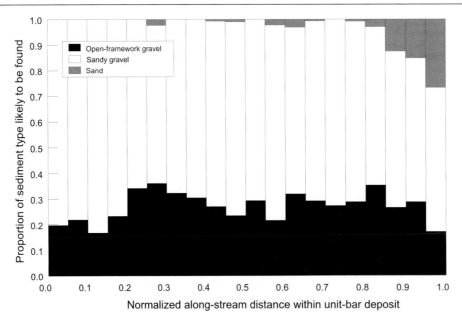

FIG. 8.—Distribution of sediment types along the normalized length of nontruncated unit-bar deposits. Lateral changes in sediment type are averaged over the unit-bar thickness and are interpreted from trenches. 0 is upstream, and 1 is downstream.

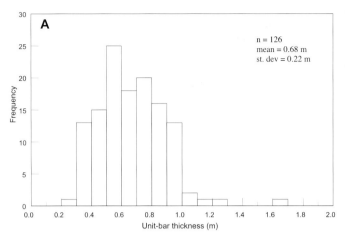

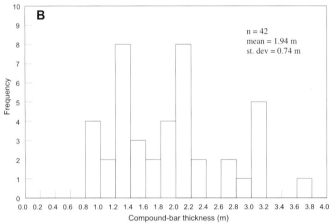

FIG. 9.—Histograms of truncated thickness of **A)** unit-bar deposits and **B)** compound-bar deposits, from core interpretations. Thickness of unit-bar deposit is unimodal and skewed, whereas thickness of compound-bar deposit is polymodal. All measurements are taken from the modern channel belt.

identifying medium-scale cross sets on the inclined surfaces of simple sets of large-scale strata.

Compound Bars.—

Compound bars, formed by the amalgamation of unit bars, may be either braid bars or point bars, and they evolve through time from one form to the other (Ashmore, 1982; Lunt and Bridge, in press). Braid bars (Fig. 4A) are compound bars bounded on both sides by channels. The experiments of Ashmore (1982, 1991) and field studies (Bristow, 1987; McLelland et al., 1999; Best et al., 2003; Lunt and Bridge, in press) show that braid bars form from the amalgamation of unit bars, from cut-off point bars, and by reoccupation of abandoned channels. Point bars (Fig. 4A) are compound bars that occur on the convex, inner banks of single, curved channels. Both point bars and braid bars have bar-head lobes on their upstream ends and scroll bars separated by swales in downstream regions (bar tails). Cross-bar channels (Fig. 4A) are common on compound bars. Compound bars migrate laterally and downstream, by deposition of unit bars on upstream, lateral, and downstream margins and by erosion of upstream and lateral margins. Lateral migration of compound bars is commonly associated with erosion of an adjacent concave channel

bank. Compound channel bars are hundreds of meters in width and length and are 1 to 4 m thick. Smaller bedforms superimposed on compound bar surfaces include pebble clusters, bedload sheets, and dunes. Mean grain size of the surfaces of compound bars generally decreases downstream from greater than 8 mm in bar-head regions to between 2 and 6 mm in bar-tail regions. Sand strata up to decimeters thick drape scroll-bar swales in bar-tail regions. Grain-size variations over tens of meters on surfaces of compound bars are determined by the occurrence of unit bars. Mean grain size of cross-bar channels is greater than of adjacent bar surfaces, and decreases downstream, from 10 mm to 6 mm. Cross-bar channels may be draped by sands at their downstream ends.

Migration of a compound channel bar forms a compound set of large-scale strata (Figs. 5F, G). In across-stream GPR profiles, compound large-scale strata dip towards the thalweg of the adjacent channel. Commonly, the large-scale strata increase in dip into the adjacent channel, and the set thickness increases accordingly. In cross sections through braid bars, the compound large-scale strata dip in opposite directions away from the middle of the braid bar and into the adjacent channels. In cross sections through confluences with adjacent side bars, the compound large-scale strata associated with the side bars dip in opposite directions into the confluence (Fig. 5F). In some cases, braid-bar sections are superimposed upon confluence sections (Fig. 5G). Along-stream sections through compound bars show low-angle (<5°), upstream-dipping large-scale strata in upstream regions of compound bars and downstream-dipping strata in downstream regions. Downstream-dipping large-scale strata are more voluminous than upstream-dipping strata. The thickness of compound sets of large-scale strata increases in the downstream direction and then decreases over the length of the compound bar. Commonly, between two and five simple large-scale sets (unit-bar deposits) constitute the thickness of a compound set.

Compound-bar deposits commonly fine upwards (from 32 mm to around 4 mm; –5 to –2 phi) or show no vertical trend in grain size. Some compound-bar deposits fine upwards and then coarsen again towards the top. Relatively thick parts of compound-bar deposits in confluence scour, mid-bar, and bar-tail regions commonly fine upwards. Compound-bar deposits that fine upward and coarsen toward the top occur in bar-head regions. Compound-bar deposits that show no vertical grain-size trend commonly form in mid-bar regions or in relatively thin compound-bar deposits. Open-framework gravel occurs throughout compound-bar deposits, but most commonly near their bases and tops (e.g., Fig. 12). Sands also occur throughout the compound-bar deposits, but most commonly towards the top. The thickness of medium-scale cross sets decreases towards the tops of compound large-scale sets (Fig. 12). In the upper parts of compound sets, individual large-scale strata pass laterally into, or are truncated by, small channel fills. Compound large-scale sets in cores and GPR profiles (i.e., truncated) are between 1 and 3.8 m thick, with a mean of 1.94 m (Fig. 9B). They extend laterally for hundreds of meters in both along-stream and across-stream directions. Ratios of length to thickness of compound sets are between 100 and 500, and do not appear to vary with orientation (Fig. 6C). The thickness and length of compound sets are comparable to, but less than, the height and length of the compound bars.

The maximum thickness of a compound-bar deposit is determined by the maximum bankfull depth of the adjacent channels. This depth varies in space around the bar, and varies over time as the bankfull discharge of individual channels and the whole channel belt vary. Spatial variations in the thickness of compound-bar deposits, their vertical sequences of grain size, and the inclination of their large-scale strata (Figs. 5F, G) are explained here in terms of channel geometry, surface distribution of sediment type, and migration pattern using the models of Willis (1989, 1993a) and Bridge (1993). Compound bars that grow in size and migrate downstream and laterally produce relatively thick upward-fining sequences, particularly where braid-bar tails prograde into confluences, and where point (side)-bar tails prograde into curved channel thalwegs. Relatively thick sequences that fine upwards and coarsen towards the top occur in the upstream parts of compound channel bars as bar heads migrate over bar tails. Relatively thin sequences that have little vertical variation in grain size are formed in riffle (crossover) sections.

Channels and Channel Fills

The Sagavanirktok River is anastomosing, meandering, and braided (Fig. 1). Anastomosing channel segments are separated by areas of floodplain (i.e., bar assemblages), whereas braided channel segments are separated by active channel bars. The degree of braiding and sinuosity of the main channels at low-flow stage are given in Lunt et al. (in press). Bankfull level in the study area was defined arbitrarily as the spatially averaged elevation of the top of the cut bank on the eastern side of the channel belt (approximately 11.4 m above mean sea level). However, the average elevation of the top of the western channel-belt bank (13.4 m above mean sea level) is higher than on the eastern side.

The western channel-belt bank was not used to define bankfull level, because there are no overbank deposits there. The main channels have bankfull widths of 50 to 250 m. The maximum bankfull depth of the main channel, determined from GPR profiles over frozen channels, is 3.9 m, although the median bankfull depth is around 1 to 2 m (Fig. 10). Channels are deepest towards the outer banks of bends and in confluences. In straight reaches, channels have symmetrical profiles, whereas in bends they have a triangular cross section with a gently sloping inner bank and a steep outer bank (Fig. 10). Channels migrate by eroding the concave (outer) banks at bends and depositing sediment on the convex (inner) banks. Channel bends migrate by downstream translation, lateral expansion, and chute cutoff. Bank erosion rate between 1949 and 2001 averages between 0.5 and 1.5 m/yr at different positions bends (Lunt and Bridge, in press). Maximum rates of erosion over shorter time spans reach 5 m/yr (cf. 0.1 to 4.0 m/yr with a mean of 1.6 m/yr on the Colville River; Walker et al., 1987). Cross-bar channels have bankfull depths less than 1 m and widths of 5 to 40 m.

Channel filling takes place when discharge through a channel reach is reduced, as a result of flow diversion and/or accumulation of sediment in the channel entrance or at its downstream end (Bridge, 1993). In one example in the Sagavanirktok River, channel filling occurs by expansion of point-bar deposits into the channel entrance and deposition of lobate unit bars in the channel at high flow stage (Fig. 4H). These bars are gravelly, but sands are

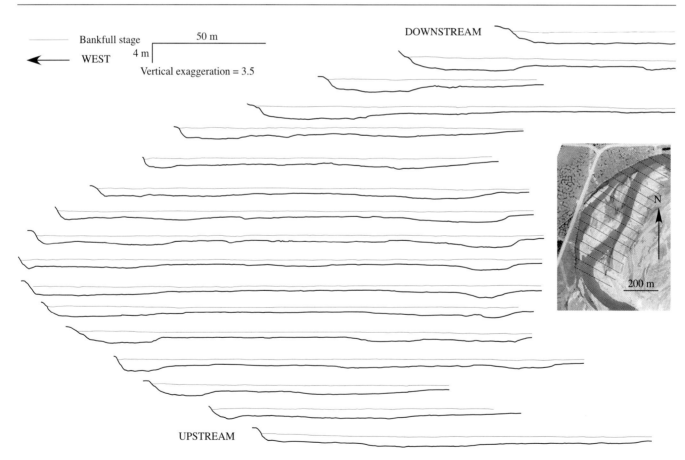

FIG. 10.—Channel geometry determined from east–west oriented 450 MHz GPR profiles collected over the frozen river channel. Profile locations are shown on aerial photograph. Radar profiles are spaced 50 m apart, and were processed using a velocity of 0.16 m/ns. Bankfull elevation was determined from the height of the eastern channel-belt cutbank. Deepest parts of active channel are on the outer banks of channel bends and in channel confluence.

deposited in the lee of the bars as channel abandonment proceeds. Water continues to flow through these channels at high flow stages, transporting gravel and sand. The final stage of channel filling is deposition of sands over the bar topography.

Sets of large-scale inclined strata deposited by bars commonly pass laterally into, or are truncated by, channel fills. Most channel fills are truncated by basal erosion surfaces of overlying compound-bar deposits. Small channel fills (up to 1 m thick) near the tops of unit-bar or compound-bar deposits are distinguished from large channel fills (between 1 and 3.5 m thick), which have a thickness similar to adjacent compound-bar deposits. Channel fills have across-stream widths of meters to tens of meters and extend along-stream for tens to hundreds of meters. Maximum thickness (truncated) ranges from 0.1 m to 3.5 m. Ratios of channel-fill width to maximum thickness vary between 30 and 100. Along-stream sections through channel fills are hard to recognize on GPR profiles.

Small channels are filled with sand, sandy gravel, and open-framework gravel (Fig. 5H). Strata sets in channel fills are concave upward in across-stream view (Fig. 5H). Sandy channel fills are generally made up of small- to medium-scale cross strata, with planar and medium-scale cross-stratified sandy gravel interspersed. Other small channels are filled with medium-scale cross-stratified gravel deposited by dunes. These bedforms were probably active only during the highest flow stages.

Large channel fills are composed of unit-bar deposits containing medium-scale and small-scale cross sets (Fig. 5I). These deposits are generally finer grained than those within the main channel bars. Open-framework gravels are present in all parts of large channel fills but are more common in upstream parts (up to 15% of the deposit) than in downstream parts (< 1% deposit volume). The proportion of sand increases downchannel and towards the tops of channel fills.

Channel Belts

The channel-belt width of the Sagavanirktok River is 2.4 km, is defined by the extent of flow during bankfull flood events, and comprises active and partially abandoned channels, simple and compound bars, and bar assemblages (Fig. 4A). There is no systematic variation in grain size across the channel belt. Channel belts have erosional bases defined by the maximum depth of channel scour over the lifetime of the channel belt. The tops of channel belts show soil horizons (containing roots and burrows) between 0.4 and 1 m thick. The thickness of the active channel belt (up to 7 m) is greater than present maximum channel depths (3.9 m). This may be due to variation in maximum channel depths over time and/or aggradation of the channel belt. Preserved channel fills range in thickness from 1 to 3.5 m. Although there is evidence of truncation at the tops of channel fills, there are no channel fills with the same maximum thickness as the channel belt. This suggests that up to 3 m of aggradation may have occurred during deposition of the modern channel belt.

Core logs and optically stimulated luminescence (OSL) dates of core samples show that the modern Sagavanirktok River channel belt is up to 7 m thick (Fig. 11). Sediments at the base of the channel belt are not significantly coarser grained than strata higher in the channel belt. The channel belt is made up of two to five compound sets of large-scale inclined strata that show no consistent spatial trends in thickness or sediment texture across the channel belt. Sandy strata and soils in the upper parts of channel belts may be present (Fig. 12) or truncated by a subsequent channel-belt deposit. In the absence of thick cosets of sandy strata underlying a channel-belt deposit, the base of the channel belt may not be obvious from core data alone. In the Sagavanirktok

River, the ratio of the modern channel-belt width (2400 m) to maximum channel-belt deposit thickness (7 m) is 343:1. Comparisons with other fluvial deposits show a wide range in the ratio of channel-belt width to thickness and significant overlap in this ratio between braided and meandering fluvial deposits. Detailed mapping from laterally extensive sandy braided fluvial outcrops in the Siwaliks of Northern Pakistan give channel-belt width-to-thickness ratios of 140 to more than 235 (Willis, 1993b; Khan et al., 1997). These paleochannels are comparable to modern braided rivers on the Indo-Gangetic plains. Extensive outcrops of meandering and braided fluvial sandstones in the Chubut Group of Argentina have channel-belt width-to-thickness ratios of 17 to 53 (Bridge et al., 2000). Channel-belt width-to-thickness ratio for the braided Brahmaputra is about 250. Core data from the deposits of the meandering lower Mississippi River show channel-belt width-to-thickness ratios greater than 200, with a mean of 375 (Bridge, 2002). Channel-belt width-to-thickness ratios of individual anastomosed channels of the Rhine–Meuse delta are less than 85 (Törnqvist, 1993). Cores from the meandering Brazos River in Texas show channel-belt width-to-thickness ratios of 132 to 172 (Bernard et al., 1970). A clear distinction should be made between bankfull channel depth and channel-belt thickness because the channel-belt thickness is usually larger than the maximum bankfull channel depth. In the Sagavanirktok River, the maximum modern bankfull channel depth is 3.9 m, whereas the modern channel-belt depth is around 7 m.

RELATIONSHIP BETWEEN CORES, WIRELINE LOGS, AND GPR PROFILES

Three wireline logs were taken in each of the 17 boreholes: gamma-ray, resistivity, and neutron-density logs (e.g., Fig. 12). The gamma-ray log values vary between 10 and 50 API. Sandy strata or soil horizons greater than 0.2 m thick are 20–40 API higher than adjacent strata: however, similar peaks also occur in sandy gravel deposits. Gamma-ray logs have a cyclic character

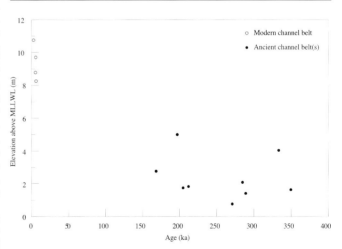

FIG. 11.—Graph showing optically stimulated luminescence (OSL) age dates against elevation above sea level. A distinct age difference is noted between active-channel-belt deposits (< 6 ka; 8–11 m above mean lowest low water level, MLLWL) and the Pleistocene channel-belt deposit(s) (> 160 ka; < 5 m above MLLWL). Ages and depths indicate that the modern channel belt is less than 7 m thick. Interpreted modern and ancient deposits are indicated by open and closed circles, respectively.

with peaks that occur at intervals of 0.1 to 0.2 m, similar to the mean thickness of medium-scale cross sets. Resistivity-log values range between 80 and 180 ohm m, with typical values between 100 and 120 ohm m (Fig. 12). They do not show any correspondence with sediment texture in the core logs. Neutron-density log values range from 1.7 to 2.3 g cm^{-3}, with typical values between 1.9 and 2.1 g cm^{-3}. Density is inversely proportional to the sediment porosity. However, there is no consistent correspondence between the neutron-density log and sediment texture between cores or within a single core. It is probable that variations in grain density due to differences in clast lithology are more significant than variations in bulk density due to porosity.

Vertical variation of radar velocities was determined from CMP analyses at 11 of the borehole locations (e.g., Fig. 13). Radar velocities from CMPs generally vary between 0.09 to 0.12 m/ns and commonly increase with distance below the surface (down to 5 m). Radar velocities depend on the dielectric permittivity of the deposit, which depends on the mineralogy of the sediment and on the amount and composition of pore-filling material (air, water, ice) (van Dam and Schlager, 2000; Kowalsky et al., 2001). In frozen sediment, radar velocities are relatively large (e.g., 0.14 m/ns). In such deposits, the porosity does not strongly influence radar velocity, because the velocities of radar waves in sediment and ice are similar. In water-saturated sediment, radar velocities are relatively low (e.g., 0.06 m/ns), and decrease as porosity increases, because the velocity of radar waves in water is less than in sediment. The downward increase in radar velocity seen in the Sagavanirktok deposits is related to the increasing proportion of ice filling the pores. Vertical variations in radar velocity are difficult to interpret in terms of porosity variations measured in core samples, because the relative proportions of ice and water in the pores are not known. In water-saturated sediment, porosity should be closely related to radar velocity.

Amplitude of radar reflections depends on contrasts in radar velocities between vertically adjacent strata, and the thickness of strata (Kowalsky et al., 2001). High-amplitude reflections are related to the occurrence of open-framework gravels and sands adjacent to each other or to sandy gravels. Above the water table, this is due to variations in water saturation. In water-saturated sediment, this is due mainly to variations in porosity. Below the permafrost, this is probably due to variations in the relative proportion of water and ice in pores, and the porosity. In the absence of information about the volumes of ice and water in the sediment pores, it is not possible to determine variations in sediment texture from radar amplitudes.

Cores provide only one-dimensional information about the thickness, texture, and internal structure of the strata. It is not possible to uniquely determine the nature and origin of sedimentary textures and structures observed in cores without understanding their three-dimensional geometry determined from radar profiles. Interpretations of unit-bar, compound-bar, and channel-fill deposits in sedimentary logs were made using orthogonal 110 MHz and 450 MHz GPR profiles through each borehole location (Fig. 12). OSL age dates confirm the existence of two distinct channel-belt deposits, indicated by a gap in the OSL dates between 6000 years and 120,000 years (Fig. 11). 110 MHz GPR profiles are up to 6 m deep and penetrate most of the active channel belt. Cores up to 10 m long penetrate the upper parts of the ancient channel- belt deposit (Fig. 12). The upper part of the ancient channel belt contains sandy small-scale cross strata, roots, burrows, and organic fragments (i.e., soils) in some cores (e.g., Fig. 12). Table 2 compares the proportion of each sediment type observed in cores with proportions derived from trenches. Trenches have less open-framework gravel and more sand than the cores, because trenches sample only deposits close to the surface. Sands occur in the upper parts of active channel bars and fills, and therefore have a low preservation potential. Hence, sands are overrepresented in trenches compared to cores. Trenches do not sample the bases of compound bars, which have high proportions of open-framework gravel (Fig. 12). Thickness of large-scale sets from untruncated unit bars observed in trench photomosaics tend to be thicker than those measured from cores. Also, thickness of medium-scale cross-sets in trenches may not be representative of those observed in cores, because the formative dunes may have larger heights (hence from thicker cross sets) in the deeper parts of channels represented in the cores.

SEDIMENT TEXTURES AND POROSITY–PERMEABILITY DATA

Porosity and permeability samples taken from undisturbed cores were classified into four sediment types: sands, gravelly sands, sandy gravels, and open-framework gravels. The classifications were based on grain-size properties (mean grain size and sorting) that were measured from grain-size distributions of 270 surface sediment samples (Fig. 14). These grain-size distributions are similar to those obtained from samples from trenches and cores. Sands have a unimodal grain-size distribution with mean grain size less than 2 mm (-1 phi) and greater than 0.063 mm (4 phi), and a sorting coefficient less than 2 phi. Most sands in the study area have mean grain size less than 0.5 mm (1 phi). Gravelly sands are bimodal, have mean grain size less than 2 mm (-1 phi) and greater than 0.063 mm (4 phi), and sorting coefficients greater than 2 phi. Sandy gravels have bimodal grain-size distributions, with mean grain size greater than 2 mm and sorting coefficients generally greater than 2 phi. Most sandy gravels have mean grain sizes in the range 3 to 12 mm. Open-framework gravels have a unimodal grain-size distribution with mean grain size greater than 2 mm, negligible sand content, and sorting coefficients generally less than 2.5 phi. Most open-framework gravels have mean grain sizes of 4 to 16 mm. Textures vary gradually between sands and sandy gravels, and between sandy gravels and open-framework gravels.

Figure 15 shows that porosity and permeability are related to sediment texture. Open-framework gravels have the highest permeabilities (greater than 10 darcys), sandy gravels and gravelly sands have the next highest permeabilities (between 1 and 20 darcys), and sands have the lowest permeabilities (less than 7 darcys). The difference between the permeabilities of sand, gravelly sand, and sandy gravel is not as great as that between sandy gravel and open-framework gravel (Fig. 15). Porosities are also related to sediment texture, though the overlap in values between different sediment types is large. Sands have the highest porosities (mean 25%; range 17 to 30%), followed by open-framework gravels (mean 20%; range 16 to 24%), and then sandy gravels (mean 18%; range 14 to 26%). These trends in permeability and porosity are similar to those reported by Huggenberger (1993). Permeabilities presented here are lower than those reported by other sources for similar sediments (Table 3). The Sagavanirktok River samples processed by Corelab, Inc. (Table 3) suffered disturbance during handling, resulting in redistribution of sand grains within the sample and significantly reduced permeability. Also, the air permeameter used by Corelab, Inc. was inaccurate, and could not measure permeabilities greater than 20 darcys. Our own measurements of the permeabilities of sand and open-framework gravels, using a constant-head water permeameter, are shown in Table 3 for comparison. Variations in published permeabilities in Table 3 are probably due to differences in experimental technique.

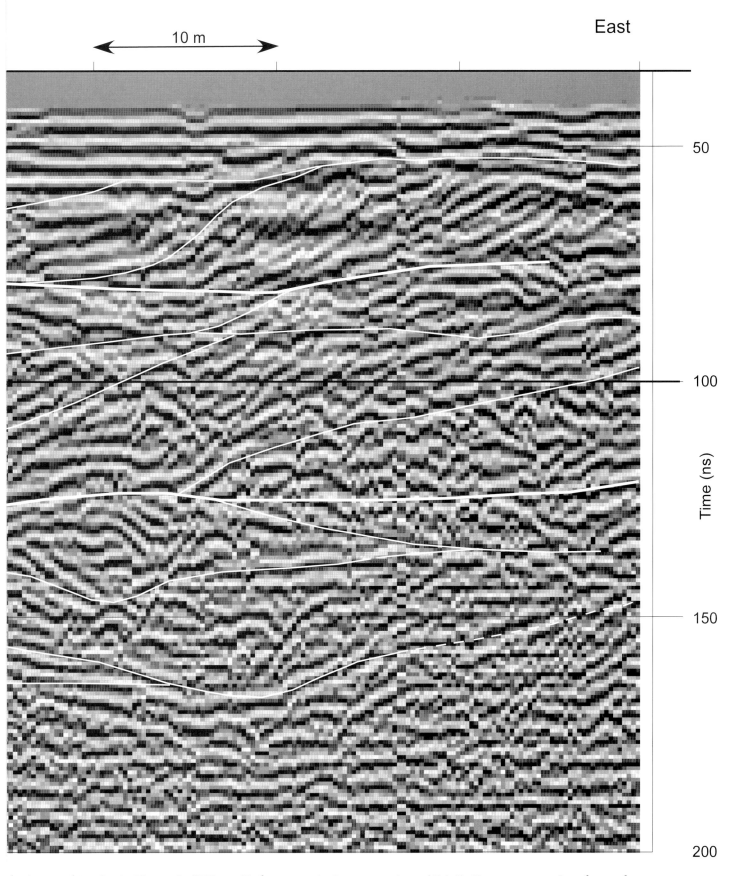

the large white dot in Figure 2. GPR profile has a vertical exaggeration of 5:1. Sedimentary core log shows three
gure) and along-stream 110 MHz GPR profiles and 450 MHz GPR profiles. The base of the active channel belt is
ent channel-belt deposits is confirmed by OSL dates of 289 ka and 271 ka from the rooted and burrowed sands.
ge-scale inclined strata. The base of the channel belt is not visible on the GPR profile. Legend for sedimentary log

channel fills may contain relatively high proportions of small- and medium-scale cross-stratified sand.

Relationship of Geometry of Stratasets to Geometry of Bedforms and Channels

Length-to-thickness ratios of stratasets are similar to wave-length-to-height ratios of their formative bedforms irrespective of scale, with a few exceptions (Table 1). Because the dimensions (i.e., length and height) of dunes and bars scale with channel depth and width, the length-to-thickness ratios of the deposits should be applicable to rivers of different size. Bridge and Tye (2000) have shown that quantitative relationships between thickness distributions of medium-scale cross sets and the height of formative dunes can be used to estimate paleochannel depth and channel-belt widths. These relationships can be used as an independent check on the interpreted thickness of channel fills or compound large-scale sets. Other checks can also be made on the relative thickness of different scales of strata set. In general, three to seven simple sets of large-scale strata (unit-bar deposits) occur within the thickness of one compound large-scale set, and two to five compound large-scale sets occur within the channel-belt thickness. The number of compound sets in the channel-belt thickness may be dependent on the specific aggradation rate of the Sagavanirktok. Recognition of all these scales of strata set is important in order to independently verify their thicknesses. Widths of different scales of strata set can be estimated (using information in Table 1) from the stratal thicknesses measured in boreholes. It should be remembered that parts of channel belts can be eroded, such that they may not be preserved in their entirety. However, the proportions of sediment textures and stratasets preserved in eroded channel belts are similar to those of complete channel-belt deposits. Also, individual channel-belt deposits are commonly interbedded with other older or younger channel-belt deposits and floodplain deposits in alluvial successions.

USE OF THE DEPOSITIONAL MODEL IN CHARACTERIZATION OF AQUIFERS

The value of this new depositional model is to remove much of the uncertainty in interpreting the origin of gravelly fluvial strata, in establishing the lateral continuity of different types and scales of strata, and in predicting the three-dimensional distribution of sediment properties. This will greatly improve predictions of groundwater flow and contaminant transport in gravelly fluvial aquifers. The procedure for incorporating this model into the characterization procedure is outlined below under three headings: (1) use of model to interpret deposits and predict lateral extent of different scales of strataset; (2) use of this information for numerical simulation of 3-D distribution of sediment textures; and (3) assignment of porosity and permeability to sediment textures.

Use of the Model to Interpret Deposits and Predict the Lateral Extent of Different Scales of Strataset

GPR profiles and borehole data should be used to provide site-specific dimensions of key features such as medium-scale cross sets, simple and compound sets of large-scale strata, and channel fills. Although the length-to-thickness ratios (Table 1) of different scales of strata are valid for all gravelly fluvial deposits, absolute thicknesses of cross sets depend on the scale of the ancient river, and vary between aquifers. Stratal dimensions can be cross-checked using relationships between different scales of strata, as described previously.

Numerical Simulation of 3-D Distribution of Sediment Types, Porosity, and Permeability

Once the dimensions of each scale of strataset have been determined, these stratasets (objects) must be placed in their correct spatial positions within a simulated aquifer volume. Predicting the exact positions of medium-scale cross sets and smaller scales of strata is not essential, because they influence the spatial distribution of permeability only over length scales less than 5 m, and their occurrence can be simulated randomly. The spatial distribution of sediment textures in the aquifer is determined mostly by their occurrence within simple and compound sets of large-scale strata and channel fills. Therefore, it is important that simple and compound sets of large-scale strata and channel fills be positioned correctly and given the correct internal distribution of sediment texture. The spatial distribution of sediment texture within simple and compound sets of large-scale strata and channel fills is shown in the depositional model (Fig. 16). Borehole data and GPR profiles are used to condition the simulation with the dimensions and position of different scales of strata. Cores, split-spoon samples, wireline logs, or flowmeter tests should be used to provide information on the proportions of open-framework gravels, sandy gravels, gravelly sands, and sand in the aquifer. These specific proportions can be used to condition the proportions of these sediment types in the simulation.

The distribution of sediment within an aquifer can be simulated using stochastic or process-based models (summarized in Koltermann and Gorelick, 1996, and Bridge, 2002, 2003). Stochastic models can be divided into object-based models, continuous (pixel-based) models, or a combined approach. Object-based models commonly involve sampling empirical distributions of the dimensions and orientation of particular objects with defined shapes and placing these objects in the correct proportions and positions within the aquifer volume until the aquifer is filled with objects. Borehole data are used to condition the simulation such that the model output honors the field data. Continuous models predict the probability of finding a particular value of a variable (such as sediment texture, porosity, etc.) at any point in the aquifer volume given the value at neighboring points. Two- or three-dimensional models are possible by combining probabilities in three orthogonal directions. Hierarchical relationships between parameters (i.e., different scales of strata) can be included in both types of model. Combined approaches might use an object-based model to distribute objects within the aquifer volume and then use a continuous model to simulate the distribution of variables such as porosity or permeability within the objects. In both object-based and continuous models, the spatial arrangement of sediment types within the model volume may be purely random (e.g., Webb, 1994; Bierkens and Weerts, 1994; Jussel et al., 1994; Rauber et al., 1998; Anderson et al., 1999) or nonrandom (e.g., Fogg et al., 1998; Weissmann and Fogg, 1999; Ritzi et al., 2000). Random stochastic simulations can easily be made to match available data, but they do not represent the spatial relationships between adjacent sediment types realistically. A nonrandom stochastic model is much more realistic because it uses spatial correlations (e.g.,

TABLE 2.—Proportion of sediment types measured from trenches and core logs.

Overall %	Sandy gravel	Sand	Open-framework gravel
Trenches	80.8	4.4	14.8
Cores	67.8	1.6	30.6

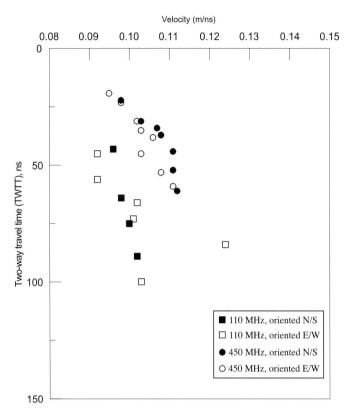

FIG. 13.—CMP velocities. CMP determined in two orthogonal directions using 110 MHz and 450 MHz antennae. 110 MHz velocities range between 0.092 and 0.103 m/ns, and 450 MHz velocities range between 0.095 and 0.125 m/ns. 450 MHz velocities are higher on average because the dielectric permittivity of water is lower at 450 MHz than at 110 MHz.

variograms or transition probability matrices) to predict the probability of finding a particular deposit at a point within the aquifer given its occurrence at an adjacent location. Transition probability matrices can be constructed for transitions between large-scale sets and channel fills derived from GPR profiles and used for simulating the spatial transitions between these objects. Frequency distributions of the length and thickness of large-scale sets and channel fills derived from GPR and borehole data can be sampled using Monte Carlo techniques to define the geometry of the objects. Alternatively, the length and thickness of objects can be determined directly from transition probability matrices. With this method, there is no need to specify length and thickness distributions independently (Carle et al., 1998; Weissmann and Fogg, 1999; review by Bridge, 2003).

Nonstochastic approaches that predict sediment distribution within the aquifer are also feasible. Process-based models use physical principles governing the deposition of different scales of sedimentary deposits to predict the occurrence of these deposits from a given set of initial and boundary conditions

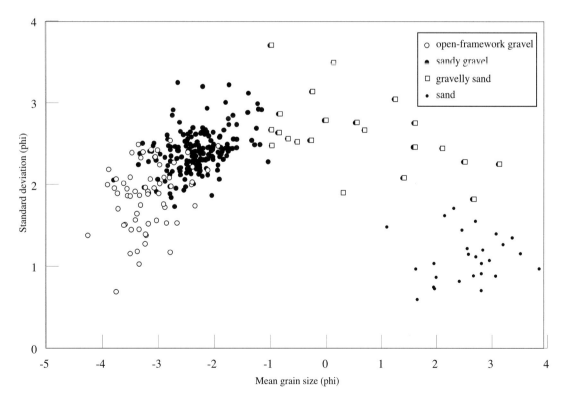

FIG. 14.—Mean grain size plotted against standard deviation (sorting) of grain-size distribution for four sediment types. Sediment types are defined on the basis of the mean and modality of the grain-size distribution measured from surface sediment samples. Open-framework gravels are unimodal, with mean grain sizes > 2 mm, sandy gravels and gravelly sands are bimodal, with mean grain sizes > 2 mm and < 2 mm, respectively. Sands are unimodal with mean grain sizes < 2 mm.

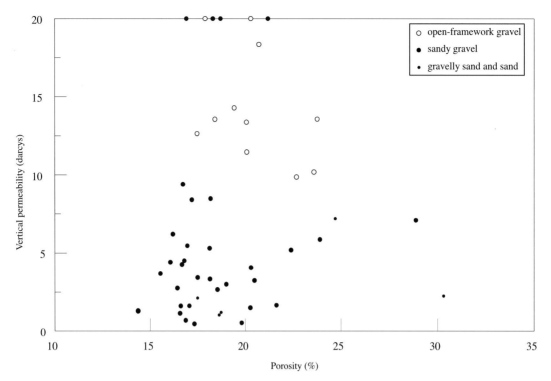

Fig. 15.—Classification of vertical permeabilities and porosity by sediment type. Sediment types are defined by the grain-size distribution of each sample. Actual definitions are included in the text and in Figure 14. Data show that the vertical permeability of open-framework gravel is > 10 darcys, sandy gravel is between 1 and > 20 darcys, and gravelly sands and sands, less than 7 darcys. Mean porosity of open-framework gravel is 20%, sandy gravel is 18%, and gravelly sand, and sand, is 25%.

(reviews by Bridge, 2002, 2003). Although these models can help understand the origin of the deposits and can predict more realistic stratigraphy than stochastic models, it is generally believed that it is difficult to make the simulated deposits fit observational data. In addition, these models are computationally intensive. However, recent hybrid simulation techniques have combined the results of multiple process-based simulations to produce a realistic channel-belt stratigraphy that is conditioned to real data (Karssenberg et al., 2001). At present, process-based models for the arrangement of fluvial deposits within channel-belts are not available.

Assignment of Porosity and Permeability to Sediment Textures

Finally, porosity and permeability measurements from wire-line logs, borehole samples, flowmeter tests, or multi-level slug tests (Zlotnik and McGuire, 1998) are related to sediment textures. Grain size and porosity are commonly used to calculate permeability using methods summarized in Sperry and Pierce (1995) and Bridge (2003). Permeabilities derived from grain-size data are notoriously inaccurate, ranging over an order of magnitude for the same grain-size properties. More rigorous approaches to predicting the permeability from grain properties have been proposed (e.g., Panda and Lake, 1994) but are difficult to apply to unconsolidated gravel deposits. Data on porosity and permeability should be site-specific. If no field data are available, such data can be taken from published sources, as summarized in Table 3. Porosity and permeability data assigned to a particular sediment texture have a wide range of values. Such data can be included in a simulation through Monte Carlo sampling of field data. Con-

tinuous simulations should be run with grid cell sizes small enough to capture the spatial variability of porosity and permeability, especially to account for thin but laterally extensive sand or open-framework gravel strata. Maximum cell thicknesses should be on the order of the thickness of a single medium-scale cross stratum (around 0.1 m in the Sagavanirktok River deposits), which varies between fluvial deposits.

CONCLUSIONS

A quantitative 3-D depositional model of gravelly braided-river deposits has been developed on the basis of extensive data from the Sagavanirktok River in northern Alaska, as well as observations from other rivers. An important aspect of this model is representation of different scales of bedform and associated stratification. *Channel-belt deposits* are composed of deposits of compound braid bars and point bars and large channel fills. Channel-belt deposits are mainly gravels, with minor sands and sandy silts. A channel belt may be capped by a sandy–silty soil horizon, unless eroded by later channel belts. Migration of compound bars forms *compound sets of large-scale inclined strata*. They are composed of simple sets of large-scale inclined strata and small channel fills. Compound sets have basal erosion surfaces and terminate laterally in large channel fills. Set thickness and vertical trends in grain size depend on the bed geometry and surface grain size of compound bars and the nature of bar migration. Thick fining-upward sequences form as bar-tail regions migrate downstream into a curved channel or confluence scour. Grain size may increase towards the top of a thick fining-upward sequence where bar-head lobes migrate over the bar-tail. Thin compound sets of large-scale strata with no vertical grain-size trend are found in riffle

TABLE 3.—Summary of permeability values for a range of fluvial sands and gravels.

Literature sources	Method	K (m/day)	K (darcys)	Porosity (%)	D_{50} (mm)	Sediment type
Anderson et al. (1999)	Grain size (Hazen)	1040	1718		9.13	OFG
		0.588	1		0.93	very fine sand?
		25.9	43		0.57	medium sand
		46–147	76–243		0.55–12.4	sandy gravel
Klingbeil et al. (1999)	Pneumatic tests	342	568	27.0		Planar/trough gravel
	and tracers	10.0	17	30.0		Bimodal gravel
		21800	36159	36.0		OFG
		95.0	158	42.0		Sand
Titzel (1997), Welch Outcrop	Air permeameter	9.7–32.8	16–54			Fine-medium sand
		54.3	90			Massive gravel
		46.7	77			Stratified gravel
Hamilton outcrop		71.5	118			Medium sand
		137	228			Stratified gravel
Welch Outcrop Mean		27.7	46			
Hamilton outcrop Mean		123	204			
Huggenberger (1993)	Permeameter and	12.1	20	20.0		Grey Gravel
	grain size (Kozeny)	2.59	4			Brown Gravel
		25.9	43	43.0		Sand
		43200	71743	35.0		OFG
		8.64–51.8	14–86	14.0		Bimodal Gravel
		0.0864	0			Silt
Jussel et al. (1994)	Permeameter	12.1–19	20–31	17.5–20.1	12.9–13.1	Grey/brown gravel
	(disturbed)	13000	21475	34.9	9.7	OFG
		147	243	43.4	0.47	Sand
Sagavanirktok River, Corelab data	Permeameter	12.1	> 20	20.7	9.02	OFG
		8.03	13	18.7	4.9	Sand and gravel
		1.51	3	21.3	0.17	sand
Lab Permeameter	(disturbed)	280	464		11.31	OFG
	(disturbed)	64.8	107		0.32	sand

Conversion between permeability and hydraulic conductivity assumes a water temperature of 7.6°C (Sagavanirktok River groundwater temperature). OFG = open-framework gravel

regions. Compound sets are composed mainly of sandy gravel, but open-framework gravel is common near set bases. *Large channel fills* (of the main channels in the channel belt) are also composed mainly of simple sets of large-scale inclined strata but are capped with sandy strata containing small-scale and medium-scale cross sets, and planar strata. These deposits are also generally sandier with progression downstream in the channel fill. Between two and five compound-bar deposits or large channel fills occur within the thickness of a fully preserved channel-belt deposit.

Migration of unit bars forms *simple sets of large-scale inclined strata*. They generally fine upwards, although they may show no grain-size trend. Between three and seven simple sets of large-

scale strata make up the thickness of a compound large-scale set. Open-framework gravels are common at the base of a simple large-scale set. *Small channel fills* (associated with cross-bar channels) are made up of small-scale and medium-scale cross sets, and planar strata. They occur at the tops of simple sets of large-scale strata, especially where simple large-scale sets occur at the tops of compound large-scale sets.

Dune migration forms *medium-scale sets of cross strata*. They contain isolated open-framework gravel cross strata and sandy trough drapes. The thickness of medium-scale cross sets decreases upwards in compound-bar deposits. *Planar strata* are formed by bedload sheets and may be made up of sandy gravel, open-framework gravel, or sand. Imbricated pebbles and pebble clusters are commonly found at the base of planar strata. *Small-scale sets of cross strata,* formed by ripples, generally occur in channel fills, as trough drapes, and as overbank deposits. Small-scale cross sets are always composed of sand and may contain organic remains, root traces, or burrows where they occur in channel fills or overbank deposits.

The geometry of the different scales of strataset is related to the geometry and migration of their formative bedforms. In particular, the wavelength-to-height ratio of bedforms is similar to the length-to-thickness ratio of their associated deposits. Furthermore, the wavelength and height of bedforms like dunes and bars are related to channel depth and width. Therefore, the thickness of a particular scale of strataset (i.e., medium-scale cross sets and large-scale sets of inclined strata) vary with the scale of the paleoriver. These relationships between the dimensions of stratasets, bedforms, and channels mean that the depositional model developed from the Sagavanirktok River can be applied to other gravelly fluvial deposits.

Porosity and permeability in the model are related to sediment texture (e.g., mean grain size and sorting) and how texture is distributed within the different scales of strataset. Textural classes are sand, gravelly sand, sandy gravel, and open-framework gravel. Sands and gravelly sands have the highest porosities (20 to 30%) but lowest permeabilities (1 to 100s of darcys), open-framework gravels have intermediate porosities (15 to 25%) and very high permeabilities (1000s to 10,000s of darcys), and sandy gravels also have intermediate porosities and permeabilities of 10s to 1000s of darcys.

The depositional model represents quantitatively the geometry of the different scales of strataset (related to geometry and migration of bedforms and channels), the spatial relationships between the different scales of strataset, and the distribution of sediment texture within these stratasets. This means that the depositional model can be used to guide geostatistical simulation of gravelly fluvial aquifers, given sparse site-specific data on sediment textures (or porosity and permeability) and the thickness of different scales of strataset.

ACKNOWLEDGMENTS

This work was supported by a National Science Foundation grant awarded to J.S. Bridge. Logistical support in the field was graciously provided by ARCO Alaska, BP Exploration Ltd., and Phillips Petroleum Co. OSL dates were carried out by Ron Goble in the Department of Geological Sciences, University of Nebraska, Lincoln. Porosity and permeability of core samples were determined by Corelab, Inc., Houston, Texas. This project would not have been possible without the hard work of many field assistants and technical staff.

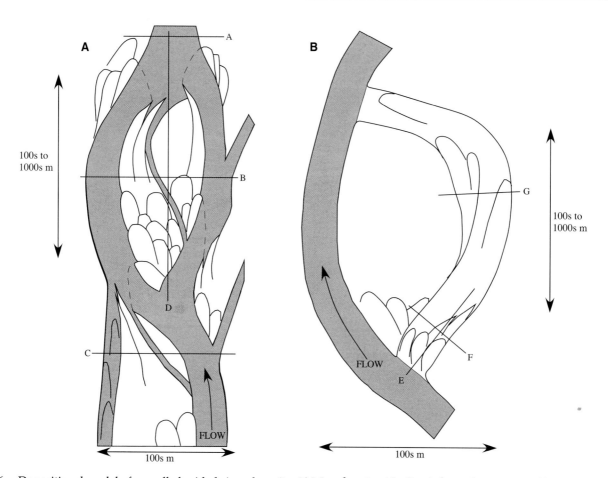

FIG. 16.—Depositional model of gravelly braided-river deposits. **A)** Map showing idealized channels, compound bars, and simple (unit) bars. Cross sections A to D correspond to those shown in Part C. **B)** Map showing idealized abandoned channel containing unit bars. Cross sections E to G correspond to those identified in Part C (shown on the following page).

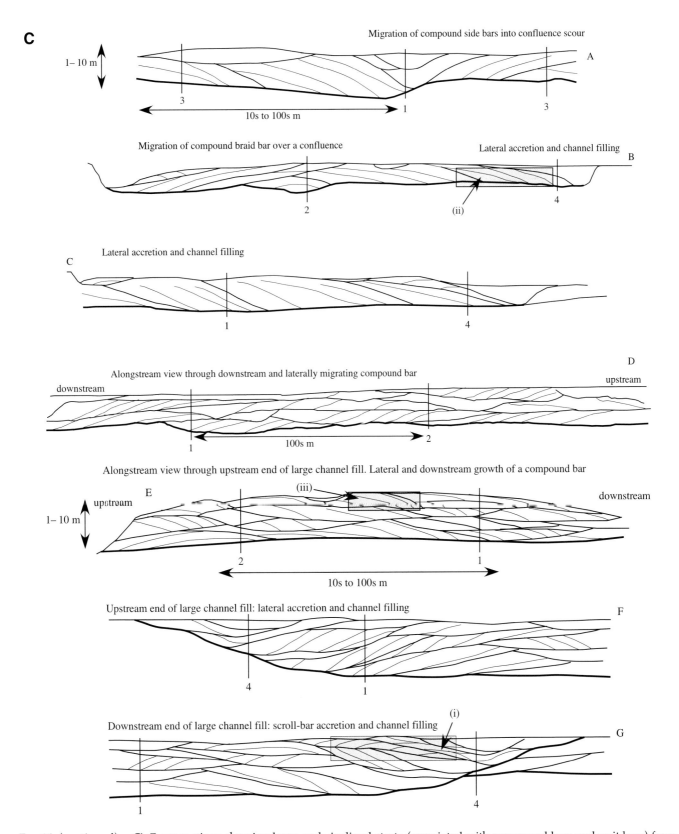

FIG. 16. (continued).—**C)** Cross sections showing large-scale inclined strata (associated with compound bars and unit bars) from deposits in different parts of the channel belt (Parts A and B). Numbered vertical logs (1–4) are shown in Part D. Numbered insets (i to iii) are expanded in Part E. Vertical exaggeration is 2:1. Thin lines represent large-scale strata, medium weight lines represent bases of large-scale sets, and thick lines represent bases of compound sets. Large-scale strata generally dip at less than 12 degrees but may be up to the angle of repose.

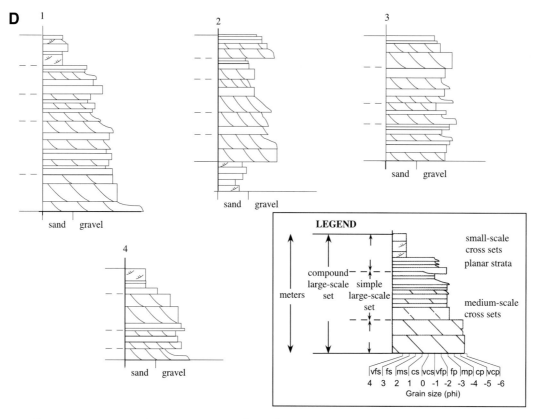

FIG. 16. (continued).—**D)** Vertical logs of typical sequences through different parts of compound-bar deposits and channel fills are shown in Part C. Symbols are explained in the legend.

REFERENCES

ALLEN, J.R.L., 1982, Sedimentary Structures; Their Character and Physical Basis, Volume 1: Amsterdam, Elsevier, 593 p.

ANDERSON, M.P., AIKEN, J.S., WEBB, E.K., AND MICKELSON, D.M., 1999, Sedimentology and hydrogeology of two braided stream deposits: Sedimentary Geology, v. 129, p. 189–199.

ASHMORE, P.E., 1982, Laboratory modelling of gravel braided stream morphology: Earth Surface Processes, v. 7, p. 2201–2225.

ASHMORE, P.E., 1991, How do gravel-bed rivers braid?: Canadian Journal of Earth Sciences, v. 28, p. 326–341.

BERES, M., HUGGENBERGER, P., GREEN, A.G., AND HORSTMEYER, H., 1999, Using two- and three-dimensional georadar methods to characterize glaciofluvial architecture: Sedimentary Geology, v. 129, p. 1–24.

BENNETT, S.J., AND BRIDGE, J.S., 1995, The geometry and dynamics of low-relief bedforms in heterogeneous sediment in a laboratory channel, and their relationship to water flow and sediment transport: Journal of Sedimentary Research, v. A65, p. 29–39.

BERNARD, H.A., MAJOR, C.F., JR., PARROTT, B.S., AND LE BLANC, R.J., SR., 1970, Recent sediments of Southeast Texas: A field guide to the Brazos alluvial and deltaic plains and the Galveston barrier island complex: University of Texas at Austin, Bureau of Economic Geology, Guidebook 11.

BEST, J.L., 1996, The fluid dynamics of small-scale alluvial bedforms, *in* Carling, P.A., and Dawson, M.R., eds., Advances in Fluvial Stratigraphy: New York, John Wiley & Sons, p. 67–125.

BEST, J.L., ASHWORTH, P.J., BRISTOW, C., AND RODEN, J., 2003, Three-dimensional sedimentary architecture of a large, mid-channel sand braid bar, Jamuna River, Bangladesh: Journal of Sedimentary Research, v. 73, p. 516–530.

BIERKENS, M.F.P., 1996, Modeling hydraulic conductivity of a complex confining layer at various spatial scales: Water Resources Research, v. 32, p. 2369–2382.

BIERKENS, M.F.P., AND WEERTS, H.J.T., 1994, Block hydraulic conductivity of cross-bedded fluvial sediments: Water Resources Research, v. 30, p. 2665–2678.

BLUCK, B.J., 1979, Structure of coarse grained braided stream alluvium: Royal Society of Edinburgh, Transactions, v. 70, p. 181–221.

BRAYSHAW, A.D., 1984, Characteristics and origin of cluster bedforms in coarse-grained alluvial channels, *in* Koster, E.H., and Steel, R.J., eds., Sedimentology of Gravels and Conglomerates: Canadian Society of Petroleum Geologists, Memoir 10, p. 77–85.

BRIDGE, J.S., 1993, The interaction between channel geometry, water flow, sediment transport and deposition in braided rivers, *in* Best, J.L., and Bristow, C.S., eds, Braided Rivers: Geological Society of London, Special Publication 75, p. 13–71.

BRIDGE, J.S., 1997, Thickness of sets of cross strata and planar strata as a function of formative bedwave geometry and migration, and aggradation rate: Geology, v. 25, p. 971–974.

BRIDGE, J.S., 2002, Characterization of fluvial hydrocarbon reservoirs and aquifers: Problems and solutions: Asociación Argentina de Sedimentología, Revista, v. 8, p. 87–114.

BRIDGE, J.S., 2003, Rivers and Floodplains: Oxford, U.K., Blackwell, 491 p.

BRIDGE, J.S., ALEXANDER, J., COLLIER, R.E.LL., GAWTHORPE, R.L., AND JARVIS, J., 1995, Ground-penetrating radar and coring used to document the large-scale structure of point-bar deposits in 3-D: Sedimentology, v. 42, p. 839–852.

BRIDGE, J.S., COLLIER, R.E.LL., AND ALEXANDER, J., 1998, Large-scale structure of Calamus river deposits revealed using ground-penetrating radar: Sedimentology, v. 45, p. 977–985.

E

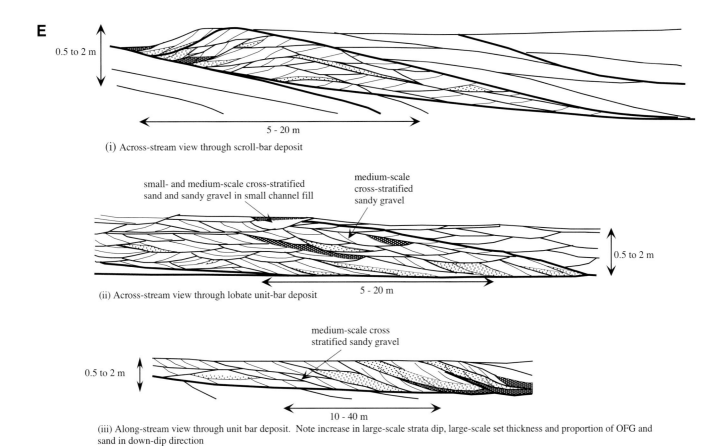

(i) Across-stream view through scroll-bar deposit

small- and medium-scale cross-stratified sand and sandy gravel in small channel fill

medium-scale cross-stratified sandy gravel

(ii) Across-stream view through lobate unit-bar deposit

medium-scale cross stratified sandy gravel

(iii) Along-stream view through unit bar deposit. Note increase in large-scale strata dip, large-scale set thickness and proportion of OFG and sand in down-dip direction

☐ **Sandy gravel**. Occurs throughout all scales of strata

▒ **Open-framework gravel (OFG)**. Occurs in steeply dipping large-scale strata at the margins of unit bars. More common towards base of unit bar.

▓ **Sand**. Occurs in steep dipping large-scale strata interspersed with OFG, in the troughs of medium- and large-scale sets (unit bars), and underlies unit bars.

FIG. 16. (continued).—E) Two-dimensional sections showing details of unit-bar deposits. Locations of figures are shown in Part C.

BRIDGE, J.S., AND TYE, R.S., 2000, Interpreting the dimensions of ancient fluvial channel bars, channels, and channel belts from wireline-logs and cores: American Association of Petroleum Geologists, Bulletin, v. 84, p. 1205–1228.

BRIDGE, J.S., JALFIN, G.A., AND GEORGIEFF, S.M., 2000, Geometry, lithofacies and spatial distribution of Cretaceous fluvial sandstone bodies, San Jorge Basin, Argentina: Outcrop analog for the hydrocarbon-bearing Chubut Group: Journal of Sedimentary Research, v. 70, p. 341–359.

BRISTOW, C.S., 1987, Brahmaputra River: channel migration and deposition, in Ethridge, F.G., Flores, R.M., and Harvey, M.D., eds., Recent Developments in Fluvial Sedimentology: SEPM, Special Publication 39, p. 63–74.

CARLE, S.F., LABOLLE, E.M., WEISSMANN, G.S., VAN BROCKLIN, D., AND FOGG, G.E., 1998, Conditional simulation of hydrofacies architecture: a transition probability / Markov approach, in Fraser, G.S., and Davis, J.M., eds., Hydrogeologic Models of Sedimentary Aquifers: SEPM, Concepts in Hydrogeology and Environmental Geology, v. 1, p. 147–170.

CARLING, P.A., 1999, Subaqueous gravel dunes: Journal of Sedimentary Research, v. 69, p. 534–545.

CHURCH, M.A., HASSAN, M.A., AND WOLCOTT, J.F., 1998, Stabilizing self-organized structures in gravel-bed stream channels: Field and experimental observations: Water Resources Research, v. 34, p. 3169–3179.

CHURCH, M.A., MCLEAN, D.G., AND WOLCOTT, J.F., 1987, River bed gravels: Sampling and analysis, in Thorne, C.R., Bathurst, J.C., and Hey, R.D., eds., Sediment Transport in Gravel Bed Rivers: New York, John Wiley & Sons, p. 43–79.

COLLINSON, J.D., 1996, Alluvial sediments, in Reading, H.G., ed., Sedimentary Environments; Processes, Facies and Stratigraphy: Cambridge, Massachusetts, Blackwell Science Ltd., p. 37–82.

DAWSON, M., 1989, Flood deposits present within the Severn Main Terrace, in Beven, K., and Carling, P., eds., Floods; Hydrological, Sedimentological and Geomorphological Implications: New York, John Wiley & Sons, p. 253–264.

DIETRICH, W.E., KIRCHNER, H., IKEDA, H., AND ISEYA, F., 1989, Sediment supply and the development of the coarse surface layers in gravel-bed rivers: Nature, v. 340, p. 215–217.

DINEHART, R.L., 1992, Evolution of coarse gravel bed forms: Field measurements at flood stage: Water Resources Research, v. 28, p. 2667–2689.

ECOLOGICAL RESEARCH ASSOCIATES, 1983, Sagavanirktok River: Hydrology and Hydraulics: Environmental Summer Studies (1982) for the Endicott Development, Vol II: Physical Processes, p. 31–43.

FOGG, G.E., NOYES, C.D., AND CARLE, S.F., 1998, Geologically based model of heterogeneous hydraulic conductivity in an alluvial setting: Hydrogeology Journal, v. 6, p. 131–143.

HUGGENBERGER, P., 1993, Radar facies: recognition of characteristic braided river structures of the Pleistocene Rhine gravel (NE part of Switzerland), in Best, J.L., and Bristow, C.S., eds., Braided Rivers: Geological Society of London, Special Publication 75, p. 163–176.

JUSSEL, P., STAUFFER, F., AND DRACOS, T., 1994, Transport modeling in heterogeneous aquifers: 1. Statistical description and numerical generation of gravel deposits: Water Resources Research, v. 30, p. 1803–1817.

KARSSENBERG, D., TÖRNQVIST, T.E., AND BRIDGE, J.S., 2001, Conditioning a process-based model of sedimentary architecture to well data: Journal of Sedimentary Research, v. 71, p. 868–879.

KHAN, I.A., BRIDGE, J.S., KAPPELMAN, J., AND WILSON, R., 1997, Evolution of Miocene fluvial environments, eastern Potwar plateau, northern Pakistan: Sedimentology, v. 44, p. 221–251.

KLINGBEIL, R., KLEINEDAM, S., ASPRION, U., AIGNER, T., AND TEUTSCH, G., 1999, Relating lithofacies to hydrofacies: outcrop-based hydrogeological characterization of Quaternary gravel deposits: Sedimentary Geology, v. 129, p. 299–310.

KOLTERMANN, C.E., AND GORELICK, S.M., 1996, Heterogeneity in sedimentary deposits: A review of structure-imitating, process-imitating and descriptive approaches: Water Resources Research, v. 32, p. 2617–2658.

KOWALSKY, M.B., DIETRICH, P., TEUTSCH, G., AND RUBIN, Y., 2001, Forward modeling of ground-penetrating radar data using digitized outcrop images and multiple scenarios of water saturation: Water Resources Research, v. 37, p. 1615–1625.

KUHNLE, R.A., AND SOUTHARD, J.B., 1988, Bed load transport fluctuations in a gravel bed laboratory channel: Water Resources Research, v. 24, p. 247–260.

LANZONI, S., 2000a, Experiments on bar formation in a straight flume 1. Uniform sediment: Water Resources Research, v. 36, p. 3337–3349.

LANZONI, S., 2000b, Experiments on bar formation in a straight flume 2. Graded sediment: Water Resources Research, v. 36, p. 3351–3363.

LECLAIR, S.F., 2002, Preservation of cross-strata due to the migration of subaqueous dunes: an experimental investigation: Sedimentology, v. 49, p. 1157–1180.

LECLAIR, S.F., BRIDGE, J.S., AND WANG, F., 1997, Preservation of cross-strata due to migration of subaqueous dunes over aggrading and non-aggrading beds: comparison of experimental data with theory: Geoscience Canada, v. 24, p. 55–66.

LECLAIR, S.F., AND BRIDGE, J.S., 2001, Quantitative interpretation of sedimentary structures formed by river dunes: Journal of Sedimentary Research, v. 71, p. 713–716.

LEWIN, J., 1976, Initiation of bedforms and meanders in coarse-grained sediment: Geological Society of America, Bulletin, v. 87, p. 281–285.

LIVESEY, J.R., BENNETT, S., ASHWORTH, P.J., AND BEST ,J.L., 1998, Flow structure, sediment transport and bedform dynamics for a bimodal sediment mixture, in Klingeman, P.C., Beschta, R.L., Komar, P.D., and Bradley, J.B., eds., Gravel-Bed Rivers in the Environment: Colorado, Water Resources Publications, LLC, p. 149–176.

LUNT, I.A., BRIDGE, J.S., AND TYE, R.S., 2004, A quantitative three-dimensional depositional model of gravelly braided rivers: Sedimentology, v. 51, p. 377–414.

LUNT, I.A., AND BRIDGE, J.S., 2004, Evolution and deposits of a gravelly braid bar and channel fill, Sagavanirlatok River, Alaska: Sedimentology, v. 51, p. 415–432.

MANAEUS, J.M., AND HASSAN, M.A., 2002, Simulation of individual particle movement in a gravel streambed: Earth Surface Processes and Landforms, v. 27, p. 81–97.

MCLELLAND, S.J., ASHWORTH R.J., BEST, J.L., RODEN, J., AND KLAASSEN, G.J., 1999, Flow structure and transport of sand-grade suspended sediment around an evolving braid bar, Jamuna River, Bangladesh, in Smith, N.D., and Rogers, J., eds., Fluvial Sedimentology VI: International Association of Sedimentologists, Special Publication 28, p. 43–57.

MIALL, A.D., 1977, A review of the braided river depositional environment: Earth-Science Reviews, v. 13, p. 1–62.

MIALL, A.D., 1992, Alluvial deposits, in Walker, R.G., and James, N.P., eds., Facies Models: Response to Sea Level Change: St. John's, Newfoundland, Geological Association of Canada, p. 119–142.

MIALL, A.D., 1996, The Geology of Fluvial Deposits: New York, Springer-Verlag, 582 p.

PANDA, M.N., AND LAKE, L.W., 1994, Estimation of single-phase permeability from parameters of particle-size distribution: American Association of Petroleum Geologists, Bulletin, v. 78, p. 1028–1039.

RAMOS, A., SOPEÑA, A., AND PEREZ-ARLUCEA, M., 1986, Evolution of Bundsandstein fluvial sedimentation in the Northwest Iberian Ranges (Central Spain): Journal of Sedimentary Petrology, v. 56, p. 862–875.

RAUBER, M., STAUFFER, F., HUGGENBERGER, P., AND DRACOS, T., 1998, A numerical three-dimensional conditioned/unconditioned stochastic facies type model applied to a remediation well system: Water Resources Research, v. 34, p. 2225–2233.

REGLI, C., HUGGENBERGER, P., AND RAUBER, M., 2002, Interpretation of drill core and georadar data of coarse gravel deposits: Journal of Hydrology, v. 255, p. 234–252.

RITZI, R.W., DOMINIC, D.F., SLESERS, A.J., GREER, C.B., REBOULET, E.C., TELFORD, J.A., MASTERS, R.W., KLOHE, C.A., BOGLE, J.L., AND MEANS, B.P., 2000, Comparing statistical models of physical heterogeneity in buried-valley aquifers: Water Resources Research, v. 36, p. 3179–3192.

RUST, B.R., 1978, Depositional models for braided alluvium, in Miall, A.D., ed., Fluvial Sedimentology: Canadian Society of Petroleum Geologists, Memoir 5, p. 605–625.

SCHEIBE, T.D., AND FREYBERG, D.L., 1995, Use of sedimentological information for geometric simulation of natural porous media structure: Water Resources Research, v. 31, p. 3259–3270.

SIEGENTHALER, C., AND HUGGENBERGER, P., 1993, Pleistocene Rhine gravel: deposits of a braided river system with dominant pool preservation, in Best, J.L., and Bristow, C.S., eds., Braided Rivers: Geological Society of London, Special Publication 75, p. 147–162.

SKELLY, R.L., BRISTOW, C.S., AND ETHRIDGE, F.G., 2003, Architecture of channel-belt deposits in an aggrading shallow sandbed braided river: the lower Niobrara River, northeast Nebraska: Sedimentary Geology, v. 158, p. 249–270.

SMITH, N.D., 1974, Sedimentology and bar formation in the upper Kicking Horse River, a braided outwash stream: Journal of Geology, v. 81, p. 205–223.

SMITH, N.D., 1978, Some comments on terminology for bars in shallow rivers, in Miall, A.D., ed., Fluvial Sedimentology: Canadian Society of Petroleum Geologists, Memoir 5, p. 85–88.

SPERRY, J.M., AND PIERCE, J.J., 1995, A model for estimating the hydraulic conductivity of granular material based on grain shape, grain size and porosity: Groundwater, v. 33, p. 892–898.

STEEL, R.J., AND THOMPSON, D.B., 1983, Structures and textures in Triassic braided stream conglomerates ('Bunter' Pebble Beds) in the Sherwood Sandstone Group, North Staffordshire, England: Sedimentology, v. 30, p. 341–367.

STOKES, S., 1999, Luminescence dating applications in geomorphological research: Geomorphology, v. 29, p. 153–171.

TITZEL, C.S., 1997, Quantification of the permeability distribution within sand and gravel lithofacies in a southern portion of the Miami Valley aquifer: unpublished M.Sc. Thesis, Wright State University, Dayton, Ohio, 197 p.

TÖRNQVIST, T.E., 1993, Holocene alternation of meandering and anastomosing fluvial systems in the Rhine–Meuse delta (central Netherlands) controlled by sea-level rise and subsoil erodibility: Journal of Sedimentary Petrology, v. 63, p. 683–693.

TUBINO, M., REPETTO, R., AND ZOLEZZI, G., 1999, Free bars in rivers: Journal of Hydraulic Research, v. 37, p. 759–775.

VAN DAM, R.L., AND SCHLAGER, W., 2000, Identifying causes of ground-penetrating radar reflections using time-domain reflectometry and sedimentological analyses: Sedimentology, v. 47, p. 435–449.

WALKER, J., ARNBORG, L., AND PEIPPO, J., 1987, Riverbank erosion in the Colville delta, Alaska: Geografiska Annaler, v. 69A, p. 61–70.

WEBB, E.K., 1994, Simulating the three-dimensional distribution of sediment units in braided stream deposits: Journal of Sedimentary Research, v. B64, p. 219–231.

WEISSMANN, G.S., AND FOGG, G.E., 1999, Multi-scale alluvial fan heterogeneity modeled with transition probability geostatistics in a sequence stratigraphic framework: Journal of Hydrology, v. 226, p. 48–65.

WHITING, P.J., DIETRICH, W.E., LEOPOLD, L.B., DRAKE T.G., AND SHREVE R.L., 1988, Bedload sheets in heterogeneous sediment: Geology, v. 16, p. 105–108.

WHITING, P.J., AND DIETRICH, W.E., 1993, Experimental studies of bed topography and flow patterns in large-amplitude meanders 1. Observations: Water Resources Research, v. 29, p. 3605–3614.

WILCOCK, P.R., 1992, Experimental investigation of the effect of mixture properties on transport dynamics, *in* Billi, P., Hey, R.D., Thorne, C.R., and Tacconi, P., eds., Dynamics of Gravel-Bed Rivers: New York, John Wiley & Sons., p. 109–139.

WILLIS, B.J., 1989, Palaeochannel reconstructions from point bar deposits: a three dimensional perspective: Sedimentology, v. 36, p. 757–766.

WILLIS, B.J., 1993a, Interpretation of bedding geometry within ancient point-bar deposits, *in* Marzo, M., and Puigdefabregas, C., eds., Alluvial Sedimentation: International Association of Sedimentologists, Special Publication 17, p. 101–114.

WILLIS, B.J., 1993b, Evolution of Miocene fluvial systems in Chinji area, Potwar plateau, northern Pakistan: unpublished Ph.D. Thesis, SUNY-Binghamton, Binghamton, New York, U.S.A., 279 p.

YALIN, M.S., 1992, River Mechanics: Oxford, U.K., Pergamon Press, 219 p.

ZLOTNIK, V.A., AND MCGUIRE, V.L., 1998, Multi-level slug tests in highly permeable formations: 2. Hydraulic conductivity identification, method verification, and field applications: Journal of Hydrology, v. 204, p. 283–296.

Index

Aquifer Characterization
SEPM Special Publication No. 80, Copyright © 2004
SEPM (Society for Sedimentary Geology), ISBN 1-56576-107-3, p. 171–172.